Today's shoe designer has an infinite number of available options when choosing materials for new footwear designs. Learning how to select and specify footwear materials accurately is a critical skill you will need to become a successful, professional shoe designer. The wrong choices can make a footwear mess, and the right choices can create a modern masterpiece!

You must take great care to pick materials appropriate for the demands of footwear marketing, performance, and manufacturing. The right material choices will make your shoe designs comfortable, compelling, and long-lasting.

SHOEMAKERS ACADEMY

Online Shoemaking Courses for all levels of Shoemakers, Shoe Designers, Developers, and Brand builders.

Expand your skills and knowledge in modern shoe design, manufacturing sourcing, and footwear brand development.

Jumpstart your career. Launch your shoe brand.

Available worldwide, On-demand, Online, and on your schedule. Start Today!

Textbooks Available now:
How Shoes are Made
Footwear Pattern Making and Last Design
Shoe Material Design Guide
How to Start Your Own Shoe Company
How to Spot Fake Sneakers
Cómo se hacen los zapatos
Cómo empezar tu propia empresa de calzado
Guía para el diseño de materiales de calzado
Patronaje de calzado y diseño de hormas
鞋子是怎样制成的

Shoe Material Design Guide

Written and Edited by
Wade and Andrea Motawi

USA Copyright © Wade Motawi 2017
ISBN-13: 978-0998707044
ISBN-10: 099870704X
Wade Motawi 2017 Revised Jan 2024

Online Shoemaking Courses
Shoemaking for Designers and Brand Builders
How to Select Shoe Materials
Sneaker Authentication Basics
Creating Footwear Specifications
Footwear Cost Calculation
Footwear Cost Engineering
Footwear Inspection and Quality Control
Building a Modern Shoe Factory
Footwear Sustainability Strategies
Footwear Fitting & Comfort
Footwear Import Duty
Starting Your Shoe Business
Shoe Types and Constructions
How to Design Shoes
DIY Shoemaking for Beginners
The Footwear Process Development to Production
Footwear Development Factory Communications
Footwear Marketing & Merchandising

Dear Readers,
This book was written to educate, inform, and inspire the next generation of shoe designers, shoe developers, shoemakers, and footwear entrepreneurs. Our goal is to help prepare people for fulfilling careers in the world of shoes.

Enjoy!
Special thanks to:
Andrea, Alex & Erik, Karim, Halla, Mom, Joanne, Dave, Alfredo, Jason, David, Lizzie, Johnson, Steve, Lenny, Bernie, Jenny, Simon, Ben, David, Jack, Gary, Jean Marc, Suresh, Abdón and Paolo.

Thanks to all my working friends in the USA, China, Hong Kong, Korea, Taiwan, Vietnam and Europe.

Shoe Material Design Guide

WADE MOTAWI

SHOE MATERIAL DESIGN GUIDE

SHOE MATERIAL DESIGN GUIDE

HOW TO USE THIS BOOK

How to select the right materials for your shoes
This book was written to help shoe designers, product managers, footwear developers, and students select the right materials for their footwear projects. After reading this book, you will have a better understanding of the material types available and the many options for each material type.

You will learn how to qualify your material choices; making sure they meet the performance requirements for your shoe. Once you have selected your materials, you will need to communicate your material choices to the factory.

Section 1: Material options for the shoe designer
The first section of the book details the many materials available to the shoe designer. Each chapter will focus on a specific material type or component. You will study the manufacturing processes and available options for each material. Once you have an understanding of your material choices, we will review how to use each material type to maximize its effect in your shoe designs.

Section 2: How to qualify and specify shoe materials
The second section of the book details exactly how to qualify and specify materials. We explain how to test materials, how to manage vendor relations, and how to build your material library. You will also learn about the challenges of sourcing, ordering, and managing the shoe material supply chain.

Section 3: How materials are used in shoe production
For this section, we have cut a sampling of shoes in half to identify what materials are used and where they are used to make many popular styles of modern and classic shoes. Use this section as a reference for common materials used to create many footwear styles.

Section 4: Who makes the best shoe materials?
To help you find the best material suppliers, we list the top vendors for major material categories.

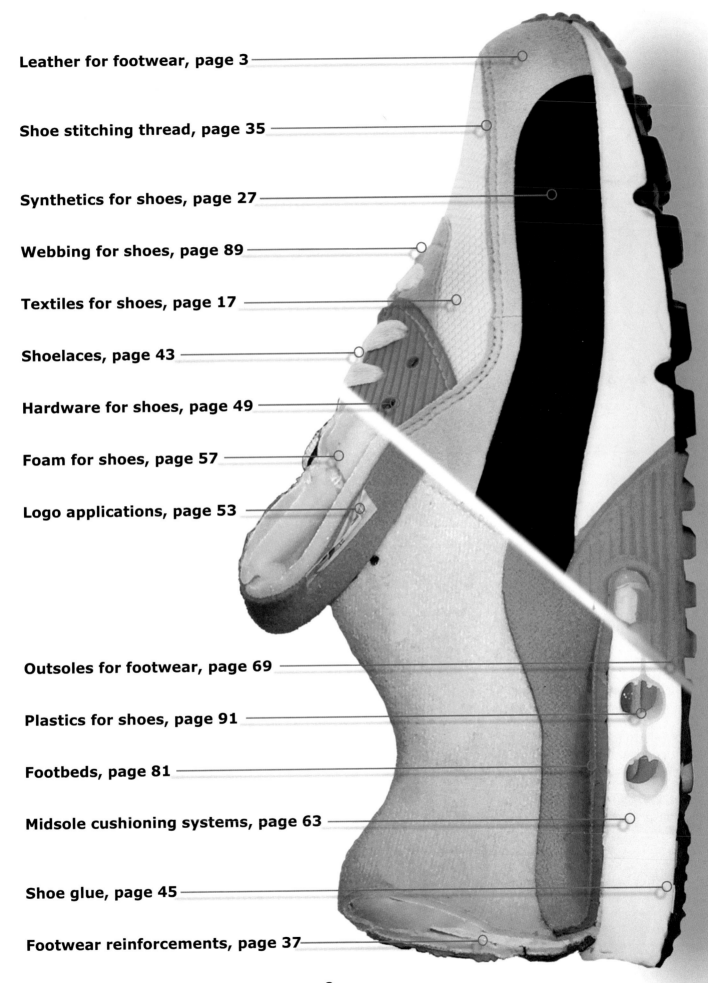

CHAPTER 1

LEATHER FOR FOOTWEAR

Why use leather to make shoes?

Natural leather is the most commonly used material for shoemaking. With the right leather, you can make rich, beautiful, functional, and fashionable shoes. Natural leather is a durable, flexible, breathable, and stretchable material that conforms to the wearer like no other material. Leather ages gracefully, acquiring a patina that records the life of its use and user. Leather shoes can accept unique polishing, buffing, and staining effects. The most expensive, luxurious, exotic, and desirable shoes are constructed with craft-made leathers.

Leather is available in thousands of styles, colors, finishes, and prices. While natural leather is ideal for dress, casual, and fashion shoes, it does have some drawbacks. Natural leather can be heavy, hot, and susceptible to water damage if not handled correctly.

While modern, man-made materials have replaced leather in many applications, genuine leather confers status. High-end basketball shoes are made of full-grain leather and the gripping texture of real split suede is preferred by both professional and amateur skateboarders. Basic leather is a relatively expensive material when compared to fabric or other man-made materials, but leather does enjoy some favorable import regulations.

3

What is the best leather for shoes?

There are hundreds of shoe types, each with different functional requirements. There is an equal number of different leather types to choose from to satisfy these functional requirements.

Today, most leather is made from cowhide, but many other animals have skin suitable for leather production. Lamb and deerskin are used in expensive apparel for their soft leather. Deer and elk skin are widely used in work gloves and indoor shoes. Pigskin is used in apparel and on seats of saddles. Buffalo, goat, alligator, snake, ostrich, calf, bull, ox, and yak skins may also be used for leather. Some motorcyclists favor kangaroo leather because of its abrasion resistance and lightweight. Kangaroo leather is also a favorite for soccer shoes and boxing speed bags.

Each of these leathers have a different grain appearance and average thickness. The pores of the individual animal species can be seen in the unique grain of the leather surface.

Leather character

When specifying leather, the designer needs to consider several aspects of the leather's character. First, it is essential to consider the aesthetic qualities of color and grain structure. Beyond the aesthetic, the designer needs to think about the function of the shoe. What leather thickness and temper are appropriate for the shoe design?

Color

Leather colors vary widely depending on the animal, tanning method, dyeing process, and pigment applications. Leathers can be crafted to have deep, rich, lustrous colors that have a natural range, or can be coated and pigmented to look like pink plastic. Natural leathers may have penetrating dyes that create unique variations, while pigment sprayed leathers can be any color you choose.

Grain

The grain of a leather hide is the top layer that carries the surface markings of the living animal's skin. The grain of cowhide is very different from the grain of goat, pig, snake, or ostrich leather. It is the grain that gives real leather its unique character. Leather grain can be left in its natural state or can be enhanced, corrected, and even created, by pressing or using rollers.

Thickness

Leather is available in varying thicknesses from 0.4mm for silky smooth goat leather linings, to 6.0mm full-grain buffalo leather used for boot soles. The most commonly used full-grain and split leathers range in thickness from 1.5mm to 2.4mm.

Temper

The temper of leather is a measure of its pliability and softness.

Firm leather has hard and rigid characteristics. This leather has very little flexibility and is best used to make soles, stacked heels, heel counters, belts, and sandal straps.

Regular leather is slightly firm and does not have rigid qualities. Regular leathers have smooth, even folds, and are perfect for shoes and boots.

Mellow leather is very limber and pliant. This leather is great for handbags, soft sneakers, and baby shoes.

Soft leather is extremely flexible and pliant. Baby shoes, slippers, gloves, garments, and upholstery are made of soft temper leather.

What is leather and how is it made?

Leather can be made from almost any animal hide. The most common are cow and calf leather, followed by pig, goat, buffalo, sheep, alligator, ostrich, lizard, and snake. Even fish skin can be made into leather. Each type of hide requires a different tanning procedure and creates leather with characteristics unique to each animal.

As cowhide is the most popular, it will be our focus. Different parts of the cowhide will have a different thickness, grain density, and stretch direction. The dense, strong leather from the bend of the hide is good for vamps, while the softer, belly leather is best used for linings and trim.

If you imagine how the hide lays over the animal, you can understand how the leather will have different characteristics depending on its location. The leather of the bend is always in tension; as it is stretched from the spine of the animal. The belly leather hangs from the bottom with no tension, it is softer with a less defined grain structure.

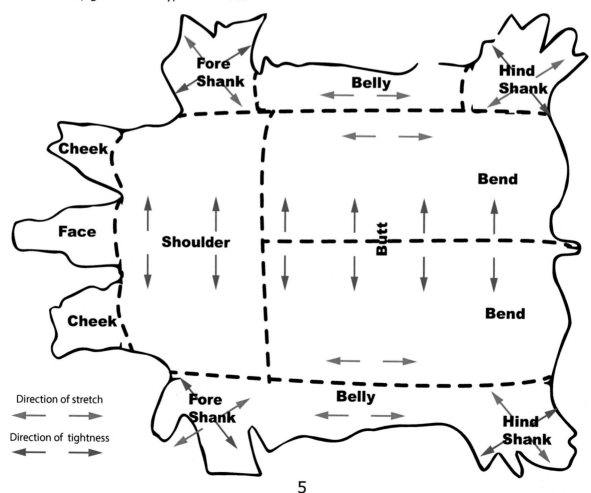

Inside the leather hide

Starting at the skin or outside, the hide has three layers.

The epidermis is about 1% of the thickness of the hide. It contains the hair, fur, follicles, sebaceous, and sweat glands. This layer is completely removed during leather processing.

The dermis is 85% of the thickness of the hide. The dermis is the layer that is transformed into leather during the tanning process. The dermis is made of bundles of connective fibers, which in turn are made up of even smaller fibrils. The fibrils are interwoven to form a three-dimensional "mesh." The fibrils are composed of the protein collagen. 30% to 35% of the dermis is collagen. The complex protein globulin cements the collagen fibrils together.

The sub-cutaneous flesh layer makes up the remaining 14% of the hide. This layer, made mostly of connective tissue and fat, is removed during processing.

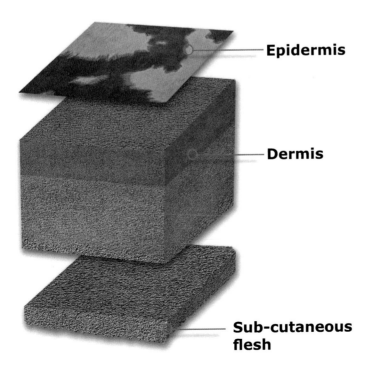

Epidermis

Dermis

Sub-cutaneous flesh

The dermis

Leather is made from the dermis layer by the process of "tanning" the raw animal hide. The protein collagen is the main structural element of the dermis. The tanning process converts the collagen protein of the raw hide into a stable and durable material.

Tanning chemicals transform the raw hide into leather by creating cross-links in the collagen structure, thus stabilizing it against the effects of acids, alkalis, heat, water, and the action of micro-organisms. The process is called tanning because the compound Tannin, extracted from oak trees, was originally used to promote the stabilizing of the collagen protein.

The fibril bundles in the upper layers of the dermis are dense and strong. This part of the hide is called the top-grain. Full-grain, top-grain, and nu-buck leathers are made from this top layer. This is the smoothest surface of leather and the most valuable part of the hide. Thin, high-quality garment leather is made by splitting off just the very top surface of the dermis.

Top grain

Split suede

Split suede

The lower layers of the dermis are called corium. The fibril bundles in the corium are less dense and do not have the same strength as the fibers in the top grain. The inner corium layers are "split" from the hide to make suede or split suede leathers.

A hide can produce three or four layers of leather depending on the thickness of the splits.

How leather is made: step-by-step

There are many operations involved in the tanning process. It takes about ten days to transform the hide of a living animal into a finished leather ready for the shoe factory. Because most raw hides are transported and stored before processing, it may take an individual hide many months to be transformed from a living skin to a finished leather product. The leather supply chain often starts with animals being slaughtered for food in South America or Australia. The animal hides are then processed in China, and the finished shoes ship back to the Americas or Europe.

Curing

The raw animal hides must be preserved to stop them from deteriorating before the leather tanning process can begin. Leather tanneries often purchase the raw hides from other countries. The hides must be cured before they can be transported. Methods of preservation include salting, chilling, or freezing. These hides are then called "wet blue." When touring a leather tannery, it is best to avoid the "blue room" as handling the blue hides is a difficult, terribly smelly, wet, and dirty job.

Soaking

When cured hides are selected for processing, they must first be soaked in water to replace any water they may have lost during curing and transportation. Hides may be soaked for several hours to several days. Soaking will also help clean the hides, removing dirt and curing salts that may interfere with the tanning processes.

Liming

Liming removes the epidermis and hair from the hide. Liming with alkaline compounds promotes the swelling of the hide. This will cause a controlled breaking of some of the chemical crosslinks of the collagen proteins. The chemically dissolved hair is scraped off and washed out of the hide.

Fleshing

After liming, the hide is passed through a machine to mechanically remove the remaining animal flesh from the inside or "flesh" side of the hide. Hides may be split into layers at this stage or after tanning.

Deliming

The deliming process works to neutralize the alkali pH in the hide. High alkali levels can damage the collagen so the pH levels must be carefully controlled during the entire tanning process.

Bating

Bating is an enzyme process that further stabilizes the raw hide, removing the last of the alkali compounds and thoroughly cleaning the hide. At the conclusion of this process, the hide is fully saturated with water, flat, relaxed, clean, and ready for the pickling and tanning processes.

Pickling

Most tanning processes require a mildly acidic pH. Acids and salt solutions are used to bring the hide to the state required. This process is called pickling. Pickled hides are stable and can be stored or transported.

Degreasing

Before the tanning operations can be started, solvents or water-based chemicals are used to remove any excess grease or fat from the animal hides.

Tanning

Now the hide is ready for the actual "tanning" procedure that creates the protein cross-links in the collagen. The hides are loaded into a rotating drum along with the tanning chemicals. The modern chemical process takes just a few hours to penetrate the entire hide. There are many different tanning methods and chemicals. The tanning process will depend on the animal hide, the end use of the leather, and any special requirements.

Chrome or mineral tanning

Today, 80% to 90% of all leather is tanned by chrome or mineral process. Invented in 1858, chrome tanning uses a chemical solution of acids and salts including chromium sulfate to transform the collagen. Chrome tanning has almost entirely replaced vegetable tanning due to its ability to create a leather product that is supple, pliable, and does not discolor or distort when wet. Chrome tanning has the advantage of being relatively fast and inexpensive. The chromium salt leaves behind a pale blue color you can see before the leather is dyed. For coated leather products you can see the blue tint on the cut edge. The chrome tanning method usually takes one working day to process. Chrome tanning also allows for a wide range of colors. Almost all leather for shoe production is chrome tanned.

Vegetable tanning

Vegetable tanning is the oldest type of tanning and uses plant extracts instead of man-made chemicals to transform the collagen inside the leather fibers. Vegetable tanning uses the tannin found in different vegetable matter such as tree bark, wood, leaves, fruits, and roots. These tanning materials limit the finished leather colors to browns and blacks. This type of tanning can take up to 40 days to produce a piece of dyed leather; thus it is a more expensive process. Vegetable tanned leather is not stable in water, and it will discolor. If left to soak and then dried, vegetable tanned leather will shrink and stiffen. Vegetable tanned leathers tend to be thick and firm and are used to produce sole leather, belting leather, and leathers for shoe linings, bags, and cases.

Aldehyde or wet-white tanning

Aldehyde or wet-white is a new organic tanning method. New types of biosynthetic compounds are used to stabilize and transform the collagen. Aldehyde tanned leather is tanned using glutaraldehyde or oxazolidine compounds. This is the leather that most tanners refer to as wet-white leather due to its pale cream or white color. It is the main type of "chrome-free" leather, often seen in shoes for infants and automobile interiors. Aldehyde tanning produces very soft leathers with excellent hand feel. Aldehyde oil tanning can be used to produce dry-cleanable and washable fashion leather. Chamois leather is made using this process. This method of tanning has been gaining popularity due to the increased concern for water quality and the environment.

Other tanning methods

There are many other exotic leather tanning processes such as brain, alum, oil, and rose tanning but these are not used to make shoe leather.

Splitting

Once the leather fiber has been stabilized by the tanning process, the hide can be divided into multiple layers. A leather splitting machine uses rollers to guide the leather into a steel splitting blade. A thick leather hide can be divided creating a layer with the top grain surface and leaving a second "split" that can be processed into suede leather or coated to create action leather.

Shaving

To create thin leather with uniform thickness, a machine with helical blades mounted to a rotating cylinder will shave the back (non-grain) side of the leather. A splitting machine alone cannot make the thinnest leathers; thus a shaving machine is used for this delicate work.

Neutralization

Neutralizing removes residual chemicals leftover from the tanning process. This process halts the tanning process, making the leather stable and ready for any additional processing and finishing.

Dyeing

The leather is now ready for the dye process. There are many different dyeing methods and compounds. It is essential for the shoe designer to know if the leather is surface dyed or if the dye completely penetrates the hide. In general, grain leather can be surface dyed, while suede must be fully penetrated.

Fat liquoring

Fat liquoring introduces oils to lubricate the fibers and keep the leather flexible and soft. Without these oils, the leather will become hard and inflexible as it dries out.

Samming

This process reduces the water content to about 55% and can be achieved by a number of machines, the most common being like a large mangle with felt covered rollers. The water is pressed out of the hide.

Setting out

The leather is stretched out, and the grain side is smoothed. This process also reduces the water content to about 40%.

Final drying

Leather is normally dried to 10-20% water content. This can be achieved in many ways, and each method has a different effect on the finished leather:

Staking and dry drumming

A staking machine makes the leather softer and more flexible by massaging it to separate the fibers. The leather may be softened by the tumbling action inside a rotating drum.

Buffing and brushing

The flesh surface is removed by mechanical abrasion to produce a suede effect or to reduce the thickness. In some cases, the grain surface is buffed to produce a very fine nap, e.g., nu-buck leathers. After buffing, the leather is brushed to remove excess dust.

Leather finishing operations

The goals of leather finishing are to level the color, cover grain defects, control the gloss, and provide a protective surface with resistance to water, chemicals, and abrasion. The finishing operations can drastically transform the outer surface of the leather. These include:

Oiling
Brushing
Padding
Impregnation
Buffing
Spraying
Roller coating
Curtain coating
Polishing
Plating
Embossing
Glazing
Tumbling

In most cases, the designer will select the leather from the tannery's swatch catalog. The exact recipe and schedule of the finishing operations may be a secret.

Final grading

The leather will be graded before shipping to the customer. Grading will take into account the color intensity and uniformity, feel of the leather, visual appearance, thickness, softness, design effects, and natural defects such as scratches.

Main types of shoemaking leather

Full-grain leather refers to hides that have not had the top surface modified by sanding, buffing, or embossing. The grain remains, allowing the fibers strength and durability. The grain also has breathability, resulting in less moisture from prolonged contact. Rather than wearing out, it develops a patina during its expected useful lifetime. High-quality leather furniture and footwear are often made from full-grain leather.

Full-grain leathers are available in many finish types:

Aniline leather

Aniline leather is the most natural looking leather. The unique surface characteristics of the animal hide remain visible. Aniline leather is colored only with soluble, penetrating, aniline dyes, and not with surface coatings of polymer and pigment. Aniline leather takes on a natural patina and darkens with age. Shoes made with aniline leather must be protected from the elements. A light surface polish may be applied to enhance appearance and offer some protection against spillage and soiling.

Semi-aniline leather

Semi-aniline leather is more durable than aniline while still retaining a natural appearance. The increased durability is provided by the application of a light surface coating which contains a small amount of pigment. This coating ensures consistent color and imparts some stain resistance. Semi-aniline footwear is easier to care for and retains a natural look.

Nu-buck leather

Nu-buck is a full grain leather which the very top grain surface has been sanded or buffed. Once the smooth top skin surface is removed, the fine grain's dense protein fibers give the leather a velvet-like nap. Full grain leathers with slightly irregular surfaces or coloring can be made into nu-buck. For light color, high-quality nu-buck, only the finest hides can be used. Nu-buck leather is often treated with water-resistant compounds as it is easily soiled.

11

Pigmented leather

Pigmented leather is the most durable leather. It is used in the majority of furniture upholstery and almost all car upholstery. The durability is provided by a polymer surface coating that contains color pigments. The surface coating allows the manufacturer more control over the properties of the leather, e.g., resistance to scuffing or fading. Pigmented leather can be made in any color. Due to the surface treatment, pigmented leather does not develop a natural patina.

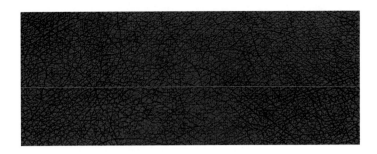

Full-grain pigmented leather

The natural grain surface is left intact before applying the polymer surface coating.

Top-grain leather

Top-grain is very commonly used to make high-end leather garments. All of the corium "split" layers and most of the grain layer has been separated, making it thinner and more pliable than full-grain. Its surface has been sanded, and a finish coat added which produces a colder, plastic feel with less breathability. Top-grain does not develop a natural patina. It is typically less expensive and has greater stain resistance than full-grain leather if the finish remains unbroken.

Corrected-grain leather

Corrected-grain leather is any leather that has had an artificial grain applied to its surface. The hides used to create corrected leather do not meet the standards for use in aniline leather. The imperfections are corrected or sanded off, and an artificial grain is embossed into the surface and dressed with stain or dyes. Most corrected-grain leather is used to make pigmented leather, as the solid pigment helps hide the corrections or imperfections. Corrected grain leathers can mainly be bought as two finish types: semi-aniline and pigmented.

12

Crazy horse oiled leather

What we in the shoe trade call "crazy horse leather" is cowhide. To make crazy horse leather, low quality, full-grain hide is brushed to remove the top surface of the grain's texture. The leather is then treated with a heavy, waxy, and oily compound that will darken the leather. This creates a rough and rugged style of leather. You may see scratches, bug bites, scars, and fat wrinkles on the surface. That's okay; it's crazy horse! This leather will show color changes when flexed. Crazy horse is a popular choice for work boots and outdoor shoes.

Splits

Other leather types can be made from the inner layers of the hide. These products are made from what is left behind once the grain leather layer has been "split" off the hide.

Split leather

Split leather is leather created from the fibrous part of the hide under the top-grain. During the splitting operation, the top-grain and split are separated. The split side of the hide can be further split (thickness allowing) into a middle split and a flesh split. In very thick hides, the middle split can be separated into multiple layers until the thickness prevents further splitting. The strongest suedes are usually made from grain splits that have the grain completely removed, or from the flesh split that has been shaved to the correct thickness.

Cow Suede

Pig Suede

Reversed suede

A reversed suede is a grained leather that is used with the grain facing away from the visible surface. A sandal strap may have a suede outlook but have a smooth lining surface.

Patent leather

Patent leather is a staple for high fashion and uniform shoes. Patent leather was originally a full-grain leather that had been given a high-gloss finish. Inventor Seth Boyden developed the finishing process in Newark, New Jersey, in 1818.

Today, high gloss patent leather is usually created from a plastic coating and is considered bycast or action leather. The plastic finish can have a mirror gloss surface which requires little polishing. Modern day patent leather costs approximately one quarter of the price of full-grain patent leather.

Action leather

Action leather, or bycast leather, is a split leather with a layer of polyurethane plastic film laminated to the surface and then embossed. Bycast was originally made for the shoe industry and later adopted by the furniture industry. This man-made material is slightly stiffer but much less expensive than top-grain leather. Action leather also has a consistent color and grain texture.

The leather surface is completely covered in plastic, so it is waterproof, and easy to clean and maintain. Action leather is the least expensive of all the leather products. It enjoys favorable duty classifications: thus it's very commonly specified for service boots and low priced casual court shoes.

Action leather is available in an almost infinite number of colors and emboss patterns. It is generally an inexpensive product. There are factories that produce more expensive action leather which may have special coatings and high durability finishes.

Designing shoes with leather

Over 6,000 year ago, the first leather shoes were made from animal hide. Leather is still a popular choice for shoes today. It's strength, durability, and comfort are timeless attributes.

Environmental factors

Leather is a great material, but it is not suitable for every type of shoe. Its surface can be scratched and penetrated by water. Wet leather is particularity susceptible to stretching. Leather may need special treatments to adapt to different shoe types. Study the environment in which your shoes will be performing to ensure you make the best material choice.

Bonding

As with textiles and synthetics, leathers require specific bonding procedures. Depending on the type of leather surface, the shoe factory will need to adjust their process. Suede leather is easy to bond, primer and cement quickly penetrate the porous surface. Action leather will require roughing to remove its plastic surface. The plastic surface resists penetration of the cement and also creates a solid bond with the cement which can cause the plastic layer to separate from the inner leather layer. Nu-buck and full-grain leather bonding can be improved with light roughing.

Waxed or oiled leather is difficult to bond, but it can be done. Careful buffing and priming usually work. Consider welted or another stitch down construction for leather types which are challenging to bond.

Lasting

Leather is the champion material for manual and machine lasting. Its ability to stretch and conform in all directions makes leather the ideal material for making smooth and sleek footwear. To ensure the leather isn't damaged and the final shape is fixed, a leather vamp will have some fabric or mold-able plastic backing inside.

Leathers special challenge: color range

Leather hides each come from an individual animal. No matter how carefully a tannery prepares the leather, there will always be color variations between hides. Natural leathers, including nu-buck and split leather, may need to be cut and matched shoe-by-shoe. This means each pair of shoes must be cut from the same hide to ensure the leather colors of each part match. This extra step reduces the cutting productivity and can complicate the stitching operations.

Surface finishing

Leather shoes often have some post-assembly finishing effects. Unlike textile and synthetic footwear, leather shoes can stained, buffed, oiled, polished, scuffed, or dyed to create special effects.

Some treatments, such as oiling and waxing, interfere with bonding so they must be done after the shoes are made. The pulling, stretching, heating, and handling of the manufacturing process itself can also leave the leather dried and in need of reconditioning.

Edge treatments

Leather, if carefully cut, can have a smooth, clean edge that does not require any special treatments. Unlike fabric, cut leather edges do not have loose fibers which may unravel.

When using leather, you want to consider how to finish any exposed edges. You need to know if your leather is 100% dyed through. Some leathers with treated surfaces will have edges that do not match the hide's surface color.

For example, white and black action leather will have a visible edge that is light blue from the chrome tanning process. You may choose to have the factory paint these edges. After cutting, the leather parts are stacked with only the cut edges exposed; a worker with an air brush then carefully sprays the edges with paint matching the surface color.

Leather has an advantage over textiles in that thick edges may be skived down to be thin. The thin edges can then be wrapped to create a very clean, smooth, and color matched effect.

This eyestay has both wrapped and cut edges.

Fine leather shoes will often have a "gimped," "pinked," or zig-zag cut edge. This strengthens the cut edge of the leather. The cut leather edge on handmade shoes may also be singed or stained.

Import duty and tariffs

Leather shoes enjoy a relatively low duty rate of 9.5% for import into the USA and Europe. To take advantage of this low duty rate, companies will design shoes that are 51% leather and 49% PU or textile. For shoes with more than 51% textile surface area, the tariff is 20%!

This classic court shoe is designed to fit the lower, leather duty classifications while avoiding the higher cost of an all leather construction.

◎ The toe tip, vamp, and quarter panel parts are action leather. You can see the leather has perforated accents.

◎ The mudguard and eyestay overlays are made from foam backed PVC synthetic. The PVC is compression molded to create interest. This is a very efficient and inexpensive way to make a "leather" shoe.

How to specify leathers

When you specify leather, you will need to consider a few basic parameters. As a designer, you need to be concerned with the color and grain. As a developer, your focus will be physical performance attributes such as the temper and thickness. Working directly with the leather tannery will give you the advantage of their insight and experience.

Color specifications

Top grain, corrected gain, action leather and any pigmented leather can usually be specified by Pantone™ color number. Natural leathers without pigmented surfaces will need to be specified by the manufacturer's color number or provided swatches. The Pantone™ color system has many brown hues, but the tannery may have a difficult time matching exact colors. Remember, natural leathers will have a color range. No two hides will be exactly alike. If you are ordering large quantities, the tannery will try their best to make exactly what you want. If your orders are small, then your choices may be limited to stock items or shared colors from another larger customer.

Price per square foot

Cow leather prices start at around US$1.30 for white and black action leather. Split suedes range from $1.30 to $1.60 depending on the thickness, color, and cut location from the hide. Butt and bend suede is of higher value than shoulder, neck, or belly suede. Prices also vary depending on grade and bulk purchase agreements.

Coated action leather: $1.30 to $1.45
Cow suede: $1.30 to $1.65
Kid (goat) suede: $1.65
Pig suede: $1.85
Crazy horse: $2.85
Pebble emboss full-grain: $2.73
Nu-buck leather: $3.75
Waterproofing: add $.50 to $1.00 per foot.

Test standards for leather

There are many physical performance tests for leather. Unlike textiles and synthetics, the leather tanning process can involve the use of hazardous chemical compounds. Additional tests may be required ensure your leather is free of any unwanted chemical byproducts.

Standard physical tests for leather:
Tensile strength L & W
Elongation L & W
Stretch under load 100N
Stitch & trouser tear L & W
Color fastness water & perspiration
Stretching under load
Crocking wet & dry

CHAPTER 2

TEXTILES FOR SHOES

Textiles are tough, lightweight, resistant to the environment, long wearing, and relatively inexpensive. With an infinite variety of weaves, knits, colors, patterns, treatments, and unique features, textiles have a special place in footwear design. To design shoes, you must have an understanding of textiles.

You will find fabric used on almost every part of footwear; outside on the upper, inside as linings, hidden reinforcements, and even on shoe bottoms. The polymer fibers such as nylon and polyester are lightweight and durable. Lycra is stretchable, and cotton canvas is a must for vulcanized construction.

Selecting textiles
When considering a textile for your shoe design, there are six features to keep in mind:
thread size, fiber composition, weave pattern, backing material, sizing, and surface treatments.

Thread size
The basic building block of fabric is the thread. Thread weight is measured by denier. 1 denier (D) = 1 gram per 9000 meters of thread. Very lightweight fabric typically uses 110D thread, shoes commonly use 420D to 600D thread weight, and 1000D is used for boots and bags.

Fiber types
Footwear textiles come in many fiber types including; cotton, wool, nylon, polyester, polypropylene, rayon, and Lycra. Each has its own look and physical properties such as water absorption, stretchability, UV resistance, and colorfastness. For shoe design, polyester and nylon are the most common. Stretchable Lycra and Spandex are often used for bindings and linings. Cotton is a must for vulcanized shoes as synthetic fibers will melt in the vulcanizing ovens.

Natural fibers, like cotton or wool, will accept many unique finishing treatments. Cotton canvas shoe uppers can be salt or stone washed before assembly to give the shoes a distressed character. Cotton can also accept an oiled or waxed finish, but this must be done after the shoe is assembled. Oily or waxed canvas does not bond well to the shoe outsole during assembly.

Nylon
Nylon is a generic designation for a family of plastics; aliphatic, or semi-aromatic polyamides. First used to make parachute cord and women's stockings, nylon can now be injection molded or spun into fibers for many different fabrics. Nylon fabrics are tough, mold resistant, easy to dye, fade resistant, and absorb little water. Nylon is a well-suited fabric for the shoe exterior. Nylon fabrics are sold under the trade name Cordura™. Trivia: The U.S.A. flag flying on the moon is made of nylon.

Polyester
Polyester is a trade name for a plastic type called polyethylene terephthalate (PET). Polyester is the common name used in footwear. Like nylon, polyester fabrics are tough, mold resistant, easy to dye, fade resistant and do not absorb water. Polyester is more resistant to UV damage and has a higher melting temperature than nylon. The fibers are highly stain resistant but can be a challenge to dye. Polyester has good moisture wicking properties and can be knit into light stretchable fabric. Polyester has the advantage of being less expensive than nylon. Polyester fabric is all over the modern shoe; inside and out.

Polypropylene
Polypropylene (PP), also known as polypropene, is a thermoplastic polymer used in a wide variety of applications including ropes, thermal underwear, and various textiles. Polypropylene is rugged and unusually resistant to many chemical solvents, bases, and acids. Polypropylene has a relatively slippery "low energy surface" which means that many common types of glue will not bond with it. Its use is somewhat limited in shoes due to its bonding complications.

Spandex™, Lycra™, Elastane™
Spandex is the trade name for a synthetic polyurethane copolymer fiber known for its exceptional elasticity. Spandex by weight is stronger and more durable than natural rubber. This fiber has the remarkable ability to stretch more than 500% of its length, then return to shape. Spandex is often combined with other fibers to create fabrics with high strength and some elastic properties. Tongue gussets and binding fabric will often have spandex fibers. Due to it conforming stretchability, Spandex fabric makes for very smooth wrapped binding edges.

Rayon™
Rayon is a semi man-made fiber manufactured from wood pulp. Cellulose extracted from wood pulp is chemically solidified, resulting in synthetic fiber. Types of rayon include viscose, modal, and lyocell. Rayon has the slippery hand feel of nylon but is more absorbent and cooling. Rayon's high melting temperature makes it useful in heat resistant fabric. Its "slippery" character has an anti-static function.

Kevlar™
Kevlar™ is the registered trademark for a para-aramid synthetic fiber. Kevlar has a high tensile strength-to-weight ratio; by this measure, it is five times stronger than steel. When woven into a material it is cut resistant, abrasion resistant, puncture resistant, and has bulletproof applications. Kevlar is often combined with nylon or other high strength fiber to reduce costs. Due to its molecular structure, Kevlar cannot be dyed. Due to its high strength, Kevlar can be a challenge to die cut cleanly.

Nomex™ fiber is chemically related to Kevlar but has poorer strength. Nomex has excellent thermal, chemical, and radiation resistance making it the material of choice for fire-resistant products. Car racing shoes are often made of fire retardant suede leather and Nomex fabric.

Linen
Linen is a textile made from the fibers of the flax plant. Linen is difficult to manufacture. Fabrics made of linen are valued for their exceptional coolness and freshness in hot weather as the fiber is very absorbent. You will find linen accents in high-end causal shoes but not in performance athletic footwear.

Silk
Silk is a natural protein fiber produced from larva which can be woven into textiles. The shimmering appearance of silk is due to the triangular prism-like structure of the silk fiber, which allows the cloth to refract incoming light at different angles, thus producing different colors. Silk is expensive and strong. It loses 20% of its strength when wet. Silk has some stretch but remains elongated and must be fully backed when used in making footwear.

Wool
Wool fabric has been popular for indoor slippers and clogs and has recently found its way into more mainstream footwear applications. Unbacked wool has the unique ability to conform over time but it is also susceptible to water and wear. Modern shoes made of wool fabric will have standard internal reinforcements; these will allow the look and feel of wool without its durability drawbacks.

Weaves

There are many ways to weave the fibers together. In a woven pattern, two fibers cross each other. The fibers running the length of the fabric are called the "warp." The fibers running across the fabric, side to side, are called the "weft." The more typical "plain" square weave has an equal number of fibers in the warp and weft. There are many weaves; plain, twill, satin, basket, dobby, and ripstop to name a few.

The "knit" is the other common way fibers are joined. In knitted fabrics, the thread follows a meandering path forming symmetric linked loops. These linked and meandering loops can be easily stretched in different directions giving knit fabrics much more elasticity than woven fabrics. Depending on the fiber type and knitting pattern, a knit fabric can stretch as much as 500%.

Common knits types are jersey, interlock, double knit, and ribbed.

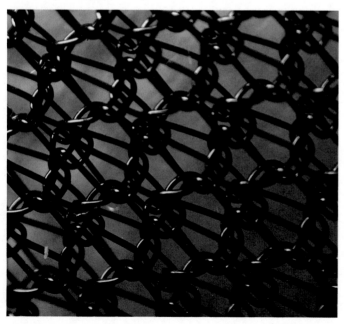

High-tech "Air" mesh, or 3D mesh, is made by knitting. Also known as sandwich mesh, the inner surface can be smooth and act as the shoe lining. There are thousands upon thousands of options for technical mesh weaving patterns. The surface pattern, thickness, color, and bottom surface are all customizable. You can even select a multi-color weave. Your imagination and the factory's minimum order quantities are your only limitations.

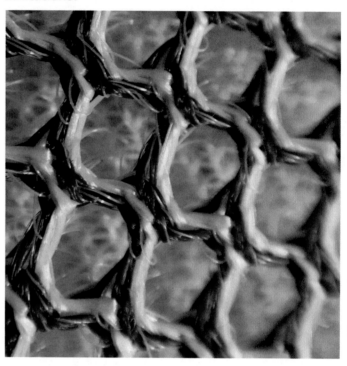

Non-woven fabric

Textiles can also be made by non-woven processes such as spunbond or weld bonded fabric. These products are made by first depositing loose fibers into mats, then securing them by heated pressure roller, embossing process, or stitch bonding.

These fabrics are tough, lightweight, durable, and breathable; suitable for linings and reinforcements but not on the outside of a shoe. Trade names are Cambrelle™ or Super-Tuff™.

Computer controlled 4D knitting

4D knitting is changing the way athletic shoes are made. A one-piece upper design is produced by a CNC knitting machine, then assembled with the tongue, lining materials, and reinforcements.

This knitting technology, once only found on expensive shoes, is rapidly expanding to lower-priced shoes. You can find this 4D knitting technology on running shoes made by Nike™, soccer shoes from Adidas™, even local market footwear in China is being made this way. In the major shoemaking areas of China, the CNC knitting machine is becoming a rather common sight.

To create the upper, a knitting machine is loaded with polyester, nylon, or spandex fibers. The machine can handle a mix of fibers and up to 10 colors at one time. It can be programmed to knit one upper, or 3 uppers at a time, with a maximum width of 90cm.

Depending on the programming and fibers selected, the upper can be thin and stretchable, or thick and stretch resistant. The design opportunities are nearly infinite with multiple fiber options, colors choices, knit densities, and opening configurations.

A single-color, polyester fiber design may cost $2.50, while a multi-color, polyester spandex combination may cost $7.50 per upper.

Fabric processing

Once the fibers are knit or woven, the fabric may need to be dyed, sized, and backed before it can be used in shoes. Some fabrics are ready to be used without extra processing. Some are woven with colored fibers and do not require any dying operations.

Before any finishing operations can be done, the fabric must be dyed. Often the weaving and dying operations are done in different factories. The material supplier will likely stock thousands of yards of material as "grey goods" or "greige." Once the material is ordered, the factory will dye and process it according to the customer's requirements. Dyeing operations take place in large heated tanks with circulating water systems to ensure the fabric is evenly dyed.

Each fiber type requires a different dying process. Some fabrics are woven with two different fibers allowing the factory to create multicolor fabrics without the hassle and expense of weaving color fibers. In many cases, a fabric may be two-tone with a fixed white or black base, and a second color that is made in the dying operations.

When a new color is ordered, the color department collects the greige and gets to work. A computer-controlled dye compounding machine mixes the dye formula based on the required color and the fiber type.

The new dye compound is tested in the color lab. The resulting samples are called "lab dips". Once the lab dips are confirmed production can be made.

Fabric backing

Freshly woven fabric is often soft and shapeless, not suitable for use in shoes. It is the sizing and backing treatments that give fabric the toughness and body to make it useful. Sizing is a liquid resin treatment applied to the fibers that help hold them together. The fabric is stretched, heated, and treated with the sizing resin; this holds the fibers in place.

The backing material is critical to the character of a fabric. There are two common backing types: PU and PVC.

PU is a thin, clear coating. It is cheaper and lighter than PVC but not reliably waterproof. You can see the fiber under the coating.

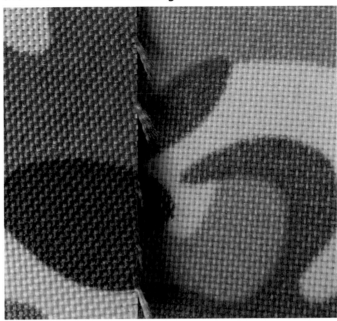

PVC backing is a dense, solid plastic coating. You cannot see the fibers through the backing. PVC is used to make very sturdy, waterproof fabric, but at the cost of breathability.

TPU is now being used to back some fabrics. It is more expensive but has the benefit of being lighter, stronger, and can be welded by heat or RF process. TPU has as additional advantage because it is NOT PVC, thus avoiding some environmental concerns.

Fabric surface treatments

Durable Water Resistant coating or DWR is also common. The woven fabric is treated while still in roll form. The fabric is coated then dried.

Brushing is another very common surface treatment. The fabric is fed into a machine with rough stone, textured metal, or wire brushes that snag on individual fibers creating a surface with a soft nap or hand. Nylex™ and Visa™, or Visa Terry™, are knit products with one side brushed to tease up the soft fibers. These polyester fabrics are the most common footwear lining materials for sports shoes.

Other treatments and special features

As mentioned before, fabrics, and their various features that can be specified are very important for shoe designers. Fabrics can be treated to be windproof, breathable, abrasion resistant, non-fraying, high friction, antimicrobial, and moisture wicking or non-wicking.

For hunting boots, fabric can be scent masking. For service and industrial shoes, fabric can have electro magnetic wave protection, thermal reflective, cut resistant, anti-static, anti-penetration, and fire retardant properties.

Fabric lamination machines are also used to apply fusible or pressure sensitive adhesive coatings and waterproof membranes.

Fabric lamination

When fabric is assembled into shoes it is quite often laminated with a thin 4mm layer of soft open cell PU foam. The foam can be attached by the application, PU glue, or flame lamination. Flame lamination heats the two materials then presses the surfaces together. This process is very common and does not damage the materials.

Foam backing controls wrinkles and makes fabric easier to handle during assembly. The foam also prevents inner layers of the shoe from x-raying through the thin fabric. Of course, the backing foam also provides the upper with a cushioning and water wicking effect. The PU foam layer will often have tricot material laminated to the back of the foam. This tricot protects the foam from snags and tears during assembly. The tricot layer is often the inside lining of the shoe.

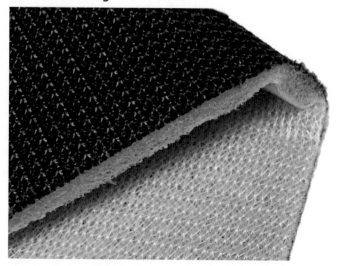

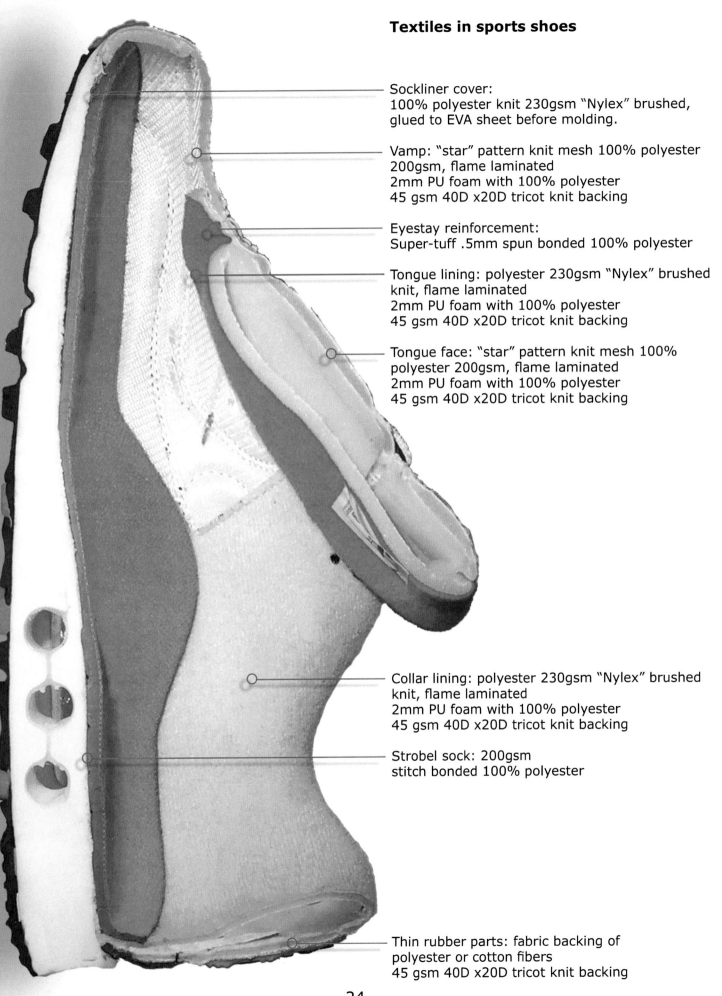

Textiles in sports shoes

Sockliner cover:
100% polyester knit 230gsm "Nylex" brushed,
glued to EVA sheet before molding.

Vamp: "star" pattern knit mesh 100% polyester
200gsm, flame laminated
2mm PU foam with 100% polyester
45 gsm 40D x20D tricot knit backing

Eyestay reinforcement:
Super-tuff .5mm spun bonded 100% polyester

Tongue lining: polyester 230gsm "Nylex" brushed
knit, flame laminated
2mm PU foam with 100% polyester
45 gsm 40D x20D tricot knit backing

Tongue face: "star" pattern knit mesh 100%
polyester 200gsm, flame laminated
2mm PU foam with 100% polyester
45 gsm 40D x20D tricot knit backing

Collar lining: polyester 230gsm "Nylex" brushed
knit, flame laminated
2mm PU foam with 100% polyester
45 gsm 40D x20D tricot knit backing

Strobel sock: 200gsm
stitch bonded 100% polyester

Thin rubber parts: fabric backing of
polyester or cotton fibers
45 gsm 40D x20D tricot knit backing

24

Designing shoes with textiles

Textiles are lightweight and strong making them ideal for use in athletic shoes. They are available in a huge range of weights, weaves, elastic or inelastic. Textiles can be specified for almost any shoe component. Textiles as a class of materials are regularly more breathable than leather or synthetics, depending on the backings specified. Textiles are commonly less expensive than leather or PU materials.

Environmental factors

Man-made textiles are quite resistant to damage by water. While the fabric weave can trap water, the individual fibers themselves do not absorb water. Textiles are ideal for river sandals, aqua shoes, and running shoes. Lightweight track racing shoes are almost entirely made of mesh.

While man-made fibers are water safe, some care must be taken with textile underlays as water can wick through the fabric allowing water to penetrate behind other materials.

3D weaves, and air mesh have the advantage of allowing water and air to flow through but also have the disadvantage of allowing sand and dust to the enter the shoe. The tightness of the weave on both sides of the fabric and any backing layers must be considered when specifying textiles for outdoor shoes.

Bonding

Textiles can also be a challenge to bond during final assembly. Depending on the weave, surface treatments, and fiber type, getting a good, high strength bond of 4kg per square centimeter may be difficult for the factory. Open weaves may absorb the glue and do not have much surface area for bonding. Fabrics with water-resistant coatings must be carefully primed to make sure the glue can penetrate the surface.

⭕ Some mesh shoes will have toe and heel foxing made of leather, PU, or welded TPU to ensure strong bonds in these critical areas.

Lasting

Textiles have high tensile strength, so they are suitable for both board lasting and force or strobel style lasting. Toe lasting textile vamps can be somewhat difficult. To get the same smooth, tight look of leather, special care must be taken to spring the pattern in order to control tension and wrinkles.

High-end running shoes often wrap the textile under the foot to make a sock. In this case, there is no strobel bottom. You can see this construction by lifting the footbed; the stitching will be running down the center of the bottom instead of along the perimeter.

Import duty and tariffs

Textile shoes have been targeted with high duty rates when importing them to the USA and Europe. The tariffs, designed to protect local shoe markets from a flood of inexpensive shoes, add 20% to 37.5% of the factory price to textile shoes. For shoes with over 51% textile surface area and a factory price below US$12.50, the tariff rate is 20% +.90 cents. For shoes which cost more than $12.50, the tariff is 20%.

The classic jogger is designed to avoid the high textile duty classifications while enjoying the lower cost of textile construction.

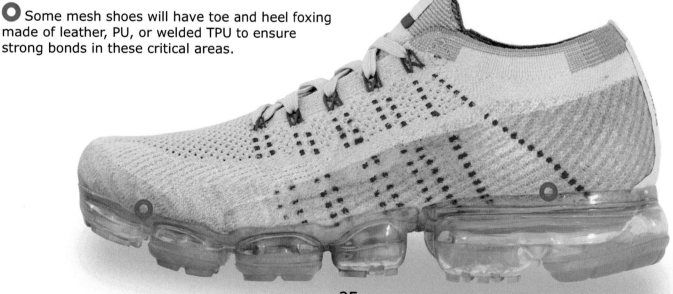

Edge treatments

When designing with textile components, you will need to consider how to finish any exposed edges. Fabric, no matter how carefully cut, will have a rough, unfinished edge. Textile edges must have a finishing treatment to prevent loose threads from unraveling, snagging, or looking unfinished. Cut fabric edges can be folded, covered with binding, hidden by overlays, stitched down, or secured by RF welding.

Here, the collar lining is finished with PU overlays and the fabric collar panel edges are finished with a turned seam.

Fabric with a relatively smooth weave and solid backing such as PVC or PU can be folded and stitched down with a zig-zag or flat lock pattern. Textiles with foam backing, textured weaves, or 3D structures must be concealed with bindings or overlays.

How to specify textiles

When you set down to specify textiles, you will need to consider a few basic parameters. As a designer, you will be concerned with the color and texture. As a developer, your focus will be the physical performance and suitability for manufacturing.

Color

Specify color with a Pantone™ number, a manufacturer's color number, or provide a swatch for matching.

Price

When analyzing the price, it is important to know how the material is manufactured. Is the fabric sold by the roll or by the sheet? 95% of all textiles are sold by linear meter or yard. Materials such as neoprene are sold by the sheet. You must also know the width of the roll and dimensions of the sheets. Fabric weight is measured in GSM (grams per square meter), or ounces per square yard.

Physical test standards for textiles:
Weight
Thickness
Tensile strength L & W
Elongation L & W
Stretch under load 100N
Martindale abrasion dry & wet
Stitch tear L & W
Trouser tear L & W
Color fastness water
Color fast perspiration
Stretching under load
Crocking dry & wet

CHAPTER 3

SYNTHETICS FOR SHOES

Synthetic, synthetic leather, PU leather, pleather, or PU; whatever you call it, this material is another must-have for modern shoes. This class of material offers the shoe designer an immense variety of colors, textures, and features at a range of prices. Synthetic materials dominate almost all categories of athletic shoe production. Many women's fashion shoes are made entirely from synthetic material. Synthetics can be made to look like natural leather, split leather, textiles, wood, metal or almost anything!

While synthetics were once considered cheap junk not suitable for high-quality shoes, times have changed. Many of the modern icons of basketball shoe design would not be possible without synthetics.

Because synthetic materials are entirely man-made, you have complete control over the outer skin layer and inner backing layers. When specifying a synthetic material, it is important to understand how it is made so you can know all your options.

Synthetic construction
Synthetic material types
Backing materials
Assembly options

This shoe features red metallic TPU with carbon fiber texture emboss. The TPU is RF-welded to PU micro fiber suede.

Synthetic material construction

Synthetic materials are often a composite made of two or more layers. An external skin surface made by either "dry" lamination process or by a liquid "wet" process. The skin surface can be printed, pigmented, and embossed. The backing layers can be made of woven, non-woven, polyester fibers, polyester microfiber, PVC, or PU foams.

Wet process synthetics

Wet process synthetic materials are made by pouring liquid resin onto the surface of textured release paper. The wet PVC or PU is carried into heating ovens by the paper material. Once the resin is cured solid, a layer of backing fabric is bonded by a heated pressure roller. The release paper is removed before the PU is shipped to the customer.

Dry process synthetics

In the dry process, the external skin is made by a printing process on PU film. Dry process PU can be thinner and have more graphic effects than wet process PU. In a second operation, the film layer is rolled together with the backing material under heat and pressure. You can tell dry process from wet process, as the wet process will almost always have a solid surface color without special effects.

Embossing rollers

The surface texture of a synthetic material can be created by release paper. More often, the texture effect is created by a heated steel embossing roller. A synthetic material supplier may have hundreds of different embossing rollers.

If you can't find a texture you like, you can order a custom roller for US$2,500 to $4,000.

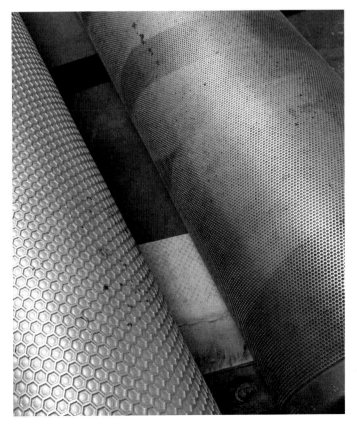

Synthetic material types

There are four common surface materials: PVC Poly(vinyl chloride), which is the cheapest; PU (Polyurethane), which can be higher quality with many surface options; TPU (Thermoplastic polyurethane); and a class of materials made of PU fibers without a surface skin. Of these four types, PVC and PU are similar in construction; a skin with backing. TPU materials tend to be a single layer of material with a finer emboss. PU materials are offered as a solid, skinless material, which can have a brushed surface to look like suede or nu-buck.

Polyvinyl chloride, PVC leather

PVC leather is the most basic synthetic leather material. Made by wet process, the surface is a sealed skin that has a textured surface.

Color matched liquid PVC is poured on a release paper, then heated to cure the PVC. This layer may be only .2 to .5mm thick. A second application of liquid PVC with an added blowing agent expands to create a soft foam layer. This layer can be 1mm to 3mm thick. Finally, a woven reinforcing cloth is rolled on to give the PVC material some structure and stretch resistance.

At this point, the PVC has a smooth, glossy surface. Before the PVC can be used, a texture must be added. PVC with a backing layer readily accepts embossing. A heated roller is used to apply the texture.

This material is the cheap stuff found on inexpensive shoes. When it is pulled tight, it may wrinkle, and the backing surface will x-ray through the surface.

Perfect for inexpensive shoes, PVC can be found on shoes as a cost cutting feature. PVC leather should not be specified for shoes that retail for more than $75.00. Thickness ranges from .5mm to 2.00mm depending on the backing layers and surface treatment.

Polyurethane, PU leather

PU leather starts with a surface of Polyurethane plastic film .2 to .5mm thick. The surface of this film is printed, embossed, scuffed, polished, or sprayed to create one of the millions of surface options. You can also choose a shiny, matte, satin, metallic, or reflective finish. You have an immense library of surface options to choose from and can create new variations if you can meet the minimum order quantity.

The large PU makers have hundreds of different embossing patterns (embossing rollers) that can be applied to hundreds of different surfaces and you can pick any color you want!

The PU surface readily accepts embossing and printing effects. The PU skin is stretchable and durable so it can be combined backing materials suitable for toe lasting. This allows PU to be used on toe-caps of sports and casual shoes. PU leather is also made in high abrasion versions and can have water-resistant backing.

PU material with microfiber backing cuts cleanly and looks great when perforated. Backings can be color matched so cut edges look clean.

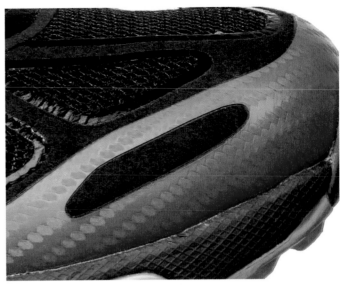

Synthetic microfiber suede

Synthetic suede, made of polyester microfibers, has a smooth, consistent, brushed surface. Known as Ultrasuede, Alcantara™, Hi-skin, Chamude, Amara, or microfiber suede, this material can be expensive, but it is great for shoes, gloves, linings, and trim.

Available in thicknesses from .3mm to 1.5mm, synthetic suede cuts cleanly for detailed designs and is available in many colors. Being colorfast and waterproof, synthetic suede replaces suede in sports shoes that will be exposed to water.

Synthetic suede is made by bonding polyester microfibers (each fiber is 1/5th the size of a human hair) into matting, then carefully brushing the surface to create the suede-like nap. Synthetic suede is available in almost any color, and its surface can be printed or embossed depending on the backing material.

Microfiber suede has hydrophilic properties, but the tiny fibers themselves, being hydrophobic, are not damaged by water.

Thermoplastic polyurethane, TPU

TPU also has many interesting properties for the footwear designer. It can be injected into flexible rubber-like parts and extruded into thin films. TPU films can be created in almost any color, including transparent, and can be made with a textured surface. TPU film is elastic, waterproof, and abrasion resistant. Once inside the shoe factory, TPU film can be die-cut, laser cut, and silkscreen-printed.

What makes TPU so interesting for footwear production is the material's thermoplastic capabilities. The thermoplastic material can be re-melted. TPU can be RF and heat welded onto the surfaces of other materials to create a high tech, stitch-less construction. TPU film is being used to create lightweight supporting structures for high-end athletic shoes.

Here is a lightweight, textile trail running shoe. Its upper is reinforced with welded thin film TPU panels. The graphics are screen printed before the TPU is cut and welded.

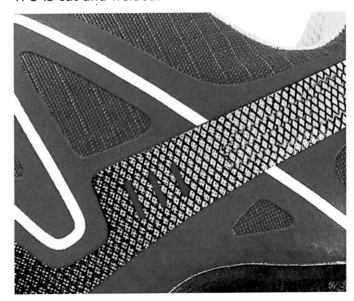

Backing materials

The surface skin of a synthetic material provides the cosmetic effect, and the backing layers are what makes the material suitable for footwear production. The backing layers of synthetic materials carry the load and help determine the performance characteristics. Synthetic materials are not colored by dyeing processes, so the backing fiber must be colored in a separate operation before lamination to the PU or PC top skins.

Backing materials can have special features such as DWR water resistant treatment to stop water from wicking into cut edges.

The backing materials fit into four classes; woven, non-woven, microfiber, and foam.

Non-woven backing

Synthetic materials with non-woven backings are more commonly found in mass-produced athletic shoes. Made of polyester fibers, the non-woven backing can be made thicker and has a dimension feel closer to natural leather. More resistant to wrinkles and stretchable synthetics, non-woven backings can be embossed and lasted. Non-woven backings die-cut cleanly and can be skived if required to roll or fold edges.

Because the non-woven backing has some thickness, the color must be specified. Synthetic materials are not colored by dyeing process so the backing fiber must be colored in a separate operation before lamination to the PU or PC top skins. The non-woven backing material has water absorbing hydrophilic properties, but the tiny fibers themselves being hydrophobic are not damaged by water. To prevent water infiltration DWR and anti-microbial compounds can be added. PU with a standard non-woven backing can cost between $4.00 to $5.00 per meter.

Woven backing

Woven backings for synthetic materials are usually made of relatively thin, non-stretchable, and inexpensive polyester fiber. Commonly used to backup PVC top skins, this combination is used to make linings, tongue faces, bindings, logos, and trim parts. Woven backing will show fiber ends on cut edges, so the material should be covered or rolled. PVC with woven backing is inexpensive, resists stretching, and bonds readily making it useful for internal reinforcements. The woven fiber backing is not suitable for emboss due to its thinness and lack of stretch. PVC with standard woven backing can cost between $1.00 to $3.00 per meter.

Microfiber backing

Microfiber backings are similar to standard non-woven backings but have improved suppleness and hand feel. Microfiber backings die-cut cleanly and can be skived if required to roll or fold edges. Microfiber backings readily accept embossing and can be very stretchable. High-end athletic shoes will use microfiber backed PU for its quality leather like feel. In all other aspects, microfiber backing can be handled like the more common non-woven polyester backing. PU with microfiber backing can cost between $7.00 to $10.00 per meter.

Foam backing

PVC sponge foam sheets can be used to back PVC and PU. Available in thicknesses from .5mm to 2.00mm, PVC sponge is relatively inexpensive and readily accepts deep emboss effects. PVC sponge is closed cell foam but is relatively heavy. PVC sponge foam is not an acceptable cushioning foam but does make an excellent filler for embossing effects if used in small quantities.

Assembly options

Synthetic materials have so many interesting variations and possible specifications. They can be handled in unique ways well beyond the capabilities of fabric and natural leather. Of course, synthetic materials can be cut and sewn conventionally, but can also be laser cut, RF welded, hot pressed, cold pressed, co-molded, perforated and over-molded; all on one shoe!

The side panels of this iconic design are produced by placing a thin metallic PU with elastic backing into a mold with expanding PU foam. With the mold closed, the foam fills the cavity, pressing the PU skin into the distinctive and dynamic shape. Thin stitching flanges are molded in around the edges, and the bottom edge is contoured to fit the outsole top line and carbon shank parts.

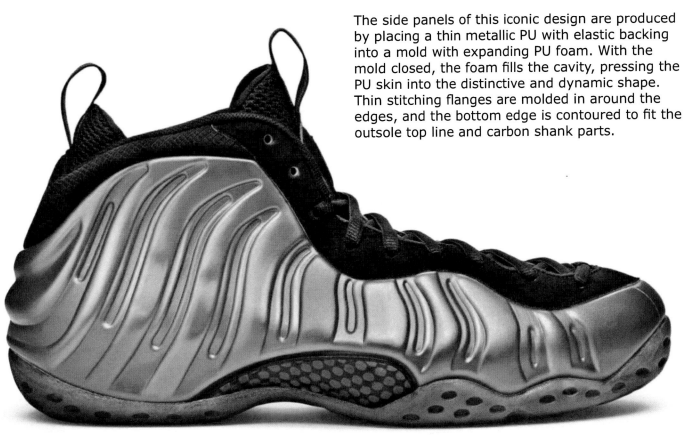

Designing shoes with synthetics

Synthetics are lightweight and strong making them ideal for use in casual and athletic shoes. As you have learned, synthetics are available in a wide range of colors and constructions.

The makers of synthetics have expertly duplicated the look of grain leather, split leather, and have emboss patterns that resemble woven textiles. Synthetics can be specified for almost any shoe style and shoe component.

Because synthetics are rolled goods and usually have a non-direction emboss, they can be very efficiently cut. The cost for most synthetics is much less than real leather; this allows the designer to create dramatic pattern parts which would be wasteful and unthinkable if made with real leather.

⊙ The narrow blue strip on the quarter panel would be expensive and wasteful if made of leather, but when made with synthetic PU or PVC, the pattern design is not overly expensive. (see below)

Environmental factors

Man-made synthetics with solid backings are resistant to damage by water. Synthetics are ideal court shoes, casual shoes, running shoes, and low price dress shoes.

Synthetics are lightweight and flexible but not always breathable. Because synthetics are essentially made of meltable plastic, great care must be taken when considering their use in vulcanized shoes. Synthetics may shrink, stretch, or peel if overheated during production.

Synthetics are easy to clean and resistant to stains and mildew. They are great for baseball, soccer and football shoes.

Bonding synthetics

Synthetics are usually easy to bond during final assembly. Depending on the surface treatments and skin type, getting a high strength bond of 4kg per square centimeter may require some light buffing.

Synthetics have the unique advantage of being weldable. If the base layer can be melted, then a synthetic material may be welded.

Lasting synthetics

Synthetics commonly have high tensile strength so they are suitable for both board lasting and force or strobel style lasting. Toe lasting synthetics can be somewhat difficult. To get the same smooth, tight look of leather, special care must be taken to spring the pattern in order to control tension and wrinkles.

Import duty and tariffs

Synthetic shoes have been targeted with high duty rates when importing them into the USA and Europe. Tariffs designed to protect local shoe markets from a flood of inexpensive shoes add 20% to 37.5% of the shoe cost to synthetic shoes.

For shoes with more than 51% synthetic surface area and a factory price below US$12.50, the tariff is 20% +.90 cents. For shoes with a price of more than $12.50, the tariff is 20%. To avoid these high duty rates, companies will design shoes that are 51% leather and 49% synthetics.

Edge treatments for synthetics

Synthetic materials offer shoe designers many options for edge finishing. If your synthetic material has a non-woven backing, the cut edges will be clean and crisp. Thinner woven backing layers, such as tricot, may also cut cleanly. Inexpensive synthetics with heavy woven backings may show loose fibers. TPU materials without backing layers cut cleanly by cutting die, laser, or welding tool.

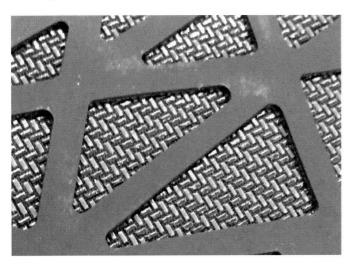

Synthetic materials have the unique feature of dye-able backing layers. The designer can specify a matched or contrasting color backing layer.

Synthetic materials with non-woven or microfiber backings can be skived allowing the edges to be neatly folded.

How to specify synthetics

When you specify synthetics you will need to consider the color, surface emboss, backing type, backing thickness, backing color, and any special treatments.

Colors

Specify colors by Pantone™ numbers, manufacturer's color numbers, or provide swatches for matching.

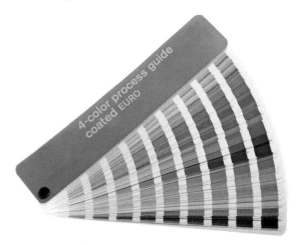

Price

Most synthetics are sold by linear meter or yard. You must know the width of the roll to make accurate price calculations. Prices for synthetics range from $1.00 per yard to over $10.00. Yes, a high-end synthetic with waterproof backing or other special features can cost more than leather!

Physical test standards for synthetics

Weight
Thickness
Tensile strength L & W
Elongation L & W
Stretch under load 100N
Martindale abrasion wet & dry
Stitch tear L & W
Trouser tear L & W
Colorfastness water
Color fast perspiration
Stretching under load
Crocking wet & dry

Because synthetics are usually made of two layers or more, it is important to look out for peeling during flex tests and elongation tests.

CHAPTER 4
SHOE STITCHING THREAD

Stitching thread is the tiny component that truly holds it all together. The right thread will make durable shoes that last for years, and the wrong thread will leave your shoes in pieces and your customers angry! Stitching technique is critical too. How many stitches per inch? How many rows of stitching? The size and type of thread must also be suited for the material you are sewing.

Shoe stitching thread is also critical to the design styling of your shoe. As a design element, the thread color choice and specification are important to the look of the shoe. Does your design have complicated stitching or simple stitching? You may choose matching stitching to help conceal poor alignment, or bright contrast stitching to highlight exceptional craftsmanship. Are you making a waterproof shoe with as few stitches as possible or a hyper-modern design with all the stitching hidden inside?

How is thread size measured?
Denier, a weight specification, states how many grams 9,000 meters of the specified thread weighs. The larger the denier number, the thicker the thread. The denier weight system also specifies the number of strands of the specified weight that are wrapped together to make the finished thread. Common deniers for shoes are 420D to 600D.

Tex is the weight in grams of 1,000 meters of thread. If 1,000 meters weighs 25 grams, it is a Tex 25. Larger Tex numbers are heavier threads. Tex is more commonly used in Europe and Canada. Thread of Tex 44 is equal to about 400D on the denier scale.

How many stitches per inch?
Shoe upper construction most commonly uses 9 to 11 stitches per inch. For outsole channel stitching, 4 to 5 stitches per inch are the norm. The number of stitches per inch detriments the strength of the seam. Too few stitches will create a weak seam, and too many stitches can lead to a perforation effect that can weaken the footwear materials. PU and leather are more susceptible to this perforation effect. Mesh fabrics are usually resistant to the perforation effect.

Plastic parts, such as nylon speed hooks and rubber parts, are very sensitive to the perforation effect. The number of stitches per inch must be tested to ensure the parts are not damaged. Try 8 per inch to start.

What are shoe threads made of?

Fibers used to make shoe thread can be natural or synthetic. Natural fibers come from plants and are spun or twisted into yarns. Cotton is the most common natural fiber used to make thread.

Synthetic fibers are made from various chemicals that are then melt-spun or wet-spun into continuous filament fibers. The most common synthetic fibers used are polyester and nylon. Other specialty synthetic fibers include polypropylene, aramid including Kevlar™, Nomex™, Spectra™, Vectran™, PPS, and PTFE.

Fiber constructions

Sewing threads are made in seven different thread constructions using either staple fibers, continuous filament fibers, or a combination of both. Staple fibers are spun into a specific yarn and then plied into a sewing thread. Continuous filaments are used in the manufacturing of five thread constructions including twisted multifilament, monocord, textured, air entangled, and monofilament.

We will focus on the threads commonly found in footwear.

Monofilament threads

Monofilament threads are made from single continuous filaments of nylon that resemble fishing line. Monofilament threads are translucent and blend in with many colors. Because it tends to be stiffer than other filament products, monofilament threads are not recommended for seams that may lay adjacent to the skin.

Twisted multifilament

Twisted multifilament threads are made from continuous filaments of polyester or nylon that are twisted together into a cohesive bundle and then plied to make the thread. They are then dyed, stretched, and heat set to achieve the desired physical characteristics. Twisted multifilament threads are available either soft or with an additional bond for better ply security and abrasion resistance.

"Bonded" finish is an additional process performed on multifilament polyester and nylon threads where a special resin is added that encapsulates the filaments forming a tough, smooth protective coating on the surface of the thread. This bonding process adds significantly to the thread's ability to resist abrasion and greatly enhances ply security during sewing.

They are exceptionally strong for their size and have excellent abrasion resistance and durability.

Monocord

Monocord threads are made from continuous filaments of polyester or nylon that have been bonded together. They have very little twist so they look like a single cord of yarn. Because of the way these threads are made, they appear to be flat and ribbon-like, which provides a low-seam profile and therefore a high degree of resistance to abrasion. Monocord threads are exceptionally strong for their size and are used in the manufacturing of furniture, shoes, and other heavy-duty applications.

Seam types found in shoes

There are 8 "classes" of stitching seams. Classes 1,2,3,& 5 are common in shoe production. Class 4 can be found in neoprene goods like wetsuit booties for example.

Class 1 – Superimposed seam
Class 2 – Lapped seam
Class 3 – Bound seams
Class 4 – Flat seams
Class 5 – Decorative/Ornamental
Class 6 – Edge finishing/neatening
Class 7 – Attaching of separate items
Class 8 – Single-ply construction

Stitching types

There are 14 standard stitch types used for commercial sewing. For shoe assembly 301,401, Multi-needle lock stitch and the Zig Zag Stitch are the most common.

101 – Single Thread Chain stitch
103 – Single Thread Blind hemming
301 – Lock stitch
401 – Chain stitch
Multi-needle lock & chainstitch 301 & 304
Zig Zag Stitch 304 and 404
406 – Cover seam
503 – Two thread overedge (serging)
504 – Three thread overedge
515 – Four thread safety stitch
516 – Five Thread full safety
602 – Twin needle cover seam with top cover
605 – Three needle cover seam with top cover
607 – Flat seam

For an in-depth description of all the seam and stitch types visit Coatsindustrial.com. The experts at Coats thread have put together an extensive informational site showing thread construction, stitching types, and seam configurations.

CHAPTER 5

FOOTWEAR REINFORCEMENTS

Reinforcements are quite often the hidden heroes inside of footwear that make a shoe design truly functional and practical. The internal reinforcements you select will allow your shoe to hold its shape, protect the foot, provide support, and stay together. The reinforcements are a significant factor in determining your shoes' performance, comfort, durability, and suitability for its designated task. The reinforcements inside hiking boots or work boots are radically different from what you will need inside a running shoe or casual footwear.

Reinforcement functions
Shaping the shoe
Upper support
Outsole stiffness
Material backing
Tear resistance
Safety requirements

Shaping the shoe
The overall shape of a shoe is determined by the last and pattern. If the upper is constructed with un-backed fabric, then it's a sock, not a shoe. Almost every shoe will have some type of shaping reinforcement to hold the shape once the last is removed. Leather will take the shape of the last, but over time, without a supporting layer, can stretch and distort. Leather is often reinforced with a fusible backing layer.

Hot melt glue is often applied between the upper layer and inner lining of a shoe. During the lasting operations and when the shoe is heated on the assembly line, the hot melt takes shape and is then set in a cooling tunnel. Hot melt glue is firm but flexible and can help a shoe "stand up" in appearance. This shoe shaping reinforcement can be overdone. Inexpensive shoes are often overly stiff. While the uppers may look crisp and wrinkle-free, they may also feel like cardboard on your feet.

Toe counters

The toe counter or toe puff may be made of a non-woven polyester fabric saturated with a heat moldable plastic. The material is die cut from flat sheets to fit the shoe pattern. When the shoe upper is processed during stitching, but before the strobel bottom is sewn on, the toe counter is heat formed. The front of the shoe is placed in a heater for a few minutes. Next, the upper is clamped into a cooling fixture with a shaped metal form to set the shape.

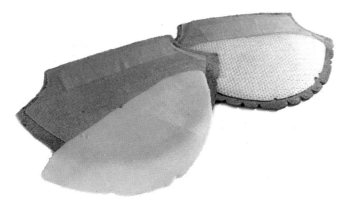

Here a worker uses a mechanical lasting machine to toe last a women's fashion shoe. The toe counter is softened in the heat tunnel and the final shape is fixed during the lasting operation.

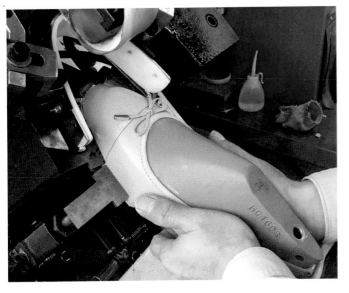

Upper support

To make a shoe with solid ankle support, it must have a heel counter. The heel counter can be hidden inside the shoe or attached to the outside of the upper, but will always be firmly attached to the outsole. The heel counter may be made using the same shaping process as the toe puff, but with a much thicker material.

Heel counters can be made from thick leather, rubber, non-woven chemical sheet, injection molded plastic, or heat moldable plastic sheet. Each material has its special properties.

Leather

Leather heel counters are found in hand-crafted leather shoes and western boots. A firm piece of leather is carefully skived to make the edges thin. The leather is saturated with a mild adhesive or water, then formed to the last. The leather counter can be very stiff depending on the thickness and temper of the leather.

Chemical sheet

Known in the shoe trades as chemi-sheet, this material is made of non-woven polyester fibers saturated with plastic resin. The material comes in sheets ranging from .5mm to 2.0mm in thickness. The counter is die-cut into shape, then dipped into or brushed with a solvent. The solvent softens the resin binder material allowing the flat sheet to conform to the upper. Chemi-sheet is only found in relatively inexpensive shoes as the material tends to crack and is not as easy to shape as other thermo-plastic materials.

Heat-molded plastic sheet

Molded counters are very popular and can be found in almost all modern mass-produced shoes.

The counter material comes in sheets ranging from .2mm to 2.5mm in thickness. The material is die-cut and bonded into the upper with hot melt glue or fusible coating. Before the shoe is closed and lasted, the unfinished upper is placed into a heater that softens the counter material.

Once the counter is soft and pliable, it is moved to a pressing machine fitted with the heel section of the shoe's last. The press squeezes the upper onto the chilled last heel, setting the shape of the counter. The materials made by Texon™ and TecnoGi™ will contain heat moldable Surlyn plastic.

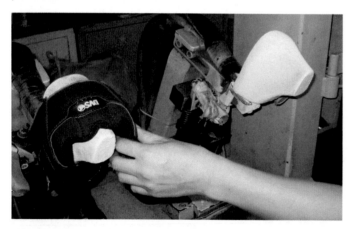

Here you can see the frost collecting on the cooling form.

Injection molded heel counters

For some high production volume shoes, the factory may use a 3D injected plastic counter. The fit can be exact, and the processing inside the stitching room can be faster. The injection molded counters can be made from Surlyn, PVC, or nylon plastics.

The 3D shape can be very precise and the material thickness adjusted to make both firm and flexible counters. You can also see injection molded heel stabilizers attached to the outside of a shoe. Close fitting soccer shoes with thinner uppers are likely to have ridged injection molded heel counters.

Vulcanized rubber

Rubber heel counters are found in vulcanized shoes. The same rubber compound used to make the sole foxing parts is re-purposed to make heel counters. Cut scraps for the sole making processes are remixed and rolled into sheets for die-cutting. The rubber edges are skived before they are cemented into the upper. The flat rubber counter takes the shape of the last when the entire shoe is vulcanized.

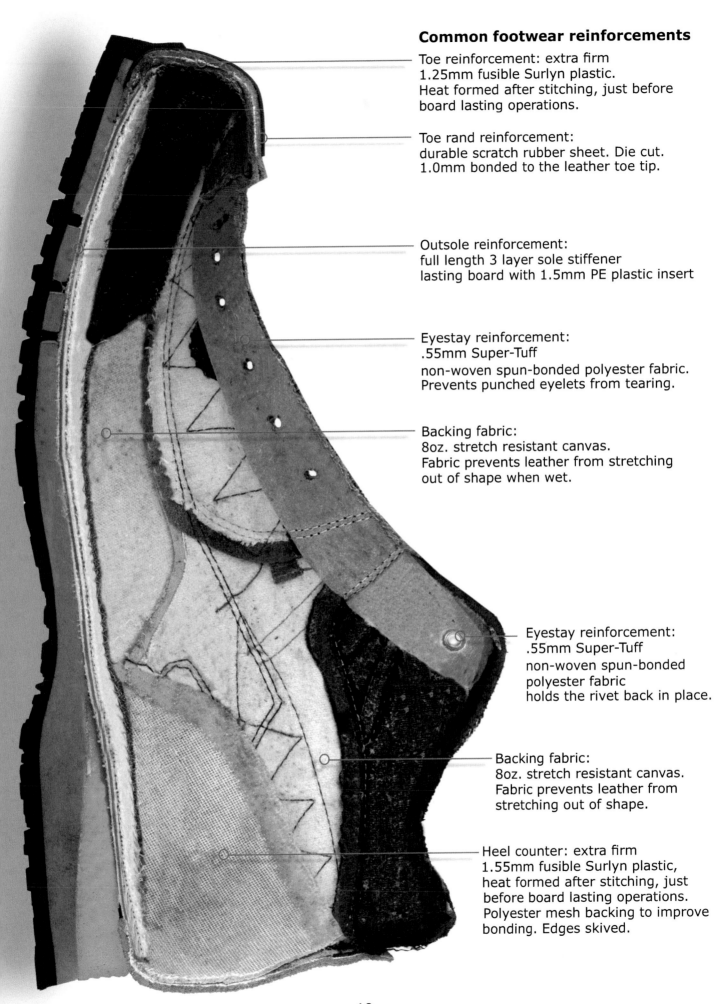

Common footwear reinforcements

Toe reinforcement: extra firm
1.25mm fusible Surlyn plastic.
Heat formed after stitching, just before
board lasting operations.

Toe rand reinforcement:
durable scratch rubber sheet. Die cut.
1.0mm bonded to the leather toe tip.

Outsole reinforcement:
full length 3 layer sole stiffener
lasting board with 1.5mm PE plastic insert

Eyestay reinforcement:
.55mm Super-Tuff
non-woven spun-bonded polyester fabric.
Prevents punched eyelets from tearing.

Backing fabric:
8oz. stretch resistant canvas.
Fabric prevents leather from stretching
out of shape when wet.

Eyestay reinforcement:
.55mm Super-Tuff
non-woven spun-bonded
polyester fabric
holds the rivet back in place.

Backing fabric:
8oz. stretch resistant canvas.
Fabric prevents leather from
stretching out of shape.

Heel counter: extra firm
1.55mm fusible Surlyn plastic,
heat formed after stitching, just
before board lasting operations.
Polyester mesh backing to improve
bonding. Edges skived.

40

Backing materials

The upper material of shoes will often need a little extra support, durability, or stretch resistance. The vamp reinforcement is often a thin layer of cotton fabric with adhesive backing. Placed on the vamp area, this material will stop the wearer's toe from stretching the material or even a toenail from wearing through. Natural leather will often have a lightweight canvas backing to protect it from stretching out of shape when wet.

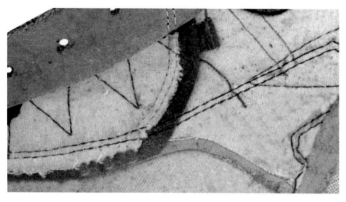

Tear resistance

Perforated eyelet holes and hardware attached by riveting require a special backing fabric to resist tearing out of the upper. The brand name for this reinforcing material is Super-Tuff™. Many material companies produce this type of reinforcing material, in the shoe trade they are all called by the common name "Super-Tuff." Super-Tuff is a thin, non-woven, spun-bonded polyester fabric. It is easy to cut but almost impossible to tear. Super-Tuff has a silver grey finish and is available in thicknesses from .25mm to 1.0mm.

Super-Tuff is found in the eyestays of almost every shoe. It is often applied with a sticky back coating allowing workers to apply quickly. Once in place, it is permanently sewn in. You will never see this material unless you cut into a pair of shoes.

Outsole reinforcements:

You may be surprised to find out that hiking boots and high heel shoes both share the common pressed steel shank.

In the hiking boot, a steel shank buried in the outsole prevents the outsole from flexing as the user walks over rocks or other obstacles that may injure the foot. Boots designed for hiking in rough conditions with heavy packs should be very stiff. A stiffer hiking boot will be needed as the terrain becomes more difficult or pack weight increases. Boots appropriate for day hikes may be flexible, while mountaineering boots may have a fiberglass or steel shank that will not bend at all.

Women's high heel shoes also require steel shanks to anchor the heel post and prevent lateral twisting. The steel shank prevents the high heel

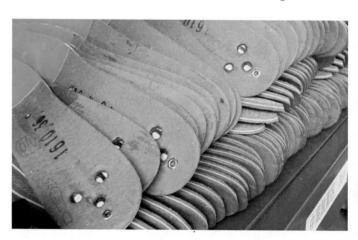

from snapping and the shoe collapsing.
You will find steel, plastic, or fiberglass composite shanks in outdoor shoes, military boots, and walking shoes.

Work boots for roofing and timber framing will have nail proof fabric inserts to prevent punctures while working on dangerous construction sites.

Cleated shoes for baseball, football, cycling, and soccer have injection molded plastic bottom units to provide stiffness. The plastic parts are often backed up with cellulose fiber lasting boards.

House slippers, driving shoes, and baby shoes do not require outsole reinforcements.

Safety

Footwear for service or industrial use will often require safety toes. Safety rated shoes are required for all types of military and civil first responders including medical, rescue, and law enforcement personnel. For example, steel toe footwear is required for personnel working on or around helicopters as soldiers and medical staff can be severely injured by the landing skids if not protected.

Extra protection is also necessary for industrial, construction, and warehouse workers in dangerous environments who handle heavy equipment. Warehouse workers may be injured by falling items or have their toes crushed under forklift wheels.

There are several rating standards for safety footwear. Some can be met with composite toe reinforcements, while others will require steel toes of various metals types or thicknesses.

Recreational shoes such as motocross boots, biker boots, mountaineering boots, and shoes for baseball umpires are not legally required to have toe reinforcements, but this feature is often included in these high-performance products.

The suppliers of steel and composite safety toes for footwear have designed their products to meet the crush standards required by the standard regulations. The designer or product manager needs only to provide the target standard. You must remember that even if the toe cap is rated to a certain standard, the finished shoe must be tested in a certified lab.

While the toe reinforcement part is the main element, the sole unit and lasting board must also be strong enough to support the toe cap and rubber hardness.

Because the toe reinforcement parts are rigid, special care must be taken to specify vamp lining materials to pad the transition to the shoe upper. The edge of the toe cap may have a rubber sheet or thick fabric layer attached to make a comfortable transition.

CHAPTER 6
SHOELACES

Shoelaces have two very simple functions. First, to hold the shoe onto your foot and second, to provide some style! The earliest leather shoes dated from 3500 B.C.E. have leather laces. 5000 years later, the function is the same, but the style has come a long way.

For the shoelace to do its job correctly, it should resist stretching and stay tied. Once these basic functions have been satisfied, more specific attributes can be studied for different shoe types. The "correct" shoelace depends on the function of your shoe. The same lace that works for a fine leather office shoe will not be suitable for hunting boots or ballerina slippers.

The aglet
The end cap on the shoelace is called the "aglet". The aglet is made of plastic tape wrapped tightly around the lace, or a metal cap crimped over the end. The plastic aglet tape may have a printed logo, while the metal aglet may have a logo stamped onto its surface. Yes, aglet is a funny sounding word! The origin is French, aiguillette, meaning 'small needle.'

The lace
The lace is simply a string. There are many material options depending upon the functional requirements of the shoe. The waxed cotton lace of an office dress shoe does not need to be high strength, 2mm diameter is okay. The lace on a hockey skate is cut resistant, wide to displace lacing pressure, and has high tensile strength so the players can pull the laces tight. The hockey skate lace may be 12mm wide. Laces with a textured surface and compressible core will stay tied better than smooth firm laces.

Style
The shoelace is also an element of style! Skateboarders often replace the standard black lace with a brightly colored lace. The boat shoe has leather laces due to tradition rather than functionality.

Shoelace constructions:
Braided, waxed, jacquard weave, reflective, oval, round, flat.

Shoelace materials:
Polyester, nylon, cotton, leather, Kevlar, elastic rubber with knit cover, stainless steel wire.

Other lacing systems

Aside from conventional woven or knit laces, there are many other ways to secure a shoe to your foot.

Steel cable lacing systems can be found on cycling shoes, snow boots, golf and running shoes. The cable reel and fittings will add US$2.00 to $10.00 to the factory price of your shoe and provide a unique function.

Of course, some shoes may not have any laces at all. The adjusting function may be velcro straps or elastic goring. The shoe brand Royal Elastics™ is based entirely on shoes without laces.

How long should a shoelace be?

There are charts available on-line that suggest the lace length based on how many lace holes are in the shoe. A basic measurement also works: starting with the shoe upper still on the last, the lace should run through every position then add 6 inches (15cm).

CHAPTER 7

SHOE GLUE

Almost every part of a modern shoe is glued or laminated in place. The outsole of the shoe is glued to the upper. Additionally, many upper parts are bonded together before they are stitched into place. Does the shoe designer need to specify the type of glue used in the shoe? Yes!

As the shoe designer or developer, you have many choices to make. The more direction you can give the factory, the better. The right glue, in the right place, will help create a flexible, strong, breathable, well-formed, and long-lasting shoe. The wrong glue may make the shoe stiff, hot, uncomfortable, or ruin carefully selected materials. Of course, the wrong glue, or an incorrect bonding process, may also cause your shoe to fall apart long before its time.

It is critical to specify a glue that will not saturate, stain, or melt the material you are bonding. It is also important to find the bonding process suitable for each material type. The glue and bonding process required for bonding oiled leather to rubber will not work when attaching mesh to EVA. Your factory's technicians will know what to do, but new materials, or higher standards, may call for expert opinions. It is in your best interest to request a consultation with the glue manufacturer.

Beyond the purely functional parameters, shoe glue is also the focus of environmental and workers' health concerns. The solvents in adhesives allow for firm bonding combined with a quick drying time which equals faster assembly line speed. These same solvents release volatile organic compounds that can harm workers and the environment. You may decide that water based glue is right for your product and brand image.

The most common types of glue in shoe production:
Polyurethane PU contact cement
White glue or PVA Poly(Vinyl Acetate)
Hot melt or fusible glue
Flame lamination

Polyurethane / PU contact cement

PU contact cement is the most common glue used in shoe production. Available in water based and solvent based formulations, PU contact cement is what a shoe factory will use to bond the outsole parts together and to bond the outsoles to the uppers. PU cement bonds well to most materials and is very flexible. PU cement is formulated to bond with itself on contact, so both objects to be bonded will need to have glue applied. For the PU bonds to be strong, the surfaces must first be prepared with a primer. Once the primer is dry, the PU cement is applied. The tacky parts are pressed together, then cooled to set the bond.

White glue / PVA, Poly(vinyl acetate)

PVA glue (commonly referred to as Elmer's glue or school glue in the USA) is also used in footwear. It is not as flexible as PU cement and is water based, so it will take longer to dry. PVA glue is used to bond some internal components, but cannot be used to assemble the upper to outsoles. PVA glue is more often found in classic handmade shoes and less often in mass-produced products.

Hot Melt / Fusible glue

Hot melting or fusible glues are now the standard for bonding the internal components of modern footwear. Hot melt glue comes in many formulations. Some are dry to the touch when cool, others tacky. Hot melt glue can be applied by a small tabletop machine that sprays the molten glue in fine looping streams onto individual parts, or the glue can be applied to rolled goods in the fabric factory. The advantage of hot glue is that once the shoe is stitched and assembled, the glue can be softened in a heat tunnel. In the heat tunnel, the hot melt glue will re-melt and set into its new shape. Shoes made with hot melt glue will be more breathable and supple than shoes made with PU or PVA glue.

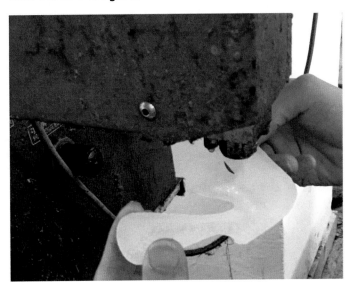

Flame lamination

Lamination is the process that combines a surface material to a second backing layer. Almost all fabrics found in shoes are laminated to at least one backing layer of foam. The flame lamination process is often used to bond fabric to PU foam. The foam sheet is heated with an open flame to melt the top layer before the molten layer has cooled the fabric is pressed to the foam bonding the two layers.

Inside a shoe, it is very common to see a thick mesh fabric layer of tricot laminated to the back of the foam and the shoe's outer skin material laminated to the top surface of the foam. The smooth polyester tricot fabric will then act as the shoe's inside lining.

PU glue can also be used to laminate fabric and foam together, but flame lamination creates a more breathable, flexible bond.

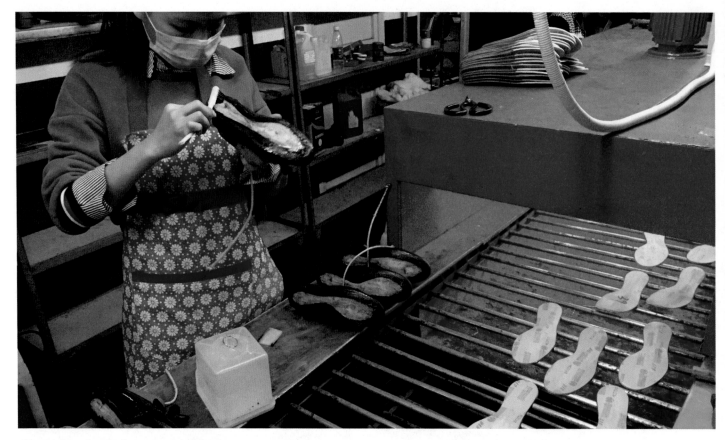

Standard gluing procedure

First, you need to make sure the parts to be bonded are clean. For the primer and cement to work properly, the gluing surfaces must be free of dirt, dust, grease, and any mold release leftover from the forming processes. Factories will often buff the surface of the midsole to break the skin and remove any mold release. This process is called "roughing." Any smooth PU or leather surfaces on the upper may also be roughed. The upper is temporarily placed on the outsole and marked so only on contact areas are roughed. It is important to remove any dust after roughing.

Once the parts are cleaned, a primer is applied to prepare the surfaces before cementing. The primer penetrates the material and allows the cement to flow onto the material for a better bond. Two coats of primer are applied and dried to assure full coverage of the material. When the second coat of primer is dry, two coats of cement will be applied. As soon as the second coat of cement is dry to the touch, the two parts can be joined together.

The technicians work quickly and carefully to make sure the upper and outsole are aligned correctly. Before the cement cures, the parts will be pressed together with a hydraulic ram. This ensures complete contact between the two surfaces being bonded. After pressing, the completed shoe will be chilled to set the bond.

How to read a glue bond

If you have a bonding failure, it is important to know how to "read" the results. The first step is to examine the broken parts to see if the material failed, or the glue failed. If you are bonding midsole foam to a rubber outsole, you will need to look at the parts closely; if you see a thin layer of foam remaining on the rubber part, the foam material failed, not the bond.

If you see a clean surface on the foam, without any glue remaining, this tells you the glue bond to the foam failed. You may need to try a different primer and make sure the foam parts are cleaned correctly to remove any dust or mold release before bonding.

If you see the remains of glue on both the foam and rubber parts, you know that the bond failed. You may need to try a different cement or adjust the temperature of the heating tunnels.

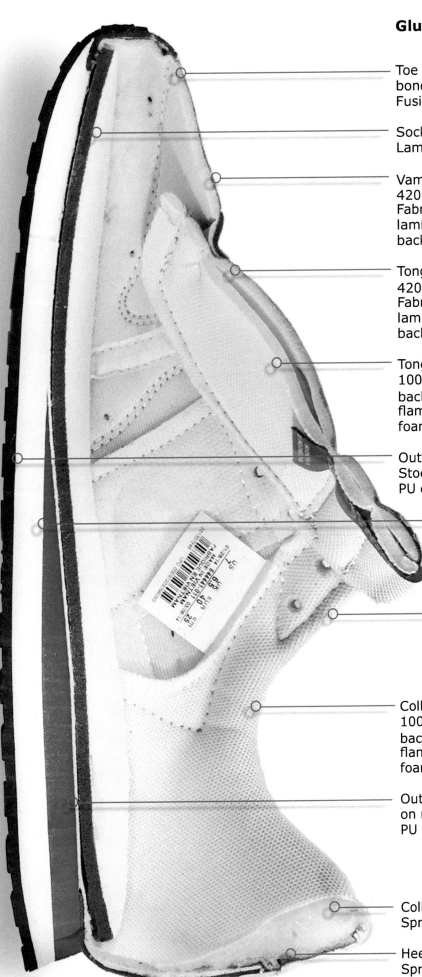

Glue holds it all together

Toe reinforcement: Surlyn plastic bonded to leather toe tip back. Fusible hot-melt glue.

Sock liner cover: 100% polyester jersey knit. Laminated to sheet foam with PU cement.

Vamp upper fabric: 420D diamond nylon with foam backing. Fabric roll laminated to foam by flame lamination. Tricot backing bonded to foam back by flame lamination.

Tongue face upper fabric: 420D diamond nylon with foam backing. Fabric roll laminated to foam by flame lamination. Tricot backing bonded to foam back by flame lamination.

Tongue lining: 100% polyester jersey knit with foam backing, fabric roll laminated to foam by flame lamination. Tricot backing bonded to foam back by flame lamination.

Outsole: rubber bonded to EVA. Stock fitting sub-assembly line. PU contact cement with primer.

Outsole: rubber bonded to EVA. Stock fitting sub-assembly line, PU contact cement with primer.

Super-Tuff eyestay reinforcement bonded to back of leather part. Spray applied hot-melt glue. Super-Tuff may have self adhesive backing.

Collar lining: 100% polyester, 200gsm 100% polyester jersey knit with foam backing, fabric roll laminated to foam by flame lamination. Tricot backing bonded to foam back by flame lamination.

Outsole unit: bonded to board lasted upper on main assembly line using PU contact cement with primer.

Collar foam: 12mm die-cut KFF PU foam. Spray applied hot-melt glue.

Heel counter: 1mm chemi-sheet fiber board. Spray applied hot-melt glue.

48

CHAPTER 8

HARDWARE FOR SHOES

Shoe hardware can be an important functional component for shoes as well as a key element of styling. Hardware can be made from many common metals or plastics. Functional parts such as eyelets, speed hooks, or buckles will have specific performance requirements. Styling parts such as logos, emblems, lace keepers, and insignia will provide the extra flash for a modern fashion shoe.

When specifying and designing hardware parts, there are many factors to consider:

Material selection
Setup costs
Unit costs
MOQ (Minimum Order Quantity)
Finishing effects
Attachment methods

This modern classic uses injection molded plastic eyestay hardware. These parts are attached by stitching.

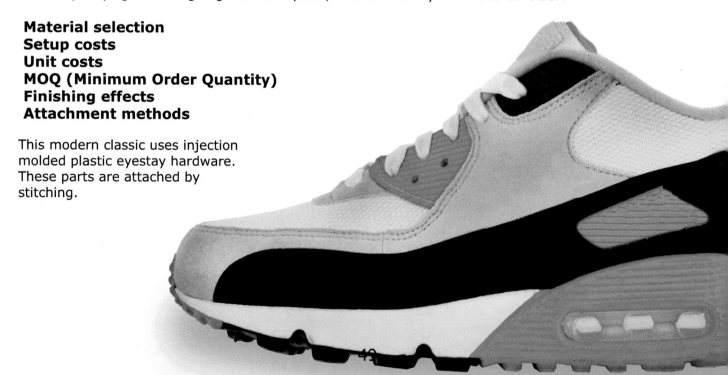

Metal hardware

Metal hardware is the traditional choice. It is strong, can be formed in many ways, and comes in a huge variety of aesthetic finishes depending on the metal type.

Metal hardware can be a shining and elegant accent to make a handmade shoe sparkle. Finishes of gold, silver, and bronze can create a feeling of luxury and high style. Stainless steel and anodized aluminum can create ultra modern high tech looks. Metal hardware also has the added benefit of being replaceable if attached by riveting.

Material selection

The common metals for hardware are steel, brass, aluminum, zinc, copper, and titanium.
Steel, aluminum, and zinc can be formed into hardware by casting. A stamping press can be used to shape steel, brass, aluminum, copper, and titanium. Of these metals, titanium is the most expensive, followed by brass, stainless steel, and aluminum. Cast zinc and stamped carbon steel are the least expensive.

Finishing effects

Most parts can be polished raw metal except cast zinc which requires plating. All metal types can be painted, while aluminum is unique; it can be anodized to create many unique colors.

Attachment methods

Metal hardware is usually riveted to the shoe. When specifying metal parts, make sure they are attached to strong materials. Extra backing layers of material, Super-Tuff, plastic sheeting, or metal washers may be required to firmly anchor metal hardware.

Set up and unit costs

A standard round metal eyelet can cost US$0.035 per part. A cast metal embellishment with glass crystals can cost $1.50 per part. Set up depends on the method of manufacturing. Simple spin casting molds may cost $100 and stamping tools $500. Die casts and lost wax tooling can cost $1000 for a custom design.

Hardware Testing

Hardware testing starts with a simple pull test. For shoes, the pull test standard for hardware is 25kg. For hunting, service, snow, and work boots a 75kg standard is applicable. Pull test machines or hand-held force gauges should be available inside the shoe factory.

For painted surfaces, UV yellowing and accelerated aging tests are recommended to ensure parts will not be damaged by the sun. For metal parts, particularly for carbon steel, corrosion tests are also recommended. Freshwater and saltwater spray tanks are used to confirm that the metal alloys and plating are correct. Make sure to test the rivet backs!

Metal hardware should also be checked for traces of heavy metals. Heavy metals are sometimes used to lubricate stamping presses. Top quality hardware vendors will have test equipment to make sure there is no nickel, cadmium, lead, mercury, or chromium that could cause your shoes to be seized by customs officials or environmental regulators.

Stamped metal parts

Die cast metal Parts

Plastic hardware

Plastic injection hardware can create entirely different looks for your shoe design. Speed hooks, multi-position eyelets, lace loops, logos, and even eyestays can be made from plastic.

Plastic hardware is very useful in many functional applications. For service boots, plastic hooks and shanks can create a metal-free boot suitable for airport security workers. Plastic hardware is also quieter and less likely to scrape in tactical situations where quiet is a must.

Plastic hardware can also be found in kids shoes, casual shoes, and some of Nike's™ modern classics.

Surface finishes can vary from raw plastic to paint, and some plastics can even be chrome plated. Plastic hardware is usually sewn on but can also be riveted to the shoe. When selecting plastic hardware, make sure it is attached to a strong material. Backing layers of extra material, or Super-Tuff, may be required to firmly anchor the hardware.

Material selection

Plastic parts can be made from all types of plastic; nylon, ABS, TPU, PVC, and PC to name a few. Plastics can be reinforced with glass fiber. 5% to 14% can make plastic tough, more than 15% can make plastic susceptible to cracking. Generally speaking, nylon and ABS are very strong, PC can be injected ice clear, while TPU and PVC can be molded in soft rubber-like durometers. PVC must be handled carefully because it can freeze solid in cold temperatures.

Each plastic will have its own surface finishing requirements. Some plastics such as TPU and ABS can have chrome like surface finishes.

Plastic parts can be painted but great care must be taken as painted parts are susceptible to chipping and may show wear prematurely.

Attachment methods

Plastic parts can be attached by sewing through a stitch flange or they can be riveted in place. Unfortunately, sewn-on parts are not readily replaceable if damaged. Also, be careful when designing the stitch flange and specifying the stitch pattern. A narrow stitch flange can be cracked during assembly and too many stitches can weaken the plastic by the perforation effect.

Set and unit costs

A standard injection speed hook can cost $0.15 per part. A chrome plated plastic emblem may cost $0.65 per part. Set up for plastic parts can be expensive. A multi-cavity injection mold can cost $2500 or more!

Hardware Testing

Hardware testing starts with a simple pull test. For shoes, the pull test standard for hardware is 25kg. For hunting, service, snow, and work boots a 75kg standard is applicable. Pull test machines or hand-held force gauges should be available inside the shoe factory.

Plastic parts should also be tested for resistance to cold. Some plastic types can freeze or become very brittle in cold weather and even crack.

Steel wire lacing systems require special plastic inserts that resist the cutting action of the wire.

(Photo to right)

Aisle 1 of 6 in a well stocked hardware supplier's retail show room. This supplier is located in Houjie, China, and stocks over 10,000 different hardware parts for shoes, clothing, and leather goods. They supply off-the-shelf parts and make custom parts for many major brands.

CHAPTER 9

LOGO APPLICATIONS

A new shoe design is not complete until you have detailed its logos. A beautiful set of logos can add value, provide information for your customers, or be a unique and special twist. A great logo can provide the center piece for your shoe design.

When you are working with a new shoe factory, it is good to know their capabilities. For example, if the factory does not have an embroidery machine in-house, it will cost more to send the cut parts out for processing. Also, if the factory has a great relationship with the woven label supplier, it will be worth your while to arrange a visit to see what the woven label supplier can do.

We will review the most common types of logos found on sports shoes and discuss what the logo parts cost, the setup charges, and designer tips.

Die cut logo

This type of logo is cut from a piece of material and sewn on. A die cut shoe logo on the shoe quarter or side panel is the most common logo treatment. The Nike™ "Swoosh™," Adidas™ "Stripes," New Balance™ "N," Vans™ "V," and Puma "Formstrip" are all classic, die cut logos. Die cut logos are great for high visibility applications and can be made from almost any material. One downside to die cut logos is that details can be limited to what can be sewn down. The die cut logo is a perfect overlay on top of any seam or pattern break. A die cut logo can also be reversed, so the logo is a window to the inside of the shoe. The price is low, just the cost of the material.

When specifying a die cut logo, make sure the backing material cuts cleanly and is appropriately colored.

Die cut RF weld

The cut weld is related to the radio frequency weld. The welding die has a crisp edge, and when the TPU material is welded down, the waste can be peeled away, leaving behind the material. The colors and surfaces are limited to what is available in the weldable TPU material. This is a great way to get a glossy logo on rough mesh, or even better, chrome! The cutting weld tools may cost $300 to $1000 depending on the logo size.

Die cut window logo

Instead of an overlay, the die cut can make a window exposing mesh or other logo treatment like a woven label or second color mesh.

Screen printing

Screen printing is a very common logo application for shoes. The setup cost is almost nothing, and color choices are nearly unlimited. There are many finishes available, such as matte, gloss, puff, or 3D styles. There are limits to the surfaces you can print on. Rough or suede surfaces will not print smooth. Elastic fabrics will cause the ink to crack. Any waxed or oiled surface is also not suitable for screen printing. However, printing is great for big, high contrast logos. Screen print logos can be several colors but watch out, registration can be difficult. Every factory will have a screen printing department. The logo can cost from $0.25 to $0.75 depending on the size and number of colors. There are not usually setup charges for silk screen printing logos.

Screen print with emboss

This is an inexpensive and great logo effect for shoes. Achieved by screen printing, then using an RF welding machine to emboss the logo for a 3D effect. The RF welding machine is an inexpensive tool, and the cut brass welding heads don't cost much. Inexpensive to set up and when it is done in-house at the factory it is cheap! The emboss tools may cost $300 depending on the logo size.

Embossed logo

The radio frequency "RF" welding machine can also be used without screen printing or TPU film. Specified as "self color emboss" the RF logo on PU, PVC, or real leather can create a cattle branding effect.

3D embroidery

This is a stunning way to make an amazing 3D effect logo. A small piece of EVA foam is placed under the embroidery head and the threads cut the edges when they are stitched down leaving behind a logo with a 2mm or 3mm 3D effect. A nice effect but also prone to snags and soiling when used on shoes. There are not usually any setup charges. The logo can cost from $0.25 to $0.75 depending on the stitch count and number of colors.

Embroidery logo

Another very common shoe logo treatment, embroidery or computer stitching, can add a touch of class. Silky threads create a rich looking logo application. Colors are limited only by your imagination. Most machines can handle 8 to 10 colors! This is a great logo application but don't go crazy, embroidery is priced by the stitch plus additional colors will cost extra. Also, the logo can run off the side of a panel part, light colors can be soiled easily, and threads can be snagged. If used in waterproof shoes, be careful, the stitching will let water in. There are not usually any setup charges. Price can vary wildly for this type of logo treatment. The logo can cost from $0.25 to $0.75 depending on the stitch count, number of colors, and if the factory has its own embroidery department.

Dye sublimation

Dye sublimation is a printing process that uses a computer to print a full-color design onto transfer paper. When the paper is applied to the material surface and heated, the ink vaporizes and transfers to the shoe material. Dye sublimation is great for 4-color process photographic designs. Sublimation printing can add $.25 to $1.00 or more depending on the size of the printed component. Direct digital printing is also gaining popularity due to its low set-up fees.

Woven labels

The woven label is another great way to create colorful logo effects. This type of label is machine made by computer control. Resolution is high for fine details and small crisp text. Colors are nearly unlimited and one logo can have as many as 15 colors. The basic tongue logos on New Balance™ or classic Nike's™ are made by this process. This process can be used to create informational labels on shoes. Setup charges are low, even zero. Woven label logos are not expensive. Prices start at $0.05 and run to $1.00 for a large multi-color patch.

Metal hardware

Metal hardware is a great way to get some custom logos on your shoe. Logo plates, custom eyelets, or lace fobs all give you another place to add your logo. This hardware can be cast, stamped, painted, plated, polished, or anodized. You have many metal choices, from steel to brass, zinc, or aluminum. Custom metal hardware will have some setup charges. Price depends on the metal type and process required. Metal parts range from $.05 to $1.00 depending on size, alloy and surface finish.

Molded logos

The modern sports shoe may have several molded components. EVA midsoles, plastic stabilizers, rubber outsole, etc. Each of these is an opportunity for logo branding your shoe design. These logos may cost you nothing once they are machined into the mold.

PVC gel bubbles

A simple way to make a unique logo is via the gel bubble. This is made by adding a clear PVC gel bubble onto a woven label or printed sticker. These logos can have a stitch flange to use as an underlay or can be self-adhesive for attachment to midsole or outsoles. Gel bubbles cost approximately $.20 each depending on the back printing effect.

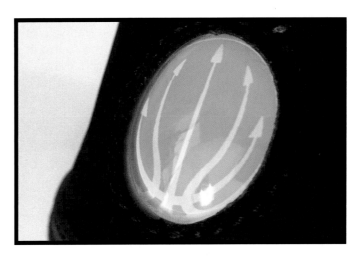

CHAPTER 10

FOAM FOR SHOES

There are many types of foam used to make shoes. In this chapter, we are going to review the types of foam found inside the uppers and outsoles of shoes. The modern sports shoe will have several types of foam inside. Foam can provide comfort, structure, cushioning and can help define the styling of your shoe's design.

Footwear designers and developers have many different types of foam available to choose from depending on the fashion or performance requirements of the shoes they are making.

What is foam?
Foam can be any plastic or rubber compound with air bubbles or cells inside. The stretchability and hardness of the materials making up the foam, combined with the size of the cells, determines the character of foam. Compounds used to make structure foams can be soft or hard, heavy or light. The compound is critical to the feeling of the foam. Does the foam have a bouncy feeling or an energy absorbing slow feeling?

Foam can be classified into two types, "open cell" or "closed cell" foam. These two types of foam have very different attributes and have many different functions inside a shoe.

Open cell foam

Open cell foam is exactly what it sounds like, the plastic compounds that make up the foam cells are open. Air and water are free to enter and exit the foam just like a dish-washing sponge. Open cell foam is water absorbing with hydrophilic properties and can be used to wick sweat away from the foot. It is usually soft and used in the shoe's upper components such and tongues and linings.

Open cell foam is most commonly made of polyurethane plastic. This open cell PU foam is available in different densities and in almost every thickness and color. It is used in the tongues and collars of shoes. Thin sheets of PU foam are used to back fabric in most shoe uppers. The PU foam allows the stitches to sink in and gives fabric, like mesh, some extra support while reducing wrinkle. Reticulated foam is the most open style of foam.

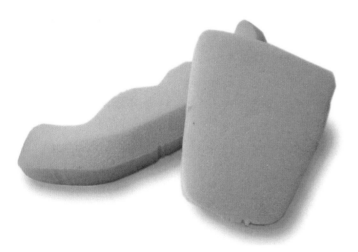

This type is often used for ventilation features. Reticulated foam is almost skeletal looking. Air and water flow freely through the foam. Memory foam is a variation of open cell polyurethane foam with additional chemicals that increase its viscosity and density.

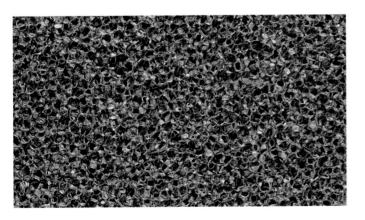

Closed cell foam

In closed cell foam, the individual air cells are closed or sealed and do not allow the foam's internal gas to escape. Closed cell foams are waterproof and can have hydrophobic properties.

Thin EVA layers can be used to create waterproof or water resistant shoes. Closed cell foams are made from many different plastic compounds and are available in all densities, from pillow soft to nearly wooden hard.

Closed cell foam is ordinarily denser than open cell foam, but it is also available is some very soft and rubber-like formulations. Midsoles of shoes are all made from this type of foam. The most common closed cell foams include EVA (ethyl vinyl acetate), PE (Polyethylene), SBR (Styrene butadiene rubber), PU (Polyurethane), Latex, and Neoprene. Each has their individual properties.

For example, EVA foam is used for backing mesh materials. A 2mm sheet of EVA will make the fabric waterproof. Neoprene and SBR are used when elastic properties are required. Latex is common for collar linings. PE foam is very light and molds well but is not very durable.

When working with foam, it is important to know what foam is appropriate for the shoe upper and what is appropriate for cushioning the shoe outsole. When specifying foam, it is critical to understand the performance attributes.

Density
Durometer
Compression set
Impact resistance
Energy return
Conformability
Moldability
Breathability
Hydrophilic vs hydrophobic

Foam density
Density is a measurement of how heavy the foam is when compared to its volume. Open cell PU foam has a low density and can be very soft. Neoprene foam has a higher density making it heavy, but it is also soft. PE foams can be very hard, but still relatively lightweight. The rigidity of the plastic material making up the foam, combined with the size of the cells, determines the density. Density is measured in pounds per square foot. A 2 lb. density foam is very light, while an 8 lb. density foam is a heavy structural foam.

Durometer
Durometer is a measurement of how firm or soft the foam is. Durometer measures the foam's resistance to surface penetration. Lower numbers indicate softer, more flexible materials, while higher numbers indicate harder materials. For EVA foam, a durometer reading of density of 25° Asker C" is okay for the upper padding but way too soft for the midsole. The stretchability and hardness of the plastic material making up the foam, combined with the size of the cells, determines the durometer of the foam.

Compression set
Compression set resistance is the foam's ability to bounce back after it is compressed. Foams with poor compression set will be crushed flat after just a few days. Foams that resist compression set can be used to make cushioning for a running shoe that will last for hundreds of miles. Softer foams can be used in the shoe upper but not underfoot.

Impact resistance
Impact resistance is the ability of foam to absorb and disperse energy. Good impact resistance protects the foot from bruising or even fractures when jumping or falling.

Energy return
Energy return is a critical attribute for the midsole cushioning of any shoe. A foam material with high-energy return rebounds quickly and can have a spring-like, lively feeling. Foam with low or slow energy return will make a very comfortable upper, but if placed under the foot can result in a shoe that feels slow, dead, tiring, and is sapping energy from every step.

Conformability
It is critical to the comfort of an upper that the foam conforms to the foot. Sheet foam that does not conform or molded foam that does not fit the contours of the foot will not be comfortable.

Moldability
Depending on the compound and process used to make the foam, it may be molded into ergonomic shapes of a shoe or not. Where and how a foam is used depends on its moldability.

Breathability
Breathability of a specific foam can be an asset or a liability depending on the functional requirements of a shoe. Breathable can mean cool in hot weather, but it can also make a shoe cold and sodden in wet weather.

Hydrophilic vs Hydrophobic
Hydrophilic open cell foams can absorb water or sweat to create a cooling function, while hydrophobic closed cell foams resist water absorption. Hydrophobic foam is great for a river shoe, allowing it to dry fast and stay lightweight even when wet.

Selecting the right foam

With the nine different performance factors in mind, the designer can select the correct foam for each functional application. Here is a listing of foams commonly found in shoes.

EVA (ethyl vinyl acetate)

EVA is the most common midsole material for sports shoes. It is lightweight, durable, easy to form, and resists compression set. EVA can be hot pressed, cold pressed, die cut, injected, and machined to make midsoles. Available in a wide range of densities and formulations, EVA can be pillow soft and flexible, or rock hard and stiff. EVA can be made in almost any color. It can be found in all different styles of shoes. EVA is also used to make footbeds, padded strobel socks, and is often laminated as a fabric backing. EVA is not breathable, but it can be perforated

Closed cell PU (Polyurethane)

Closed cell PU is also a common foam for shoes. PU foam is "blown" into molds. The liquid compound expands and forms air cells to fill molds. It is used to make durable midsoles for hiking boots. It can also be made into entire sole units which include the tread and midsole all in one. PU foam is used to directly attach midsoles to uppers. PU is expanded from a liquid allowing it to fill complex shapes. Many women's high heel outsoles are made from high-density PU. Very soft PU is used for footbeds due to its resistance to compression set. The classic Nike Foamposite™ is made of PU foam.

Open Cell PU (Polyurethane)

Open cell PU foam is found in the uppers of almost every sports shoe. Because the foam is open cell, it is breathable, be careful so it does not absorb the glue. Thin layers of PU are laminated to fabric to provide backing substance. PU foam is also used to make tongue foam and collar foam. Often called KFF foam. Due to its softness, open cell PU foam cannot be used underfoot.

PE (Polyethylene)

Expanded into sheets, PE foam is easily die cut and laminated. Parts are then pressed into shape for internal pads and tongues. Due to its weakness in compression set, PE foam is not used underfoot. PE foam is closed cell and waterproof.

SBR foam (Styrene butadiene rubber)

SBR is very soft foam often laminated between two layers of fabric. It is closed cell and is used to make parts waterproof. SBR foam is often used as a lightweight replacement for neoprene rubber, but it is not as stretchable.

PVC (PolyVinyl chloride) sponge foam

PVC sponge foam is a closed cell that is available in many formulations. Rigid PVC sponge foam is used to reinforce surfboards, while soft PVC sponge foam is used to make life jackets and other sporting goods. PVC sponge is a relatively heavy foam but responds well to compression molding. Not used for underfoot cushioning, PVC foam is used as a moldable backing material for synthetic leathers and is used in logo treatments.

Latex rubber foam

Latex foam is easily formed into complex shapes in open top molds. Latex is used for upper padding but not as a midsole material. High-density latex foam sheets can be used to make die cut footbeds. The latex footbed provides excellent comfort for in-store effect but is not a durable foam for running for other athletic shoes. Molded anatomic features inside snowboard and ski boots are often made from latex foam. Latex is also used for bonding cork granules into midsole components.

Memory foam

Memory foam consists mainly of polyurethane as well as additional chemicals increasing its viscosity and density. It is often referred to as "viscoelastic" polyurethane foam or low-resilience polyurethane foam. Higher density memory foam softens in reaction to body heat, allowing it to mold in a few minutes. Memory foam may lose its viscoelastic properties in cold weather and may shatter if exposed to subzero temperatures.

Neoprene rubber

Neoprene or polychloroprene is closed cell expanded synthetic rubber produced by polymerization of chloroprene. Neoprene is made in large blocks or buns and then skived down into the required thickness. Thickness can range from 1mm to 12mm. Neoprene maintains flexibility over a wide temperature range and is used as an insulating layer. It is the most common material used in wetsuit booties and is often used to make elastic collars in shoes. Neoprene is waterproof, but not breathable, and is relatively heavy and expensive.

Foam inside a modern athletic shoe

This baseball cleat has 12 different foam components using 8 different types of open and closed cell foam.

Midsole foam: closed cell, hot pressed compression molded EVA Durometer Asker "C" 60°

Footbed foam: closed cell, die cut 5mm sheet stock EVA Durometer Asker "C" 30°

Vamp lining: open cell foam. Padding: 4mm PU KFF foam flame laminated to fabric, 1 lb. density

Tongue face foam: closed cell, 2mm perforated SBR foam 2 lb. density

Tongue lining: open cell foam. Padding: 4mm PU KFF foam flame laminated to fabric, 1 lb. density

Tongue gusset: open cell foam. Padding: 4mm PU KFF foam flame laminated to fabric, 1 lb. density

Tongue foam padding: open cell 6mm PU KFF foam die cut, 1 lb. density

Upper foam padding: open cell 4mm PU KFF foam laminated, 1 lb. density

Midsole shock structure: closed cell, poured PU foam Durometer Asker "C" 54°

Collar lining: open cell foam. Padding: 4mm PU KFF foam flame laminated to fabric, 1 lb. density

Collar foam padding: open cell 6mm PU KFF foam die cut, 1 lb. density

Logo backing foam: closed cell, 2mm embossed PVC foam Durometer Asker "C" 25°

How to measure foam density

Measuring the density of very soft foams can be difficult. The density is measured in pounds per square foot. Very soft open cell foam is 1.2 lbs. per square foot. For denser foam, a durometer tester is needed. An Asker "C" scale durometer tester is used to test the hardness of foam shoe components. You can tell the "C" scale tester apart from other testers due to its rounded test probe.

The durometer tester will give you a reading of the density of the material. Try to test in flat spots and take several readings for each shoe part you are checking. For foam, try to cut the parts so you can test the center of the foam. EVA foam skin may give you a harder reading. A standard EVA midsole may be 55°, a soft footbed 35°.

Test Locations ◯

62

CHAPTER 11
MIDSOLE CUSHIONING SYSTEMS

The midsole is the component or structure that fills the space between the outsole and upper of the shoe. In the modern shoe, the midsole provides cushioning, support, and heel lift. Not every shoe type has a midsole, and some sole designs have the cushioning system integrated into the outsole components. The composition of the midsole depends on the shoe's price point, performance requirements, space limitations, construction technique, and believe it or not, marketing considerations.

Common midsole materials
The most common midsole cushioning materials are EVA foam, PU foam, TPU foam, air bags, rubber egg crate, TPR egg crate, blown rubber foam, gel packs, injected molded plastic, cork, and 3D printed structures. Your selection of midsole materials will depend on the price and performance requirements for your shoe design. The design style of your shoes will also play a factor. Classic leather shoes and high tech athletic shoes do not usually share the same midsole design or materials.

Before we review the common midsole materials, we should study the performance characteristics required for midsoles. Midsole performance requirements include:

Cushioning
Support
Flexibility
Weight
Impact resistance
Energy return
Compression set

Cushioning

Cushioning is the ability of the foam to absorb and disperse energy. A good cushioning system provides comfort for walking and running. It also protects the foot from bruising or even fractures when jumping or falling. The forefoot midsole for most casual and sports shoes is between 6mm to 10mm. Midsole heels measure between 10mm to 20mm. Running and basketball shoes require more cushioning, dress and casual shoes require less cushioning, and a driving moccasin will require almost no cushioning.

Support

A midsole must have some supportive feature to ensure the users can walk or run safely. Support can come from wider bases or added components such as molded plastic counters or rubber cup soles. The supporting functions are related to the shoe's purpose. A fast-moving court shoe for basketball will offer much less support than a midsole designed for hiking or military boots. The shape and density of the midsole determine its ability to provide support.

Flexibility

Depending on the intended purpose of the shoe, the midsole will require more or less flexibility. A tennis shoe or running shoe must have flexibility, while a midsole for a mountaineering boot must provide dampening and support without bending at all. While more flexibility is usually a good thing, too much flexibility can cause instability and lead to foot fatigue.

Weight

Again, depending on the intended purpose the shoe, the weight of the midsole may be a key feature. For a long distance racing shoe or track spike, every gram is critical. For a motorcycle boot, a heavy midsole is not a problem.

Energy return

Energy return is a critical attribute for the midsole cushioning of any shoe. A foam material with high-energy return rebounds quickly and can have a spring-like lively feeling. Foam with low or slow energy return will make a very comfortable upper, but when placed underfoot can result in a shoe that feels slow, dead, tiring, sapping energy from every step.

Compression set

Compression set resistance is the foam's ability to bounce back after it is compressed. Foams with poor compression set will be crushed flat after just a few days. Foams that resist compression set can be used to make cushioning for a running shoe that will last for hundreds of miles.

Common midsole materials

EVA foam (ethyl vinyl acetate)

EVA in its many forms is the most common midsole cushioning material found in modern sports and casual shoes. EVA can be hot pressed, cold pressed, die cut, injected, and machined to make midsoles. EVA is lightweight and can be formulated into a wide range of densities and characters from firm to rubbery. For sports shoes expect EVA densities from 50° to 60° in the Asker "C" durometer scale.

"Drop in" EVA die cut

The most basic EVA midsole is made by dropping die cut EVA blocks into rubber cupsoles. The EVA blocks may be located just in the heel, or an entire sheet of EVA foam may fill the inside bottom of the sole unit. This die cut or "drop-in" midsole is an inexpensive way to add comfort to a low price shoe.

TOOLING: The cost of cutting dies < $100
UNIT PRICE: $0.25 to $0.75 per pair

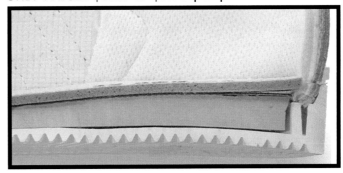

Compression Molded EVA or CMEVA

The standard two-part sole is made with a lightweight CMEVA midsole, bonded to a rubber outsole. The EVA foam is expanded into blocks, then cut down to fit into a mold. The mold is heated, causing the EVA to re-expand and fill the compression mold. The density and durometer are set by how much foam is compressed into the mold and the formula of the foam. More foam is harder and gives the sole design more definition. The midsole is bonded to the rubber in the stock fitting room before the unit meets the upper in assembly.

TOOLING: $1,500 to $2,500 per size
UNIT PRICE: $1.50 to $3.00 per pair

Polyurethane Foam

Polyurethane or PU foam is also a very popular choice for midsoles. Like EVA, it can be formulated into different densities suitable for many various types of footwear midsoles. PU foam has the unique ability to be molded from a liquid base. PU foam is a mixture of isocyanates and polyols compounds.

Once mixed, the two compounds form a viscous syrup that can be poured into an open mold at room temperature. Once the mold is closed and heated, the compound "blows" expanding to fill the mold. Unlike EVA, the forming temperature is relatively low. The liquid flows inside the mold allowing other components such as airbags, fabric linings, and shank parts to be inserted into the mold. PU flows inside the mold, thus it can be used to make very complicated shapes, like women's high-heeled shoe soles.

Liquid PU can easily fill complicated shapes. It is used to make the Nike Shox™ midsole components. PU foam can also be modified with other additives to create some special foams such as memory foam or non-Newtonian foam such as the product 3DO™.

PU foam densities can vary from 45° to 85° in the Asker "C" durometer scale.

TOOLING: $2,500 to $4,000 per size
UNIT PRICE: $2.50 to $4.00 per pair

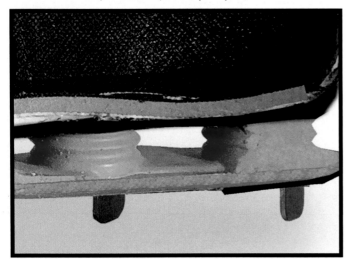

Cup, cut, and buff sole

This classic cut and buff EVA wedge midsole is made by bonding together die cut EVA blocks. The wedge profile shape of the EVA is made by pressing the EVA with a profile roller while a cutting blade splits off the bottom layers. The foam layers are bonded to the rubber bottom. All three parts are then cut and buffed to create the angled sidewall. This process requires very little tooling but is labor intensive.

TOOLING: Cutting dies and buffing stone $900
UNIT PRICE: $1.50 to $2.00 per pair

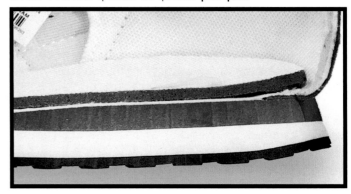

Injection molded EVA

EVA material can also be formed by injection process. The Crocs™ sandals and the modern basketball slide are both made by EVA injection process. The EVA compound is heated to a critical state under pressure to prevent air bubbles from forming inside. The compound is then injected into a mold that is about half the size of the finished product. After a few minutes, the mold springs open and the EVA part expands to full size in 1/10th of a second.

TOOLING: $2,500 to $4,000 per size
UNIT PRICE: $1.50 to $3.00 per pair

Classic airbag with PU midsole

This classic airbag shoe midsole is made by over-molding PU, but in this case, the airbag is clipped in the heel and exposed. The liquid PU flows around the airbag to fill the mold cavity. A side window made by the clamps hold the bag in place, and stop the PU from covering the bag. After the PU parts are cleaned and painted, they are bonded to the rubber parts by the stock fitting line. This outsole requires a rubber compression tool, air bag mold, and PU midsole mold.

TOOLING: $3,500 to $5,000 per size
UNIT PRICE: $3.50 to $6.00 per pair

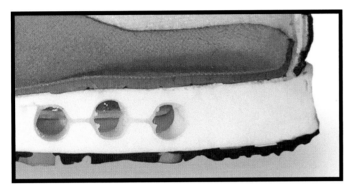

TPU foam midsole

Thermoplastic polyurethane (TPU) is a new foam material designed by BASF™. It is marketed by Adidas as Boost™ foam and is an alternative to EVA or PU foams. The TPU foam pellets are loaded into molds with an air venting function. When the midsole mold is heated, a catalyst inside the pellets causes air pockets to expand, venting the air and filling the mold with the distinctive fused pellet texture. The TPU foam cells have a unique elastic property allowing for high-energy return and making the shoe feel more "alive". BASF will be making this material available to other shoe brands sometime in 2017.

TOOLING: $2,500 to $4,000 per size
UNIT PRICE: $1.50 to $3.00 per pair

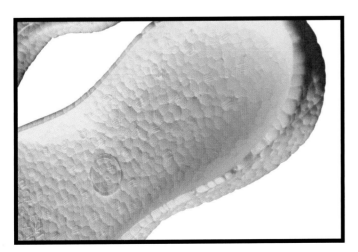

Rubber egg crate midsoles

The "egg crate" style midsole is an inexpensive way to create heel lift and a sturdy (but firm) cushioning system. The egg crate midsole is molded with the outsole. Egg crate is heavy, and there is a cost associated with the weight of the rubber, but there are no other associated costs. You will find square egg crate in the heel and a more flexible linear pattern in the forefoot. If you choose an egg crate midsole, you will need a firm lasting board or EVA sheet on top to span the open spaces. The rings are usually 3mm to 4mm wide, this allows the rubber to flow, filling the ribs and giving the lasting board enough surface area for bonding. Egg crate is very common in inexpensive casual shoes, but can also be found in hiking and hunting boots that require a firm, long-lasting cushioning system. Expect rubber densities from 50° to 60° in the Shore "A" durometer scale.

TOOLING: $2,500 to $4,000 per size
UNIT PRICE: $1.50 to $3.00 per pair

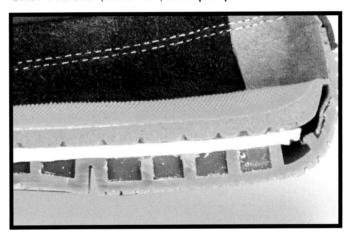

TPR (Thermo Plastic Rubber) egg crate

While you will never find a Nike™ shoe made with a TPR egg crate midsole, the construction is used commonly around the world. It is heavy, but the TPR egg crate is very inexpensive and provides elastic cushioning suitable for general use in footwear. The rib dimensions are commonly 3mm to 4mm wide. Expect TPR densities from 50° to 60° in the Shore "A" durometer scale.

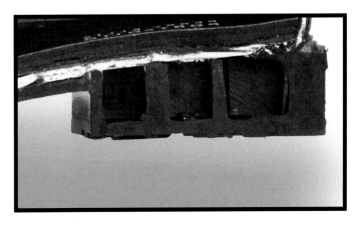

Blown rubber midsoles

Blown rubber fill is a special class of midsole only found in vulcanized shoes. Rubber scraps left over from the sole making operations are reprocessed into a spongy heat resistant compound that can survive the vulcanizing oven. Using the reprocessed, uncured rubber is convenient and cost-effective for the vulcanized shoe factory. EVA, PU, and other foam types will melt in the high heat of the vulcanizing ovens. This compound is heavy, but vulcanized shoes are not known for being lightweight. Expect blown rubber densities from 40° to 45° in the Asker "C" durometer scale.

TOOLING: $100 to $500 per size
UNIT PRICE: $1.50 to $2.00 per pair

Gel pack midsoles

Liquid and solid gel midsole materials can be found in performance shoe soles. Gel materials can be formulated to provide either an energy absorbing function or an energy returning function with bounce. Gel materials tend to be small inserts as most gel materials have a specific gravity greater than 1 (SG 1 = water). The brand name product GPact™ is a well-known gel cushioning system used in footwear.

TOOLING: $100 to $500 per size
UNIT PRICE: $1.50 to $2.00 per pair

Injection molded plastic midsoles

Many firms have been experimenting with foamless injection molded midsoles. This shoe has a stiff moderating plate under the heel to keep the shoe stable. The midsole structure is likely made of nylon, TPU, or TPE plastic. These midsoles provide a cushioning effect by spring deflection. The Adidas™ Springblade™, Saucony™ Grid™, and Mizuno™ Wave™ all feature injection molded midsole parts.

TOOLING: $2,500 to $8,000 per size
UNIT PRICE:$2.50 to $9.00 per pair

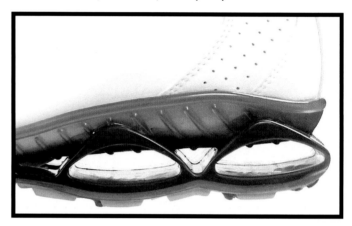

3D printed plastic midsoles

Many shoe brands are now developing and marketing shoe midsoles made of 3D printed thermo plastics. Prices will be high, and production volumes will be low, but the technology offers a way to make midsole parts custom shaped to user's feet. Materials and processes are currently trade secrets but expect this technology to expand. Don't expect 3D printed midsoles to replace traditionally molded midsoles anytime soon due to the material cost, 3D printing productivity, and machine costs.

TOOLING: $0 per size
UNIT PRICE: $5.50 to $10.00 per pair

Airbag midsole

The airbag midsole is made by the blow molding process. The midsole starts out as a hot, semi-liquid plastic extrusion tube (called a parison). A steel mold clamps around the tube and the air is injected inside to fill the bag and inflate the shape to fill the mold. The tooling and machines are very expensive. The plastic can be tinted, and the bag top and bottom surfaces can be painted. In this case, the airbag is attached to an EVA tray that is then bonded to the shoe outsole by cold cement process. This type of sole unit is great for running and cross training. The airbag looks cool, but due to the blow molding process, the plastic walls of the bag can be a little thick. This sole unit requires an EVA compression mold, rubber compression mold, and blow molds.

TOOLING: $2,500 to $8,000 per size
UNIT PRICE: $2.50 to $9.00 per pair

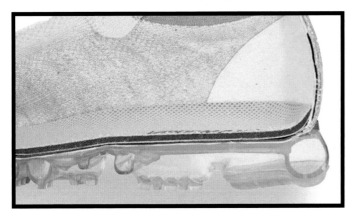

Cork midsole

The cork midsole is found in many very expensive handmade shoes. The bark of the cork tree is chopped into tiny particles then mixed with a pliable latex glue. The resulting cork paste is used to fill the forefoot of the sole before the leather bottom is sewn on.

TOOLING: $0 per size
UNIT PRICE: $1.00 per pair

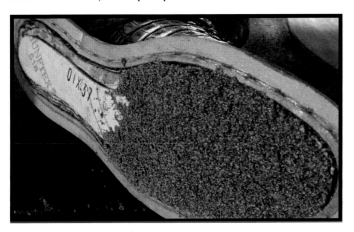

CHAPTER 12

OUTSOLES FOR FOOTWEAR

The outsole design for a shoe plays a major factor in shoe performances. The outsoles for running shoes, biker boots, and football cleats all have very different performance requirements and manufacturing methods. The shoe outsole is also one of the most expensive parts of the shoe. For low-cost shoes, the outsole can be 10% of the shoe cost, second only to the leather cost. For high-end basketball, running, or soccer shoes the outsole can be 25% to 35% of the shoe's factory price. A simple cupsole may cost $2.00, while a multi-part running sole with carbon shank could cost $8.00 to $10.00.

A set of outsole tooling is by far the most expensive equipment needed to produce a shoe. While the cutting dies required to produce a shoe upper may cost $1,000 for a complete size run, a single size of outsole tooling is a minimum of $1,400. Now, multiply that by 14 sizes, and you get $19,600! This is the cost for a simple rubber cupsole.

The cost for a complicated multi-part outsole with a rubber bottom, EVA midsole, and plastic shank plate may cost $100,000! Shoe companies must take great care in designing and developing new outsole tooling. Many shoe companies will only make one size for testing and sales samples. Only after their salesmen collect orders for the new model will the balance of the tooling be made.

I have seen designers and developers work for months to create a new design only to see production canceled before it even begins. When a weak sales report arrives, product managers have difficult choices to make.

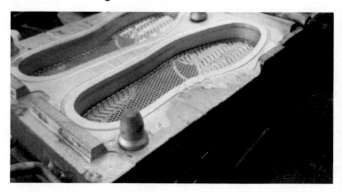

Can you risk $100,000 in tooling for a model with just a hope that it will "catch on"? Small shoe companies may be forced to use old tooling on new models until they can afford the cost of new equipment.

69

Performance factors
Performance factors for footwear outsoles include traction, support, flexibility, weight, slip resistance, and durability. These features are a function of the design geometry and materials.

Traction
Outsole traction is an important feature of any shoe outsole. The design of the outsole pattern and selection of materials controls the amount of traction. The traction requirements for hiking boots, office shoes, boat, and bowling shoes are all radically different.

When designing an outsole, it is important to understand the environment and surfaces the outsole will encounter. Traction is also directional. A mountaineering boot will require lateral traction on rough terrain, while a basketball sole needs to support quick stops on a smooth wood surface and allow spins with the foot planted.

Support
An outsole must have some supportive feature to ensure users can walk or run safely. Support can come from wider bases or added components such as molded plastic counters or rubber cut soles. A fast, lightweight running shoe designed for speed may have little support, while a mountaineering boot will have a metal shank to carry the weight of a heavy pack in rough terrain.

Flexibility
Depending on the intended purpose of the shoe, the midsole will require more or less flexibility. A tennis shoe or running shoe must be flexible, while a cowboy boot will have a steel shank to spread the load of the stirrups without bending at all. While more flexibility is usually a good thing, too much flexibility can cause instability and lead to foot fatigue. The general rule is, the heavier the load and the rougher the terrain, the stiffer the outsole.

Weight
Again, depending on the intended purpose of the shoe, the weight of the outsole may be a key feature. For a long distance racing shoe or track spike, every gram is critical. For a driving shoe or biker boot, a heavy outsole is not a problem.

Durability
The durability requirements of an outsole will depend on the environment and tasks selected for the particular shoe. The fine leather soles of women's dress shoes and men's office shoes are perfect for smooth stone hallways and carpeted offices, but would last only a few steps on a rainy construction site or mountain trail. Durability can be a selling feature for a shoe but may come at the expense of added weight or reduced flexibility.

Slip-resistance
Slip resistance is a key feature for many service shoes. Restaurant, hospital, maintenance, and warehouse staff members are required to wear shoes with certified slip-resistant rubber compounds and tread patterns. Oil resistant rubber compounds may also be a requirement for industrial footwear.

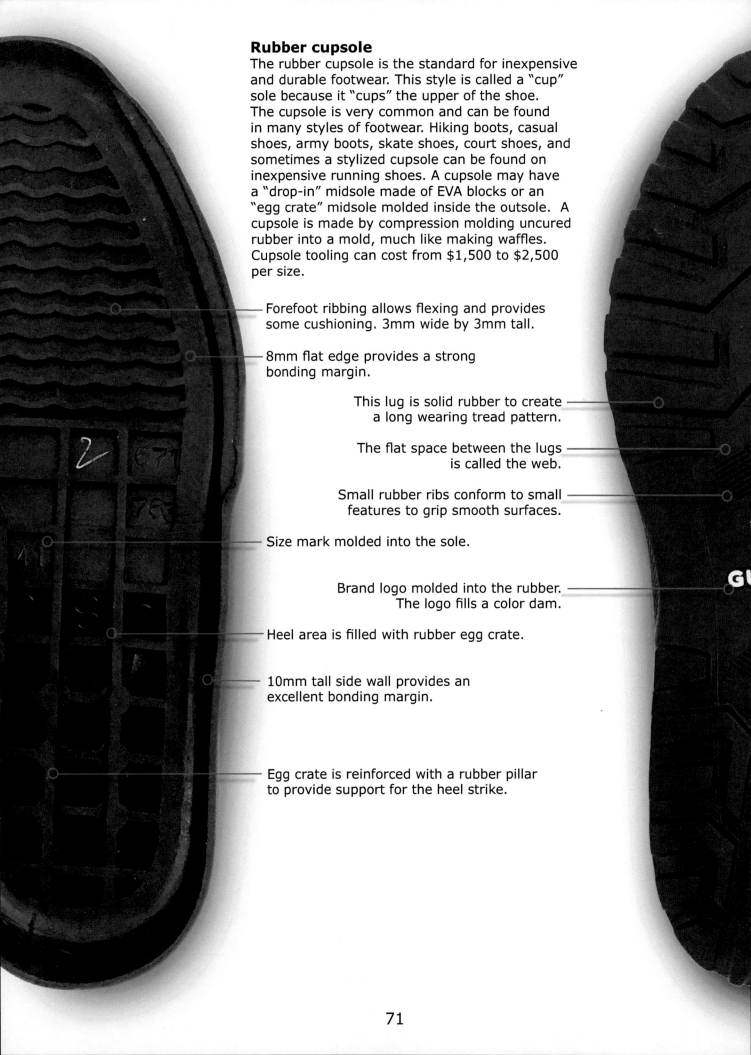

Rubber cupsole

The rubber cupsole is the standard for inexpensive and durable footwear. This style is called a "cup" sole because it "cups" the upper of the shoe. The cupsole is very common and can be found in many styles of footwear. Hiking boots, casual shoes, army boots, skate shoes, court shoes, and sometimes a stylized cupsole can be found on inexpensive running shoes. A cupsole may have a "drop-in" midsole made of EVA blocks or an "egg crate" midsole molded inside the outsole. A cupsole is made by compression molding uncured rubber into a mold, much like making waffles. Cupsole tooling can cost from $1,500 to $2,500 per size.

Forefoot ribbing allows flexing and provides some cushioning. 3mm wide by 3mm tall.

8mm flat edge provides a strong bonding margin.

This lug is solid rubber to create a long wearing tread pattern.

The flat space between the lugs is called the web.

Small rubber ribs conform to small features to grip smooth surfaces.

Size mark molded into the sole.

Brand logo molded into the rubber. The logo fills a color dam.

Heel area is filled with rubber egg crate.

10mm tall side wall provides an excellent bonding margin.

Egg crate is reinforced with a rubber pillar to provide support for the heel strike.

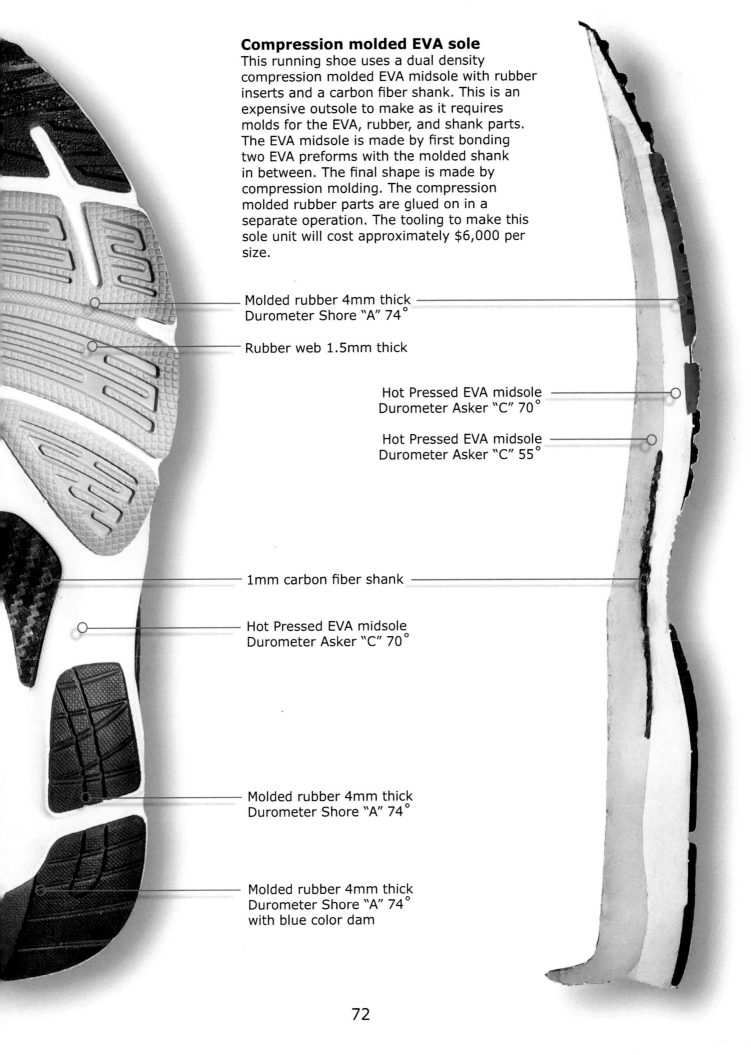

Compression molded EVA sole

This running shoe uses a dual density compression molded EVA midsole with rubber inserts and a carbon fiber shank. This is an expensive outsole to make as it requires molds for the EVA, rubber, and shank parts. The EVA midsole is made by first bonding two EVA preforms with the molded shank in between. The final shape is made by compression molding. The compression molded rubber parts are glued on in a separate operation. The tooling to make this sole unit will cost approximately $6,000 per size.

Molded rubber 4mm thick
Durometer Shore "A" 74°

Rubber web 1.5mm thick

Hot Pressed EVA midsole
Durometer Asker "C" 70°

Hot Pressed EVA midsole
Durometer Asker "C" 55°

1mm carbon fiber shank

Hot Pressed EVA midsole
Durometer Asker "C" 70°

Molded rubber 4mm thick
Durometer Shore "A" 74°

Molded rubber 4mm thick
Durometer Shore "A" 74°
with blue color dam

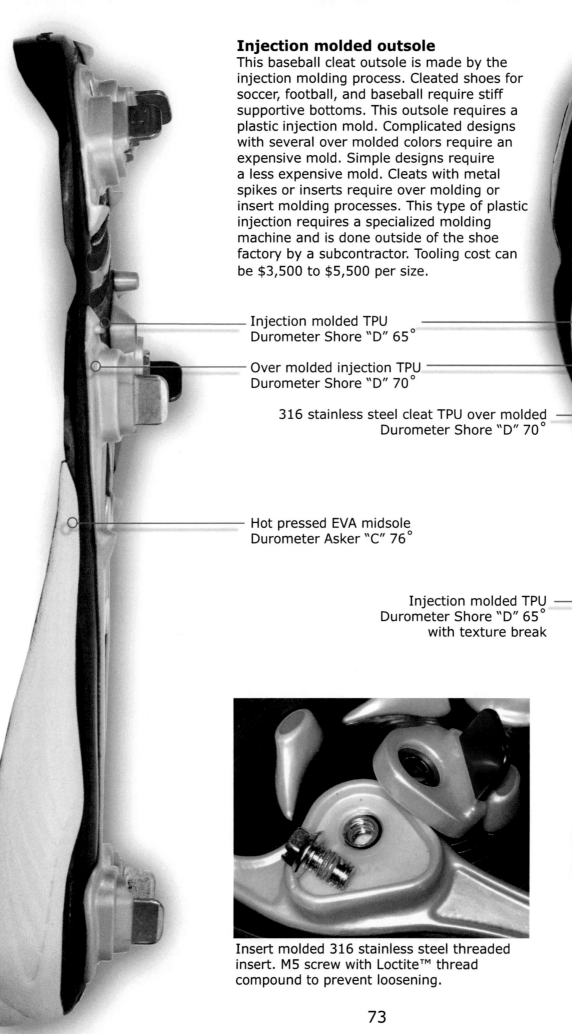

Injection molded outsole

This baseball cleat outsole is made by the injection molding process. Cleated shoes for soccer, football, and baseball require stiff supportive bottoms. This outsole requires a plastic injection mold. Complicated designs with several over molded colors require an expensive mold. Simple designs require a less expensive mold. Cleats with metal spikes or inserts require over molding or insert molding processes. This type of plastic injection requires a specialized molding machine and is done outside of the shoe factory by a subcontractor. Tooling cost can be $3,500 to $5,500 per size.

Injection molded TPU
Durometer Shore "D" 65°

Over molded injection TPU
Durometer Shore "D" 70°

316 stainless steel cleat TPU over molded
Durometer Shore "D" 70°

Hot pressed EVA midsole
Durometer Asker "C" 76°

Injection molded TPU
Durometer Shore "D" 65°
with texture break

Insert molded 316 stainless steel threaded insert. M5 screw with Loctite™ thread compound to prevent loosening.

73

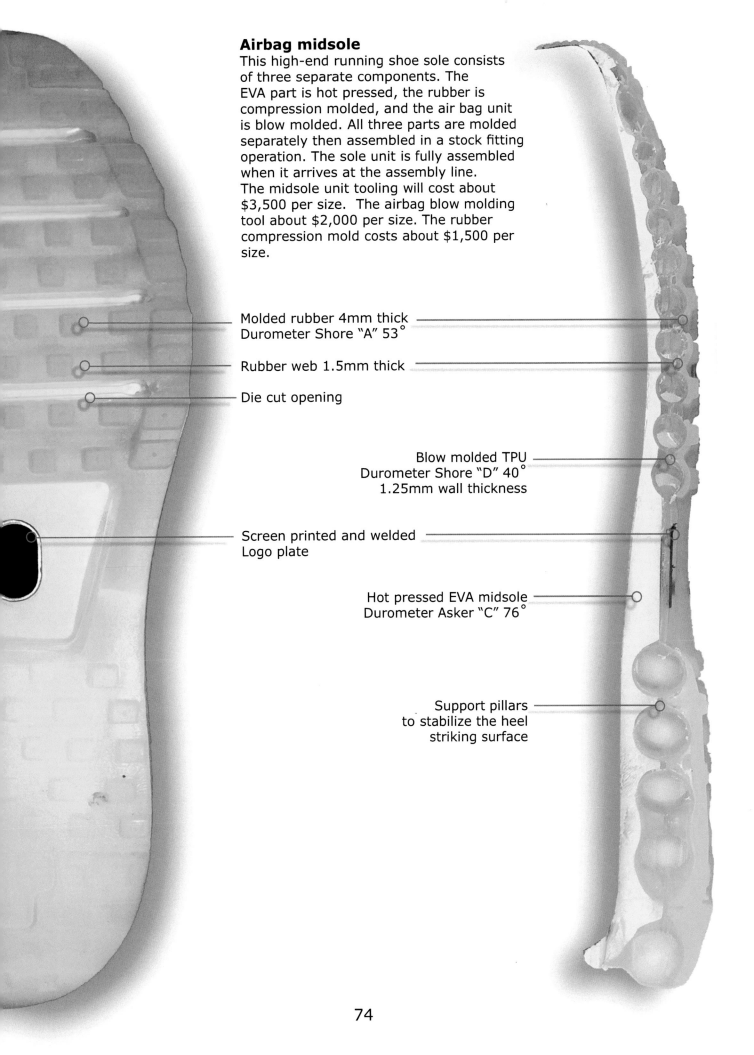

Airbag midsole

This high-end running shoe sole consists of three separate components. The EVA part is hot pressed, the rubber is compression molded, and the air bag unit is blow molded. All three parts are molded separately then assembled in a stock fitting operation. The sole unit is fully assembled when it arrives at the assembly line. The midsole unit tooling will cost about $3,500 per size. The airbag blow molding tool about $2,000 per size. The rubber compression mold costs about $1,500 per size.

Molded rubber 4mm thick
Durometer Shore "A" 53°

Rubber web 1.5mm thick

Die cut opening

Blow molded TPU
Durometer Shore "D" 40°
1.25mm wall thickness

Screen printed and welded
Logo plate

Hot pressed EVA midsole
Durometer Asker "C" 76°

Support pillars
to stabilize the heel
striking surface

74

TPR (Thermo Plastic Rubber) outsole

The TPR outsole is the price point hero for the world shoe market. While you will never find a Nike™ shoe made with TPR, it is a very common outsole material. TPR outsoles can be produced quickly in high volumes and require inexpensive low-pressure injection molds. TPR outsoles can have several outsole color breaks with a separate lower density midsole compound injected into the same mold. The outsoles are inexpensive but are very heavy. The downside to TPR outsoles is that they do not have the slip resistance or durability of "real" rubber outsoles.

Molded TPR 4mm thick
Durometer Shore "A" 74°

TPR will have silvery mold texture
and parts may show injection flow lines

Molded TPR side wall 6mm thick
Durometer Shore "A" 74°

This is not a solid foam midsole,
inside you find a ribbed egg crate design

Replaceable logo plate so the factory can sell
the same design to different customers.

Molded TPR sole units
will have smooth, perfectly clean
color dams.

This is the mold's parting line.

Inexpensive shoes have the size molded in.

Faux airbag midsole window.
Injection molded clear PVC,
back printed two color logo.

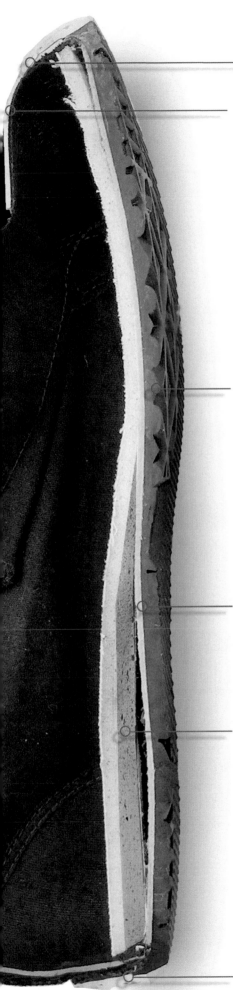

Texture rolled foxing tape toe bumper
Durometer Shore "A" 74°

Rubber toe cap
2.5mm thick Durometer Shore "A" 64°

Classic vulcanized outsole

This outsole shows the standard for vulcanized
shoe construction. The grey rubber bottom is
cemented to the upper, and then the rubber
foxing tape wraps both. A toe cap and toe bumper
are also added. Once the assembly operation is
complete, the entire shoe is cooked at 110°C
for 70 minutes to cure the rubber; this makes
the bonds permanent. This outsole requires a
rubber compression mold for the bottom and a
vulcanizing production factory to make the rubber
parts.

Compression molded rubber sole
2.5mm thick, Durometer Shore "A" 64°

This component is pre-molded but
not 100% cured. The sole rubber
is fully cured only after vulcanization.

Rubber foxing tape:
This classic design has two layers
1.5mm thick. Durometer Shore "A" 64°

Strobel board:1.5mm
100% stitch bonded polyester

Blown rubber midsole cushioning:
made of recycled rubber foxing tape.

Rubber "license plate" covers the heel seam
1.5mm thick. Durometer Shore "A" 74°

Molded rubber 4mm thick
Durometer Shore "A" 74°
The toe tip will be stitched down

The EVA wedge

This classic die cut EVA wedge, also called a "cut and buff" sole is a compression molded rubber bottom bonded to EVA sheets. The top wedge shapes of the midsole are made by pressing the EVA with a profiled roller while a blade splits off the bottom layers. The resulting EVA part tapers from forefoot to heel. The profiled EVA layers are buffed and bonded to the rubber bottom. All three parts are then profiled with a grinding stone to create the angled side wall. This process does not require expensive tooling but is labor intensive. One bottom tool can be trimmed to create an entire size run.

Molded rubber lugs: 4mm thick, Durometer Shore "A" 74°

Rubber web: 1.5mm thick

Rubber logo: molded in

Die cut EVA midsole wedge:
Durometer Asker "C" 70°
profile cut EVA, 9.0mm thick

Die cut EVA midsole wedge:
Durometer Asker "C" 70°
profile cut EVA, 9.0mm thick

The upper is board lasted.
The EVA wedge has no side wall to cover the seams.

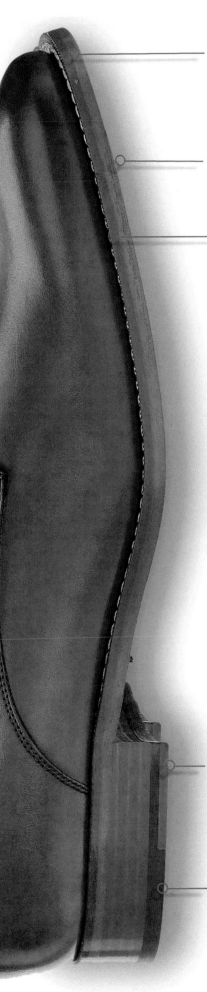

The welt layer is sewn to the
upper leather after lasting.
The stitches are hidden inside the shoe.
The welt is 4mm thick firm vegetable
tanned leather.

The sole leather is glued
and stitched to the welt.
The sole is 4mm thick firm
vegetable tanned leather.

A channel is cut into the sole leather
to sink the stitching. The stitch holes are
punched before the thread is sewn in.

Welted leather soles

High-end men's dress shoes will often have
hand stitched leather soles. The leather
parts are combined piece by piece instead
of being glued to the upper on an assembly
line. The welt is sewn to the bottom of the
lasted upper. The space between the welt is
filled with a shank and cork padding in the
forefoot. The outsole layer is sewn and glued
in place before the stacked leather heel is
attached.

The sole is 4mm thick firm
vegetable tanned leather.

The stacked layers are
held with steel nails.

A 4mm layer of firm rubber
is cemented to the stacked leather
heel.

CHAPTER 13

WATERPROOF CONSTRUCTION

As a shoe designer or developer you may be called upon to make waterproof shoes. Not just for hiking boots, waterproof constructions are required for running, hunting, military, EMS, and winter boots.

Making high quality waterproof shoes and boots can be a difficult technical challenge. It is not easy for experienced designers and professional footwear factories to make a long lasting, waterproof shoe. The shoe pattern, material selection, specific waterproof construction techniques, and conscientious testing must all come together to make it work.

Two layers
Keeping water out of a shoe requires a multilayer defense.

The first layer is an outer shell that resists and repels water from entering the shoe. The boot shell must be made from hydrophobic or waterproof materials. Textiles with closed cell foam backing and leathers with oily coating or synthetic durable water repellent (DWR) treatments are needed.

Inside the shell, all seam lines and stitching holes must be coated with a flexible waterproof glue or mastic compound to prevent leaks.

The sewing thread must also be hydrophobic to prevent water from wicking into the upper.

Once the shell is sealed, it must be examined to make sure there are no rough edges or exposed stitching that can damage the inner lining. The edges of internal reinforcements and heel counters must be skived smooth or covered.

The second inner line of defense to keep water out is a sealed inner sock or bootie made from a waterproof fabric membrane. GoreTex™ is the most widely recognized membrane product used in many high quality shoes and boots. GoreTex™ is popular because its membrane allows heat and vapor to escape, while keeping water out. Sympatex™ is another common breathable membrane product used in footwear.

The waterproof inner sock is usually made in two or three pattern parts. Sides and bottom panels, or side panels joined alone in the center of the bottom. The membrane backed fabric is sewn together, then, using a special steam heating machine, waterproof tape seals the seams. Next, this inner bootie is attached to the top of the tongue and collar parts so it "hangs" down into the shoe. The inner bootie may be cemented in place. Workers must be careful not to perforate the fabric when attaching it to the upper.

When the shoe is lasted, the inner lining is very carefully pulled onto the last so not to damage the lining. The boot can be finished by board lasting or strobal construction.

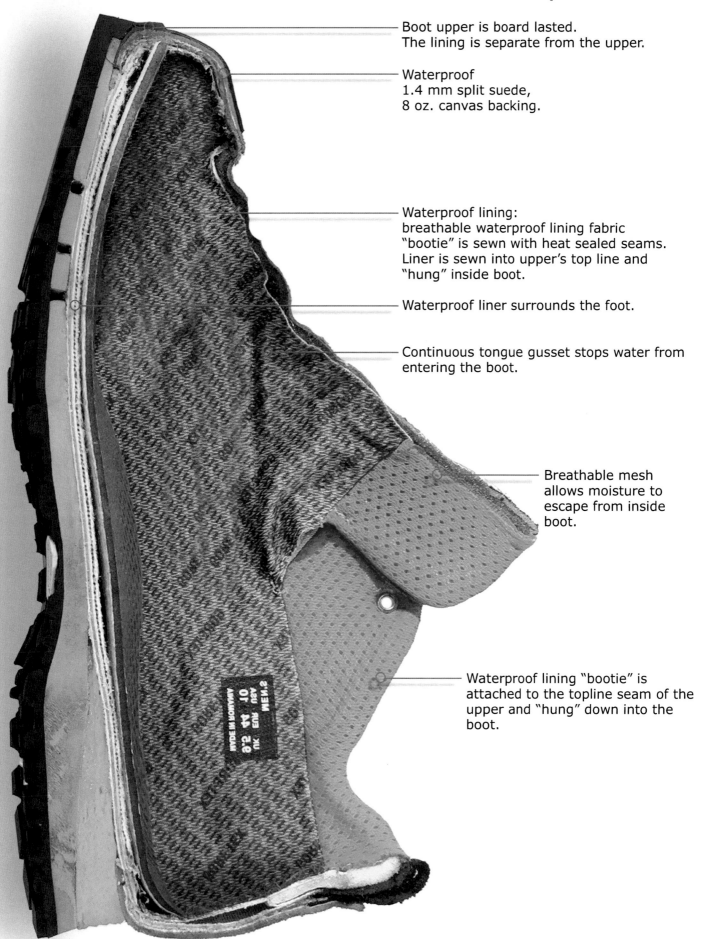

See inside a waterproof boot

Boot upper is board lasted.
The lining is separate from the upper.

Waterproof
1.4 mm split suede,
8 oz. canvas backing.

Waterproof lining:
breathable waterproof lining fabric
"bootie" is sewn with heat sealed seams.
Liner is sewn into upper's top line and
"hung" inside boot.

Waterproof liner surrounds the foot.

Continuous tongue gusset stops water from
entering the boot.

Breathable mesh
allows moisture to
escape from inside
boot.

Waterproof lining "bootie" is
attached to the topline seam of the
upper and "hung" down into the
boot.

CHAPTER 14

SELECTING FOOTBEDS

The footbed

The footbed, insole, sock, sockliner, whatever you call it, is important to the fit, feel, performance, and cost of your shoe. Footbeds come in all shapes, sizes, and materials. They may be customizable, removable, or glued in.

It is important to select a footbed which will compliment your shoe design. Is your shoe designed for hiking or wearing in the office? The footbed for a combat boot will be very different from the footbed for a running shoe or gardening shoe.

When a shoe is in development, it is important to plan for the footbed. Each shoe last will have a "sock allowance" built into the bottom, this creates space inside the shoe. The footbed can be 2mm, 4mm, 6mm thick, or more. You have to get this right, or your shoe will not fit right. Then again, a little extra foam in your footbed can be used to fine tune or fix any fitting issues your shoe may have.

The footbed is also key to the lifespan of your shoe. A thin footbed, made of overly soft and cheap foam, can collapse after just a few days. This leaves the shoes fitting loose and your customers with tired feet. A high-quality footbed, with firm resistant foam, and leather top skin, may last for years.

The ability for the foam to survive being placed underfoot is called its compression set or compression resistance. Not all foams are suitable for long-lasting footbed service! A plush footbed may help convince a customer to buy, but a collapsed footbed and ill-fitting shoe will not create a loyal, satisfied, or repeat customer.

A simple footbed will have just a few components. The top skin, which makes contact with the wearer's foot, the supporting foam, and maybe a logo. High-end technical footbeds may have molded foam, injected plastic support structures, impact absorbing gel inserts, padded top skins, or ventilation features.

sock allowance

Common footbed types

Footbeds come in two construction types: molded or die cut. Die cut footbeds are simply cut from flat stock materials. The molded footbeds are made of compression molded EVA, poured PU (polyurethane foam), latex and cork, sponge rubber, or PE (polyethylene) foam.

Generally speaking, EVA footbeds tend to have higher energy return and will give a running shoe a lively feel with some "spring." A poured PU footbed may have better energy absorbing or dampening characteristics and be more suitable for walking or standing comfort.

Die cut footbeds

The die cut footbed can be the cheapest piece of junk, or it can be very plush. Die cut does not have to mean cheap. The most basic shoe will have a thin, die cut footbed, made of soft EVA foam that will last just a few weeks. High-end shoes can have a nice, leather-covered, die cut footbed, made with multiple layers of high quality, long lasting PU foam, neoprene rubber, or gel sheet.

Fashion and casual shoes can have die cut footbeds. Soccer cleats, even expensive ones, often have thin, die cut footbeds. The die cut footbed is generally glued in place so it will not shift around inside of a shoe.

Molded footbeds

The molded footbed is the standard for performance athletic shoes. The contours will support the foot and hold the foot in place. Hiking, hunting, and military boots need a molded footbed. Inside strobel shoes, the footbed may be thinner, as the inside of the shoe will have more contours from the last and molded midsoles. Stiffer board lasted boots should have a molded footbed to provide support and fill up the square corners created by a square edged last.

Molded footbeds are usually removable. With a molded footbed you can add other features like injection molded stiffeners, support frames, gel pods, or airbags. The sky is the limit! But, you need to remember that a $4.00 footbed will add almost $20.00 to the retail price of your shoe!

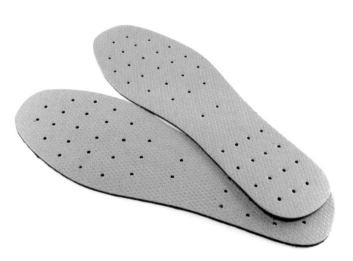

Here in the footbed factory, sheets of EVA foam with the fabric top skin already attached, are heated in an oven then pressed into cold molds to set the final shape. A cutting die will be used to trim away any extra foam.

82

Footbed cover materials

Footbeds come with different cover fabrics and linings. The best cover fabrics have enough grip to hold your feet in place. Fabric which is too smooth will not be stable and fabric which is too grippy will cause friction, heat, and can ruin your socks.

Some footbeds may not need any cover material at all. Running shoe and hiking boot footbeds need abrasion resistant materials to last for miles and miles. Some football and soccer cleat footbeds will have EVA covers. These will not absorb water, allowing the shoe to dry quickly.

Footbed cover materials must resist crocking, which is color transfer by friction or rubbing. Your shoes should not discolor your socks, even when wet.

Leather footbeds are nice for fashion shoes but are not suitable for athletic shoes. Many women's fashion shoes will have thin leather or PU footbeds and these will be glued into the shoe. Loafers, slip-on, and fine leather shoes will also have a smooth lining to allow easy entry.

The cover material for a molded footbed is laminated to the foam material in its flat pre-molded shape. The cover material will need to be somewhat stretchy to mold cleanly without wrinkles.

Fabric footbeds are the most common, but you will also find some high-end shoes that have micro-fiber suede footbeds. You can see molded micro-fiber on high-end outdoor sandals.

Other footbed features

Footbeds may have multiple densities of foam. They can also have perforations or other venting features. Moisture-wicking fabric covers, or bright graphics, are a nice touch. Most companies will have their own footbed molds with refined shapes to fit their last bottoms and molded in logos.

Another trick companies use is to include a very soft latex foam wedge under the heel. This latex will only last for a short while, and after a few days, or a week, it will be crushed flat. This is done to improve the "try on" or "in-store" feeling of the shoe.

For winter boots or hunting boots, you will find insulated footbeds with silver heat reflecting coatings. Footbeds for construction boots may have nail proof fabric, and a combat boot may have an extra grippy footbed to ensure stable footing for life and death situations.

High-end athletic footbeds will often feature impact dampening pads, injection molded supports, and removable arch "cookies."

As a designer or product manager, make sure your footbed matches the quality of your shoe. An inexpensive, poor performing footbed can cost you a repeat customer. As a shoe buyer, I am often disappointed to find cheap $0.65 footbeds in a $120 sports shoe. That said, a fancy footbed in an inexpensive shoe may hurt your profit margin or price your shoe out of the market.

Take time to shop around and make sure your footbeds are competitive, long lasting, and comfortable!

A heat reflecting layer added to the footbed of a winter boot.

A perforated footbed will help to keep you cool.

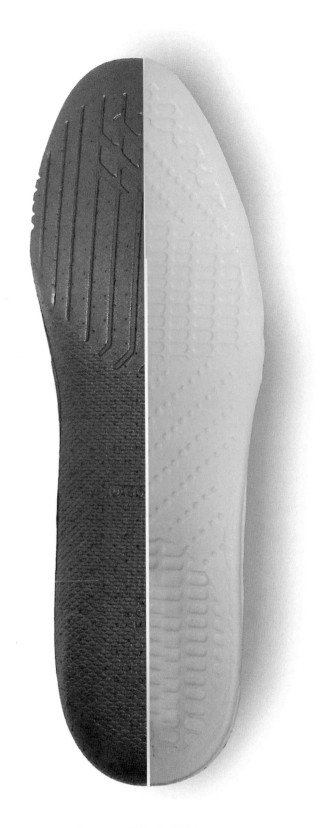

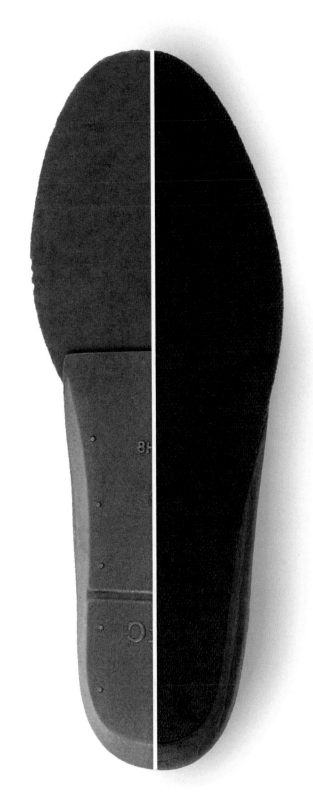

Dual-density molded EVA
This cold pressed EVA footbed features two layers of EVA, each with a different density. The green layer, closest to the foot, is a softer 30°. The grey layer, at the bottom, is a firmer 44° foam for support. This contoured footbed comes with a football cleat. The bottom surface has an aggressive texture to prevent it from sliding, while its top side does not have a fabric cover thus allowing it to dry fast between games.

Hybrid footbed
This economical footbed design is suitable for casual and dress shoes. This design combines a die cut forefoot and heel section with a cold pressed EVA heel cup. This is an efficient design. One step up from die cut, but with a molded heel cup for a more finished look. The polyester jersey top cover provides minimal traction but has some moisture wicking properties.

Molded EVA with plastic reinforcement
This performance footbed is from a high-end
snowboarding boot. The top skin is molded with
a gripping texture to prevent slipping inside the
boot. The bottom has molded flex grooves in the
forefoot and an injected nylon heel stabilizer.
This injected nylon plastic part is pre-molded in
a separate operation, then pinned into the EVA
mold during the compression operation. You can
see the pin holes in the finished product.

Multi-density poured PU footbed
This footbed is from a high-end biker boot. Liquid
PU is poured into a two-piece mold, and the
fabric (with a waterproof backing) is laid into the
mold before it is closed. The PU foam inside the
mold fills the cavity and bonds to the fabric. This
footbed is made with two molding operations. The
orange is poured first and partially cured, then
the black PU foam and fabric are combined in the
second molding operation.

 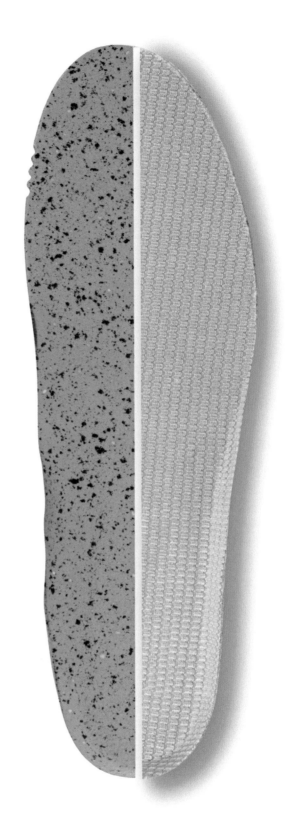

Molded EVA with gel and foam pods
This footbed is from a high performance cleated shoe. The top skin is combined with soft PU foam inserts in the heel and forefoot before being molded with the EVA footbed. The PU foam flattens while the EVA is molded, but springs back to create soft pods of foam on the top surface. On the bottom side of the pod, die cut sheets of firm plastic, also modeled with the EVA, provide a supporting function.

Crystallized PU foam footbed
This footbed, pulled from a mid-priced running shoe, features a unique foam compound made with chopped PU foam in an EVA foam matrix. Designed to provide the rebound of PU foam but with the lightweight and mold-ability of standard EVA foam. This foam is 4.5mm thick and has a density of 32°.

Injection footbed
This is an example of a very expensive aftermarket injection footbed. The heel and arch support are made of over-molded nylon plastic (the red and gray parts). After molding, this structure is bonded to a flexible injection molded TPU frame. The forefoot is padded with die cut EVA. This footbed is quite complicated and requires expensive tooling to produce.

Vulcanized footbed
This footbed was pulled from a classic high top vulcanized shoe. The top skin is cotton canvas with logo printing. The padding is blown sponge. The rubber hardness is 25° and it is 4.5mm thick. The heel wedge is made of reprocessed rubber foxing tape with a hardness of 35° to 40°. The stripe pattern is from the glue used to attach the footbed permanently. An automatic glue roller neatly applies the glue.

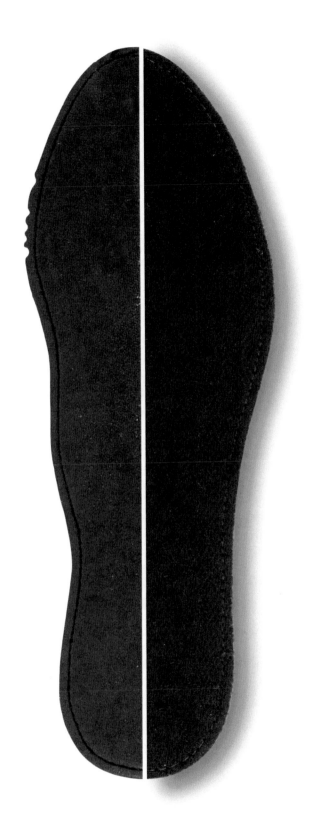

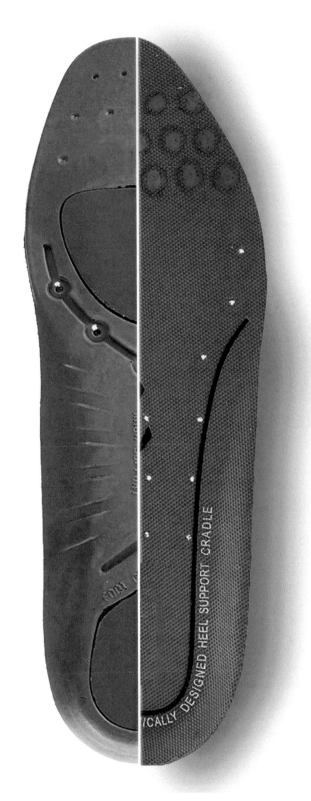

Die cut footbeds

The die cut footbed can be found in many types of footwear. Sleek fitting wrestling shoes, cleated shoes that don't require cushioning, fine dress shoes, and discount shoes. The die cut footbed can be very inexpensive if the foam is thin and the top cover is cheap. Expensive dress shoes may also have die cut footbeds, but these have calf leather top covers and plush PU foam sheets stacked to create a custom fit.

Multi-density poured PU footbed

Liquid PU is poured into a two-piece mold, and the fabric (with a waterproof backing) is laid into the mold before it is closed. The PU foam inside the mold fills the cavity and bonds to the fabric. This footbed has added pods of die-cut Sorbathan™, an energy absorbing foam. This footbed will be relatively heavy with good impact protection and it will last. This example has flex grooves and vents combined to move air inside the shoe.

CHAPTER 15

WEBBING FOR SHOES

Webbing is a very useful component on footwear. Its light weight and high strength make it perfect for use as lace loops, tongue pulls, back pull tabs, tongue anchors, and reinforcements. In the case of the classic river sandals, the entire shoe is made of webbing.

Webbing for footwear is usually made of nylon, polyester, polypropylene, or cotton. Polyester and nylon are most popular due to their higher strength, UV stability, and suitability for bonding with standard shoe cement. For high strength and fireproof applications, webbing can also be made from Kevlar™ and Nomex™ fibers.

Webbing is usually knit with color fibers, but can also be dyed to almost any color. Webbing is available in widths from 2mm to 100mm and thicknesses from .5mm to 3mm. Webbing can be soft to the touch or "sized" with a plastic resin coating to create a stiffer webbing strap that will resist wrinkling and bunching under load. Webbing can also be coated or co-extruded with PU or PVC film covers.

Webbing can be knit in almost any pattern, from solids to stripes to checks. Solid color webbing can have 3D features such as stripes, ribs, blocks, and even logos. Webbing can be woven or printed with reflective logos. Webbing can also be woven with varying widths along its length.

For extra effect, webbing can have welded logos, sublimation printing, elastic fiber, and gripping rubber stripes. While webbing knit from man-made fibers is not damaged by water, straps may have an extra DWR coating to repel water and prevent mildew.

The MOQ for a basic, solid color webbing, can be low or even zero if purchased from stock. Complicated designs that need complicated set-

CHAPTER 16

PLASTIC PARTS

In this chapter, we will look at injection, compression, and blow molded plastic parts for footwear. Technically speaking, almost every part of a modern athletic shoe is made of plastic. Textiles are woven from plastic fibers, foam is made of blown plastic, and synthetics are actually sheets of plastic with plastic fiber backings.

In fact, many shoes are made entirely of plastic. We are going to focus on the plastic accessory parts which give shoes their special functionality. It is these plastic parts that separate the modern mass-produced athletic shoe from its handmade ancestor.

Thermoplastic vs Thermosetting polymers

Plastics can be separated into two main types. Thermoplastic polymers or "thermoplastics" are melted and formed while hot. Thermoplastics can be re-melted and remolded. Thermoplastics like nylon are injection molded to create complicated 3D shapes. Thermoplastics are particularly useful in shoe production due to their ability to be reformed after molding.

Thermoplastic plastics are the most common type of plastics used in footwear. There are many different types of thermoplastics, each with individual properties and uses in footwear. Thermoplastics can be recycled. The most common thermoplastics found in shoes include nylon, ABS, polycarbonate, TPE, TPU, TPR hytel, PVC, surlyn, polyethylene, and polypropylene.

Thermosetting plastics are a class of materials that can be shaped and once heated they are transformed by an irreversible chemical reaction called curing. In the curing process, the molecules in the plastic are cross-linked. Once fully linked, these chains of molecules cannot be broken down by heat. Epoxy, polyester, EVA, and polyurethanes are thermosetting plastics.

This shoe features an injection molded TPU heel strap.

91

When to use thermoplastics versus thermosetting plastics

Material suppliers will use thermosetting plastics to produce many types of foams and fabrics. Thermoplastics are much more common for a designer to specify for a component. Thermoplastics are easy to handle and can be formed with several different machines. The most common being a plastic injection molding machine. Plastic injection machines, big and small, are ubiquitous in the industrial cities of China.

Making thermoplastics parts

Injection molding is the most common forming method for shoe accessories. Lace hardware, logo plates, shanks, internal heel counters, back-stays, eye-stays, bottoms for cleated shoes, spike plates, and buckles are all made by injection process. Injection molds can be expensive but productivity is high, and parts spring from the machine ready for assembly with little post finishing required.

Injection molding

Injection machines work by heating tiny plastic pellets until they melt to a liquid state. With the mold being held closed by steel clamps, host plastic is "shot" under tremendous pressure rapidly into the mold. After cooling for several seconds, the mold opens and the parts are released. Injection parts can be any size, from a tiny logo piece to an entire ski boot frame, or even a 60-gallon trash can! Injection parts can also have glass fibers or carbon fibers added. These reinforcing fibers are chopped down into lengths less than 1 mm and then added to the plastic formula. Plastic can have fiber reinforcements ranging from 1% to over 50%. For flexible shoes, 15% is about the maximum glass fill. Above 15% glass fill, parts are difficult to sew through and can crack instead of bending. A shank plate for a soccer shoe many have 0 or 3% glass fill while a shank plate for a mountaineering boot may have 45%.

Blow molding

Blow molding is the process used to make plastic soda bottles. Nike™ airbags are also made this way. In the blow molding process, the machine extrudes a hollow tube of molten plastic that will hang down between the two mold halves. The mold halves close on the tube as a needle pumps air into the tube, forcing the plastic to follow the shape of the mold. While an airbag will use elastic TPU, the same machine can make plastic soda bottles with ridged PET plastic.

Vacuum molding

Vacuum molding is when a sheet of plastic is held by the edges while being heated. Once the sheet is soft it will be lowered down into a mold. A vacuum pump will then be used to draw the plastic down onto the mold. Vacuum molding is most often used for packing materials.

Plastic extrusion

Extrusion is the process in which the hot plastic is forced through a die with a specific shape. Plastic piping trim is made by extrusion, as is synthetic welting material. The extrusion process is also used to saturated fabrics with plastic. Components such as lasting boards, heel counters, and toe puff fabrics are made using this process. Rubber parts for vulcanized shoes can also be extruded.

Open mold pouring

PU and TPR materials can be molded in "open" molds. These molds do not have a top. The materials are self leveling liquids and do not require injection pressure to fill the mold. The small rubber logo badges found on many shoes and clothing are made by hand; the workers apply the color drop by drop into the molds. The parts are then cured in a small oven before being peeled out of the mold.

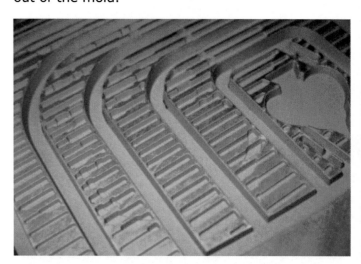

Making thermosetting plastic parts

PU foam is the most common example of thermosetting plastic found in shoes. Its two precursor chemical components are mixed creating a cross-linking catalytic process. The PU flows from the mixing machine like a heavy syrup. If left in the open air, cells inside the PU will expand the material into a cake like foam, if enclosed in a heated midsole mold, the PU will fill the cavity creating a foam part with a solid skin. More PU will produce a higher density part. Once the PU reacts, it cannot be reformed. This PU pouring process is used to make midsoles, outsoles, footbeds, and upper side panels.

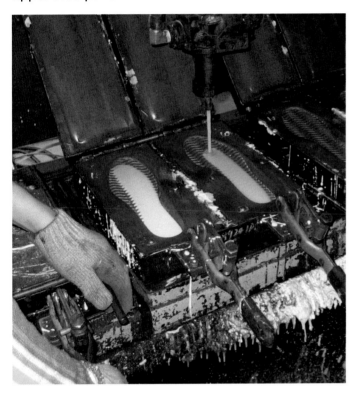

Thermosetting carbon fiber composite

What we know as carbon fiber or fiberglass parts are actually a composite made by arranging the fibers then anchoring them in place with a thermosetting plastic. The material that holds the fibers in place is called the "matrix." Epoxy and polyester are the most common thermosetting plastics used as the matrix. To make a composite part, the fibers are saturated with the matrix plastic in its liquid, uncured form. Once the liquid plastic is heated, it solidifies and cannot be re-melted. This process is usually done outside the shoe factory by a special sub-contacted factory.

Carbon and fiberglass parts are found in outsole stiffening shanks. Strangely, a women's high heel shoe and a mountaineering boot may both have composite shanks. The composite shank is also used in service boots when metal is prohibited. Safety toes for work boots can also be made of composite.

94

CHAPTER 17

FOOTWEAR PACKING SPECIFICATIONS

The design of your shoe packaging is a significant part of your product marketing presentation. In a retail store crammed with your competitors' product, first impressions are critical. A cheap shoe box may save you money, but dented or wrinkled packaging sends the wrong message to your customers. Well designed, high-quality packaging does not have to be expensive and confirms that your product is top notch. Let's not forget about your dealers. They will have a hard time selling your shoes at full price if the packaging is damaged.

In-store appearance
When designing your packaging, you need to consider where and how your products will be sold. Are your shoes being sold in a boutique where the boxes will be hidden away in a dark stock room? Maybe your shoes will be sold in a mass-market retailer with the boxes stacked for self-service sales?

There are two main types of footwear box construction. The most popular is corrugated cardboard that has been printed, cut, and folded. High-end shoe boxes are made of solid boxboard or paperboard that has been hand wrapped in printed or embossed paper. Many shoe companies offer limited edition packing made of plastic, wood, fabric, foam, or any combination of materials.

The shoe box for your average sports shoe will cost about $0.75. A reinforced box for larger work boots, designed to be stacked 10 high for self-serve retail may cost over $2.00. A luxury brand may use hand-wrapped paper with leather trim and foam inserts that may cost $5.00 or even $10.00. Add-ons may include shoe bags or shoe trees.

Remember that high-end packaging which adds $10.00 to the landed cost, adds $50.00 to the retail price of the shoe! Spend your packing budget wisely!

Corrugated cardboard

Corrugated cardboard is made of three parts that are laminated together: the outer skin paper, the inner skin paper, and the fluted or corrugated paper in the middle. Corrugated board is specified by the weight of the skin papers and the size of the flute pattern. For shoe boxes, the most common is E flute. E flute board is 1/16 of an inch thick (1.5mm) and has 94 flutes per foot. Stronger shoe boxes can be made from C flute, while boot boxes will be made from B flute board.

Boxboard or paperboard.

A less commonly used box material is a solid sheet of stiff paper known has boxboard. If you have purchased a cell phone from Apple™, you have seen boxboard packaging. (All Apple iPhones are packaged in boxboard) Boxboard has the advantage of being a perfectly flat surface, excellent for direct printing or laminating of printed paper skins.

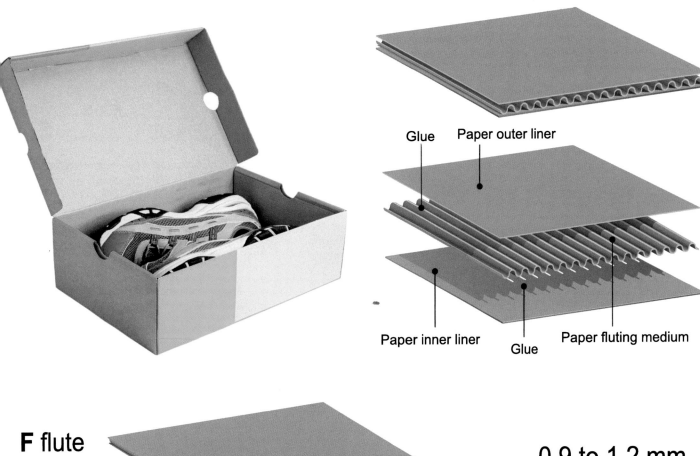

Glue   Paper outer liner

Paper inner liner   Glue   Paper fluting medium

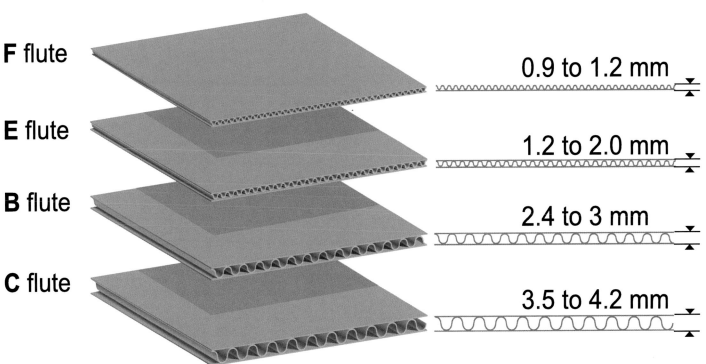

F flute

E flute

B flute

C flute

0.9 to 1.2 mm

1.2 to 2.0 mm

2.4 to 3 mm

3.5 to 4.2 mm

Die lines

The box die line is simply the outline shape of the box pattern. The die line has all the tabs, slots, folds, windows, and perforations that allow you to fold flat stock into a 3D container. The configuration of the die line determines the cost and strength of the final box. Depending on the size and design; a shoebox may be assembled by just folding tabs or may require glue and staples.

The cardboard stock materials come from the paper factory in rolls. The box printer will have rolls of different widths depending on the factories machines and common box sizes. It is important to know the box printers standard width so you can create a design that efficiently uses the paper. The box price is calculated on paper consumption. A very efficient design will use the entire width of the roll with a minimum length. Remember, just like when other shoe materials are cut, you will be paying for any waste paper that is trimmed away.

When the graphic designer works to make a new box design they will need the die line to arrange the artwork correctly. It is a good idea to hand cut a small mock-up of a new design to make sure the logos are facing the right direction.

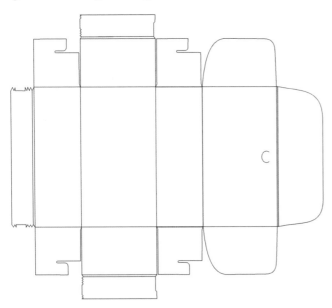

The die line is used to create the cutting die or tooling used to trim the cardboard into the correct shape. The cutting die is made by carving the box design onto a sheet of wood and then inserting the sharpened steel blades. Box cutting dies are not expensive and are easy to modify. A busy box factory will have hundreds of cutting dies from which to choose.

How corrugated shoe boxes are made

First, the factory will order the paper stock for the fluting and the outer skin for the box. A simple box design can be printed directly to the outer surface of the cardboard. For a design that requires more color or a gloss finish, the outer skin paper will be printed before it is laminated to the fluted inner skin.

Once the cardboard has the artwork applied it is ready to be cut by machine. The printed board is fed sheet by sheet into the cutting machine. Once the board is cut into shape, the flat boxes are stacked on pallets for shipment to the shoe factory. Boxes are stored flat until the very last minute. Depending on the box design, a worker will fold, staple, and apply quick setting glue to complete the box.

How hand wrapped boxes are made

The wrapped box is made by first printing the art on the skin paper and then cutting the paper into shape. Hot glue is then applied to the back of the skin paper using a roller machine. The boxboard is cut, bent into shape, and then placed on the paper. The paper is then quickly wrapped over the boxboard before the glue cools.

Graphic effects

Both corrugated cardboard and boxboard shoeboxes can have 4-color photographic art applied. Before lamination, the skin papers can also have texture emboss, metallic foil stamping, or gloss overprinting.

Inner box vs case box

In the shoe trade, what we all know as a shoe box is called the inner box. At the end of the assembly line, the shoes are placed into the inner box. The inner boxes are then labeled with the shoe size and model name before being loaded into another larger master carton or case box. This larger box will usually hold 12 inner boxes. Large boots may be six packed.

The master carton is designed to protect the inner boxes. Shoe factories may require orders to be placed in multiples of 12 to make full cases. The size of the master carton will depend on the labor regulations of the importing country. Oversized master cartons are dangerous for workers to lift and may require higher freight fees when being shipped to dealers.

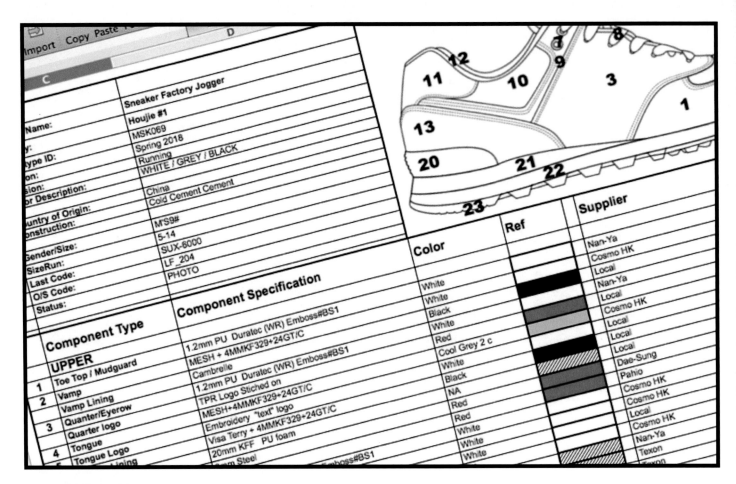

CHAPTER 18

SHOE MATERIAL SPECIFICATIONS

Once you have made your material selections, you will need to communicate your choices to the factory. As a shoe designer working for a smaller firm, you may be responsible for writing your own product specifications. If you work for a mega brand, you can pass your drawings to the development staff, and they will complete the product specifications.

In this chapter, we will describe the basic requirements for a simple specification sheet. Large shoe brands will have a database system to hold the data, and smaller shoe companies will create the spec sheet in Microsoft™ Excel™ or other spreadsheet software.

The spec sheet lists each shoe part, the material code number or thickness, color, and supplier. When you first create a spec for a new development, some of the details may be missing, that's okay. It is the developer's job to fill in the blanks as the shoe development continues. Once the spec is sent to the factory, the factory development staff will work with the developer and designers to complete it.

The spec is an important document. When it is time for production, the approved spec sheet will become the contract with the factory. The spec sheet is also a living document. As the shoe is developed, the spec sheet is changed and updated onward to production.

This is a very simple spec sheet for a basic item. A high-tech sneaker or snowboard boot spec may have many pages. For a complicated item the supplier part number of the materials must also be included.

	Project Name:	Ariss Jogger
	Factory:	**Houjie #1**
	Prototype ID:	ARJ-001
	Season:	Spring 2018
	Division:	Running
	Color Description:	WHITE / RED / BLACK
	Country of Origin:	China
	Construction:	Cold Cement Cement
		Board Lasted
	Gender/Size:	M'S9#
	SizeRun:	5-14
	Last Code:	SUX-6000
	O/S Code:	LF_204
	Status:	Photo Sample

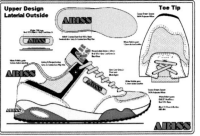
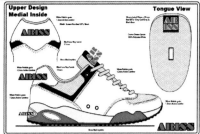
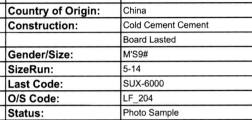
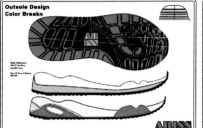
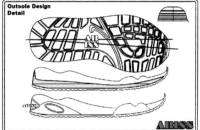

	Component Type	Component Specification	White/Red/Black	Color	Supplier
	UPPER				
10	Toe Top / Mudguard	1.2mm White Pebble grain Action Leather	White		Nan-Ya Tanning
20	Vamp	Cosmo Dream Spacer 100% Polyester	White		Cosmo HK
30	Vamp Lining	Cosmo Dream Spacer 100% Polyester	White		Local
40	Quanter/Eyerow	1.2mm White Pebble grain Action Leather	White		Nan-Ya Tanning
50	Quarter logo	TPR Logo "Ariss"	Red 187c/Black/Grey 2c		Local
60	Tongue	Cosmo Dream Spacer 100% Polyester	Cool Grey 2 c		Cosmo HK
70	Tongue Lace keeper	1.2mm White Pebble grain Action Leather	White		Nan-Ya Tanning
80	Tongue Logo	32mm x 32mm Woven Label Stacked "Ariss"	Red 187c/Black/Grey 2c		Local
90	Tongue Lining	Visa Terry + 4MMKF329+24GT/C	Cool Grey 2 c		Local
100	Tongue Foam	20mm KFF PU foam	NA		Local
110	Lace Eyelets	8mm Steel	Black		Dae-Sung
120	Medial Vents	8mm Steel	Black		Dae-Sung
130	Shoe Lace	8mm Oval	Cool Grey 2 c		Pahio
140	Collar Underlay	Low Nap Suede 1.2mm	Black		Local
150	Collar Panel	Cosmo Dream Spacer 100% Polyester	White		Cosmo HK
160	Heel Logo	Print + Emboss 55mm ARISS	Red/Black		Local
170	Heel Lining	Visa Terry + 4MMKF329+24GT/C	NA		Cosmo HK
180	Heel Counter	1.2mm White Pebble grain Action Leather	NA		Nan-Ya Tanning
190	Internal Heel Counter	Texon Rite thermoplastic 1.4mm	NA		Texon
200	Internal Toe Puff	Texon Sportflex .35mm thermoplastic film	NA		Texon
210	Eyerow Reinforcement	Super Tuff	NA		Local
220	Upper Thread	bonded nylon 6 250D 3 Ply	Matching		Coats or A&E
	OUTSOLE UNIT				
230	Midsole Wedge Top	Hot Press EVA Asker "C" 45-50	White		Local
240	Outsole	#1-44 NBS400 Shore "A" 65 +or-3 SG 1.1 +1.4	Black		CW Pressing
250	Outsole Color Break	NBS400 Shore "A" 65 +or-3 SG 1.1 +1.4	Red		CW Pressing
260	Outsole Logo	"ARISS" Logo NBS400 Shore "A" 65 +or-3 SG 1.1 +1.4	Red		CW Pressing
270	Outsole Tip Stitching	bonded nylon 6 850D 3 Ply	Red		Coats or A&E
280	Insole Strobal	Texon T28	White		Texon
290	Footbed	Cold Pressed EVA Asker "C" 45 Standard Open Mold	Black		Local
300	Foobed Skin	Cosmo Hex Weave	White		Cosmo HK
310	Foobed Logo	Screen Print Logo "ARISS" 65mm Heat Transfer	Black / Red		Local
320	Cement	Water based PU	Clear		Nan-Pou
	PACKING				
330	Inner Box	2016 Box art E-Flue - White Back PVC skin	Red		Lai-Wah
340	Out Carton	Brown	Brown		Local
350	Tongue label	3cm x 3cm White + Black Screen + Weld	Black / White		Local
360	EEC label	2cm x 2cm White + Black Print	Black / White		Local
370	HangTag	4-Color Print	Color		Lai-Wah
380	Tag pin	White	White		Local
390	Wrap Tissue	10 gram 2 sheets	White		Local
400	Toe Tissue	10 gram 2 sheets	White		Local

The spec sheet

The footwear specification sheet or "spec" sheet does a few things:

1. Tells the shoe factory the name of each part on your design.
2. Details the material you want for each part.
3. Tells the shoe factory what color every part is.
4. Tells who supplies each material to the shoe factory.

A detailed specification sheet is absolutely critical to your success. If you leave line items open without details the factory developer will choose whatever they have inside the factory for these parts. This may be good or bad and may lead to an unexpected result.

You will also use the spec sheet to check the new samples that come in from the factory. It's important to review each sample with the spec sheet to make sure that the factory followed the specification sheet. It is good to highlight differences and ask the factory why they did not follow the spec sheet. Maybe they have a suggestion that is better than what you chose? In many cases, the factory developer or pattern maker will substitute a material they have on hand, and it may work better than your original specification.

Material maps

You should make a material map when first specifying an item the factory has not seen before. It is important for the shoe factory to know the terminology you are using for each part.

Take a black-and-white drawing and give each piece a number. Make sure the numbers on your spec sheet match the drawings. This takes just a few minutes and can save you the hassle of a simple mistake. I like to count by 10's so I can add lines later if I need to. You can use letters to separate outsole parts.

Project Name:	Sneaker Factory Jogger
Story:	Haujie #1
Prototype ID:	MSK069
Season:	Spring 2016
Division:	Running
Color Description:	WHITE / GREY / BLACK
Country of Origin:	China
Construction:	Cold Cement Cement
Last/Sizes:	MT59#
SizeRun:	5-14
Last Code:	SUX-6000
EC Code:	LF_204
Value:	PHOTO

Component Type	Component Specification	Color	Ref	Supplier	Notes
UPPER					
Toy Top / Mudguard	1.2mm PU Dureloc (WR) Emboss#851	White		Nan-Ya	
Vamp	MESH + 4MMKF329+24GT/C	White		Cosmo-HK	
Vamp Lining	Cambrelle	Black		Local	
Quarter/Eyerow	1.2mm PU Dureloc (WR) Emboss#851	White		Nan-Ya	
Quarter logo	TPR Logo Stiched on	Red		Local	
Tongue	MESH+4MMKF329+24GT/C	Cool Grey 2 c		Cosmo-HK	
Tongue Logo	Embroidery "text" logo	White		Local	
Tongue Lining	Visa Terry + 4MMKF329+24GT/C	Black		Local	
Tongue Foam	20mm KFF PU foam	NA		Local	
Top Eyelet	8mm Steel	Red		Dae-Sung	
Shoe Lace	8mm Oval	Red		Paiho	
Collar Underlay	1.2mm PU Dureloc (WR) Emboss#851	White		Cosmo-HK	
Collar Panel	MESH+4MMKF329+24GT/C	White		Cosmo-HK	
Heel Logo	Embroidery "text" logo	White		Local	
Heel Lining	Visa Terry + 4MMKF329+24GT/C	NA		Cosmo-HK	
Heel Counter	1.2mm PU Dureloc (WR) Emboss#851	NA		Nan-Ya	
External Heel Counter	Texon 4mm	NA		Texon	
Internal Toe Puff	Texon 2mm	NA		Texon	
Eyerow Reinforcement	Super Tuff	NA		Local	
Upper Thread	bonded nylon 6 2500 3 Ply	Matching		Coats or A&E	
OUTSOLE UNIT					
Heel Counter	Injection Plastic Red	Red		Xie-Xie Injection	
Midsole Wedge Top	Hot Press EVA Asker "C" 45-50	Grey 2c		Local	
Midsole Wedge Bottom	Hot Press EVA Asker "C" 55-60	White		Local	
Outsole	41-44 NBS400 Shore "A" 65 +or-3 SG 1.1 +1.4	Black		CW Pressing	
Insole Strobal	Texon T28	White		Texon	
Footbed	Cold Pressed EVA Asker "C" 45 Standard Open Mold	Black		Local	
Footbed Skin	SAMPLE MESH+4MMKF329+24GT/C	White		Cosmo-HK	
Footbed Logo	Screen Print Logo "Text" 45mm x 25MM	Black / Red		Local	
Cement	Water based PU	Clear		Nan-Pou	
PACKING					
Inner Box	2016 Box art E-Flue - White Back PVC skin	Red		Lai-Wah	
Outer Carton	Brown	Brown		Local	
Tongue label	3cm x 3cm White + Black Screen + Weld	Black / White		Local	
UPC Label	2cm x 2cm White + Black Print	Black / White		Local	
HangTag	4-Color Print	Color		Lai-Wah	
Clip pin	White	White		Local	
Poly bag	Clear	Clear		Local	
Wrap Tissue	10 gram 2 sheets	White		Local	
Stuff Tissue	10 gram 2 sheets	White		Local	

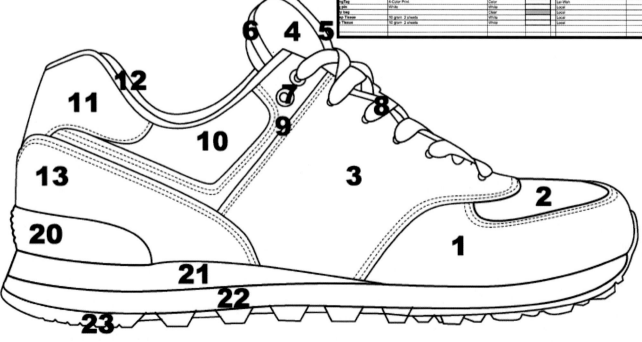

101

Spec sheet header

Big companies will have a database system to manage spec sheets, but medium and small companies can manage just fine with Microsoft Excel or other spreadsheet programs.

The specification sheet header contains lots of key information the factory will need to keep your project organized and make the samples.

Your header should include:

The development model year and season
The shoe factory name
Model name or number if it has a name
Outsole tooling code numbers
Size run information
Designer or Developer's name
Last code number
Sample color information
The sample round number

Project Name:	Ariss Jogger
Factory:	Houjie #1
Prototype ID:	ARJ-001
Season:	Spring 2018
Division:	Running
Color Description:	WHITE / RED / BLACK
Country of Origin:	China
Construction:	Cold Cement Cement
	Board Lasted
Gender/Size:	M'S9#
SizeRun:	5-14
Last Code:	SUX-6000
O/S Code:	LF_204
Status:	Photo Sample

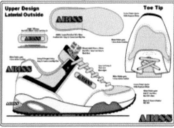

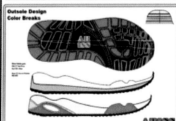

Filling in the spec sheet

When writing the spec sheet, it helps to break up the components of the shoe into several sections. The first section being the upper components of the shoe. Start with the front of the shoe and work your way backwards. Then, list the inside lining components and the reinforcing components, all those pieces that you can't see inside the shoe like the vamp lining, collar lining, etc... In this section, you can also list things like the glue, collar foam density and thickness, and the thread type you want to use.

The bulk of the information on the spec sheet will include the names of the components and what material you specified for each component. When detailing the shoe materials, list the name, the manufacturer and the code number or the swatch book.

Depending on the material, you will want to list the thickness of the material, the emboss pattern, and the backing material.

Let us look at this sample spec

#1 is the toe top:
The material thickness is 1.2mm. This material is PU (Polyurethane leather). The product name is "Duratec." In this case, it has (WR) water resistant treatment added to the backing layer. The material is available in many different surface patterns or "emboss patterns." In this case, emboss#BS1. The color is "white," the material manufacturer is "Nan-Ya."

If the material vendor is new to the factory, it is useful to add the factory contact information somewhere on your spec sheet.

	Component Type	Component Specification	Color	Ref	Supplier
	UPPER				
1	Toe Top / Mudguard	1.2mm PU Duratec (WR) Emboss#BS1	White		Nan-Ya
2	Vamp	MESH + 4MMKF329+24GT/C	White		Cosmo HK
	Vamp Lining	Cambrelle	Black		Local
3	Quanter/Eyerow	1.2mm PU Duratec (WR) Emboss#BS1	White		Nan-Ya
	Quarter logo	TPR Logo Stiched on	Red		Local
4	Tongue	MESH+4MMKF329+24GT/C	Cool Grey 2 c		Cosmo HK
5	Tongue Logo	Embroidery "text" logo	White		Local
6	Tongue Lining	Visa Terry + 4MMKF329+24GT/C	Black		Local
	Tongue Foam	20mm KFF PU foam	NA		Local
7	Lace Eyelet	8mm Steel	Red		Dae-Sung
8	Shoe Lace	8mm Oval	Red		Pahio
9	Collar Underlay	1.2mm PU Duratec (WR) Emboss#BS1	White		Cosmo HK
10	Collar Panel	MESH+4MMKF329+24GT/C	White		Cosmo HK
11	Heel Logo	Embroidery "text" logo	White		Local
12	Heel Lining	Visa Terry + 4MMKF329+24GT/C	NA		Cosmo HK

Specifying the outsole unit

The next section will call out the footwear outsole unit components. List the rubber parts, colors, and other details like the logo. You can also spec the following features:

Rubbers hardness (Shore "A" scale)
The SG or specific gravity
Rubber color
Midsole material
Midsole hardness or durometer
Sockliner foam
Sockliner cover fabric

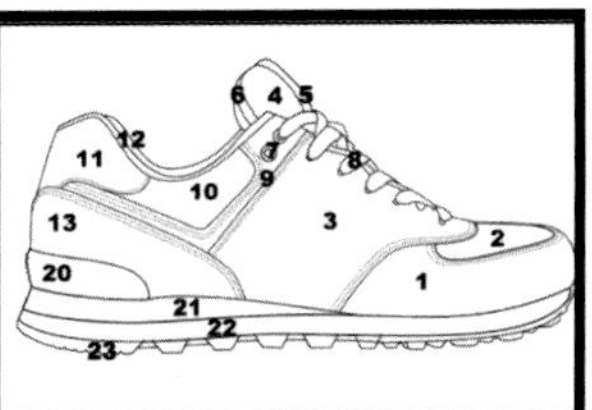

Let us look at this sample specification

#23 is the rubber outsole:
We can look at this spec and see the mold code number is #1-44, the rubber compound is an extra durable compound NBS400. The rubber hardness is measured in the "Shore A" scale. Shore "A" 65. We give the factory a range of + or- 3, the density is SG 1.1 +1.4

The midsole is hot pressed EVA with hardness measured in the Asker "C" scale, 45-50.

	OUTSOLE UNIT				
20	Heel Counter	Injection Plastic Red	Red		Xie-Xie Injection
21	Midsole Wedge Top	Hot Press EVA Asker "C" 45-50	Grey 2c		Local
22	Midsole Wedge Bottom	Hot Press EVA Asker "C" 55-60	White		Local
23	Outsole	#1-44 NBS400 Shore "A" 65 +or-3 SG 1.1 +1.4	Black		CW Pressing
	Insole Strobal	Texon T28	White		Texon
	Footbed	Cold Pressed EVA Asker "C" 45 Standard Open Mold	Black		Local
	Foobed Skin	SAMPLE MESH+4MMKF329+24GT/C	White		Cosmo HK
	Foobed Logo	Screen Print Logo "Text" 45mm x 25MM	Black / Red		Local
	Cement	Water based PU	Clear		Nom-Pou

Packing

Remember, everything you want to ship with your shoe must be included on the spec sheet.

The final section of the spec sheet should list any items that are not necessarily part of the shoe but are still part of the package.

For example, the cardboard box, the tissue paper, tags, stuffing, if you have extra shoelaces, if you have a keychain, or you have a user manual in a plastic bag. Anything like that should be included in the final section.

	PACKING				
	Inner Box	2016 Box art E-Flue - White Back PVC skin	Red		Lai-Wah
	Out Carton	Brown	Brown		Local
	Tongue label	3cm x 3cm White + Black Screen + Weld	Black		Local
	EEC label	2cm x 2cm White + Black Print	Black / White		Local
	HangTag	4-Color Print	Color		Lai-Wah
	Tag pin	White	White		Local
	Poly bag		Clear		Local
	Wrap Tissue	10 gram 2 sheets	White		Local
	Toe Tissue	10 gram 2 sheets	White		Local

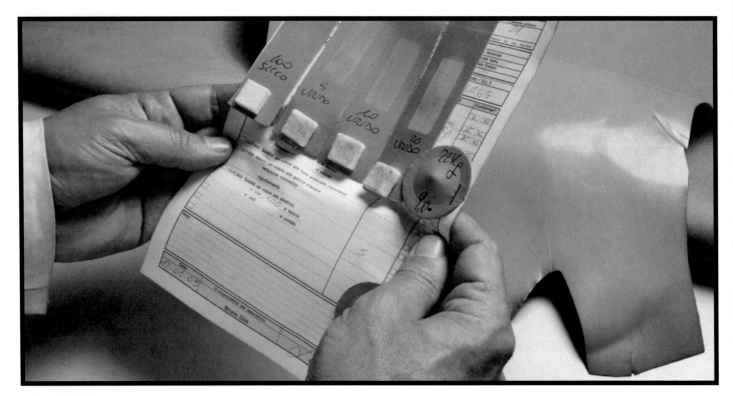

CHAPTER 19

SHOE MATERIAL TESTING

Material testing is another critical aspect of quality footwear production. A beautifully designed shoe, carefully patterned, and meticulously crafted can still fall apart in a few days if the materials selected for its construction are not appropriate or poorly manufactured. Physical testing and lab testing of materials and the finished product are required to ensure your shoes work. We will review five types of testing.

Physical testing of sample materials
Physical testing of production materials
Lab testing completed shoes
Fitting trials
Wear testing shoes

Physical testing sample materials

When you specify a new material for a particular component, you need to make sure the physical properties are appropriate for the chosen application. Most suppliers' sample books will list the physical testing lab results for all materials they sell. A typical swatch card will show color and texture options for material on the front, with lab test results listed on the back.

The specific performance property will be listed with the lab test method and the lab test result.
There are hundreds of different performance tests based on the material type, industry, and country. A lab test report may show test standards from one of the following:
ASTM™ American Section of the International Association for Testing Materials
SATRA™ Shoe and Allied Trades Research Association
DIN™ German Institute for Standardization
ISO™ International Organization for Standardization
ANSI™ American National Standards Institute
AFNOR™ French Standardization Association

These associations design the test standards which allow labs around the world to follow the same procedures. This ensures a lab test done in the Chinese factory will match the test done in a French safety lab. These standards are not all legal requirements but may provide some legal protection. In cases of safety marketing there are standard requirements for "slip resistance" and "oil resistant" products.

Standard material tests

There are dozens of material tests listed on the swatch cards of professional material suppliers. Some careful study will allow you to compare and rate a material's suitability. The material supplier's salespeople will often help you find the right material for your particular project and will be more than happy to explain the test standards. The larger brands will have a fixed set of standards for material performance requirements.

Weight

Consistent weight measurements insure the factory is delivering product with the same fiber content and composition as the sample product.

Thickness

The thickness measurements again insure the factory is delivering the same product spec. Inconsistent material thicknesses can cause fitting problems in the finished goods.

Tensile strength length & width

Tensile strength is the force required to pull a sample apart. Materials should be tested in both directions if the material surface is not directional.

Elongation length & width

The elongation test lets you know how far a material will stretch before it fails. This is important to know for elastic materials such as Lycra or neoprene and knot fabrics.

Stretching under load length & width

This test reveals the stretching "pull back" power of an elastic material.

Trouser tear length & width

This test reveals the internal strength of a material when pulled apart along a slit. Technically it is called tear-propagation resistance.

Stitch tear length & width

When joining two materials together, more stitching is usually better, but not always. The stitch tearing test shows how the material responds to the perforations caused by stitching. Some materials may lose strength as stitches are added!

Bursting strength

The bursting test is made by securing the material along the perimeter of a circle and applying pressure to the center by an inflatable bladder. The bursting strength of a material predicts its strength for lasting operations. Material with low bursting strength cannot be toe lasted without reinforcing layers.

Martindale abrasion dry & wet

The Martindale test uses a sandpaper-like material to grind on the material surface. Used on fabric and other shoe materials, the test predicts wear-ability, durability, and fiber damage. A good Martindale result makes a material suitable for use as a lining for footbed top skin.

Colorfast in water & perspiration

Colorfastness is the resistance of fabric dye to color bleed. This test is done with both water and simulated perspiration. The colorfast test ensures the lining of a running shoe will not color bleed when wet.

Crocking dry & wet

The crocking test is similar to the colorfast test but is focused on the transfer of color by friction or rubbing and is done dry.

UV color fade

The UV color fade test simulates how a material resists the damaging effects of sunlight. A material with a poor UV rating can fade while sitting on a store shelf or if left outside over a weekend. Different color pigments are more or less susceptible to UV damage. Black and blue pigments are more resistant than red pigments and the vibrating neon colors glow because the pigments are being destroyed by UV rays.

Accelerated aging

The accelerated aging test takes place inside an "oven." In the oven the environment has harsh UV lighting, humidity, and temperature cycling.

Leather flexing test

The leather flexing test machine is used on real leather, coated leather, and synthetic leather. The flex test ensures the surface of the leather remains firmly attached and does not crack.

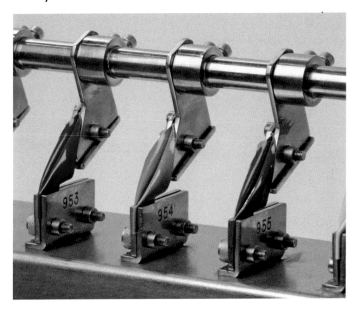

Physical testing of production materials

Physical testing of production materials inside the shoe factory helps to ensure the material performs as specified. The supply factory must deliver materials that conform to their specifications or the goods should be rejected or discounted. A strobel material that bursts during the lasting operation, or a lining that color bleeds, will result in a rejected shoe or warranty claim. The factory can be held responsible for warranty claims, thus it is in their best interest to check the materials before assembly.

Shoe factories and brands will lab test materials from new vendors and may spot check deliveries from trusted suppliers. Materials that can impact the safety of a product may be re-tested with every delivery.

Physical testing complete shoes

Even though all the materials may meet QC standards, physical testing of the completed shoes is required to ensure product performance and durability. Mishandled or improperly assembled materials can lead to product failures. These tests should be done during the development phase to qualify the shoes, and during production to ensure standards are continuously met.

The typical tests for finished shoes include:

Slip resistance

Slip resistance is an important requirement for many service and work shoes. The finished shoe is placed on a surface with a standard coefficient of friction. The force required to move the shoe is a measure of its slip resistance. Footwear for hospital and food service use will have a slip resistance rating.

Bonding trials

When a new shoe model is in preproduction, the shoe factory will make bonding trials with any new materials to ensure the bonding procedure is correct. The factory may adjust the heat tunnel settings, the viscosity of the cement, and test different primer compounds for the different materials. The manufacturer of the glue may send a technician with several different compounds for testing inside the shoe factory. The bonding trial parts will be passed to the testing lab for examination.

A 10mm wide section of the bonded surfaces is cut from the shoe. A test machine is used to pull the parts and measure the force required to separate the 10mm length. For athletic footwear, the bonding standard is usually 4.0kg per square centimeter.

Hardware pull tests

Any component that can be pulled or yanked by the customer should be lab tested to ensure it can withstand abuse. The lacing hardware of a shoe needs to withstand a 35kg pull test and snowboard boot hardware is required to pass a 75kg standard. Sandal toe posts and straps need to be tested to ensure the materials are strong enough. Webbing back pulls and tongue loops should also be tested.

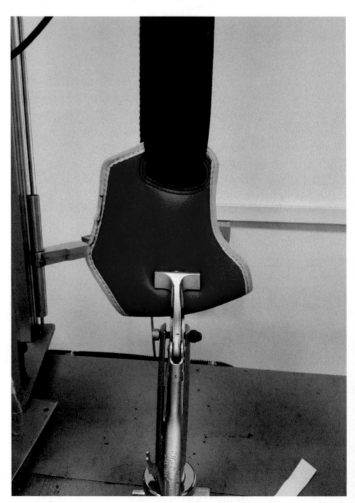

Cold crack tests

Every plastic component in footwear which is designed for cold weather use should be tested for cold cracking. Certain plastic materials such as PU and PVC can "freeze" in cold weather and instead of bending they may crack and fail. An entire snowboard boot, or just the plastic parts, is cooled and then tested. A specialized snow boot factory will have the testing machine stored inside a refrigerated enclosure.

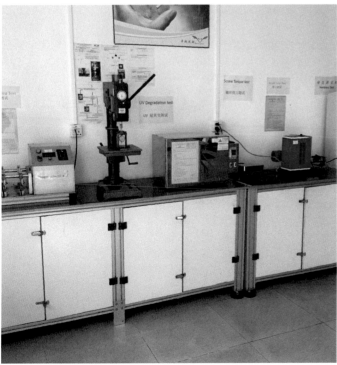

Bending test

The finished shoe-bending test will show if the pattern design, stitching location, and material all work together correctly. Poorly constructed seams may open, a material may split, and stitches may come undone. The bending test can also confirm if a shank is correctly anchored and if an outsole is properly designed.

Tests for waterproof shoes

To confirm that a waterproof shoe will remain waterproof during use requires a flex test done in a water bath. The Maeser Water Penetration Test (ASTM D2099) flexes the shoe while in a tank with color dyed water. An electrode in the shoe turns off the machine when water penetrates the upper. Passing requires 5000 flexes without any water penetration. The dyed water allows the developer to follow the path of the water entering the shoe. Like reading a map, the dye shows which component failed.

Other tests

Beyond physical performance tests, fit testing and wear testing are critical to making sure a new models fits true to size and performs appropriately for its function.

Fitting trials

Fit trials take place during the development of a new shoe. A size run of the new shoe is made in the sample room and sent to the brand for testing. The product manager or testing department will pass the shoes to testers with the appropriate sized foot for evaluation.

Wear testing shoes

Wear testing can be a functional test or long term durability tests. Shoes are supplied to athletes or company employees to wear for evaluation.

CHAPTER 20
LOCAL MARKET SHOE MATERIALS

In the major shoemaking centers in China, you will find thriving local markets for shoe materials. The local markets are storefronts large and small with every type of shoe material, shoe component, and manufacturing equipment available to buy. You will find many storefronts displaying the material swatches available to order from a nearby factory, or shoe materials in stock that you can purchase immediately for use in making samples. These market areas are very well organized; you will see streets lined with shoe material suppliers and even entire shopping malls crammed with all types of shoe materials.

I am going to describe a busy shoe material market area in the town of Houjie, China. Houjie is about a two hour drive from the Hong Kong airport. It is an industrial city, which is common to find in China. The city has a robust footwear and furniture industry. Located within a 5-minute walk from the Sheraton™ hotel you will find hundreds of shoe material and equipment dealers.

What you will find in the shoe material markets
You will find almost everything you need to make nearly every type of shoe. The one thing you may not find is a material dealer that speaks English. To make the most of a visit to the Houjie material market you may need help with translation. Make sure to take some business cards or catalogs so the dealer can see what kind of shoes you are making. Also, you should bring your Pantone™ book to check colors, and a drawing of your shoe to help the dealer understand what you are looking for. Don't forget some local money, you will need Chinese RMB if you are planning to buy any materials.

The local material market is a great place to look for new ideas. The material market is also a useful place to find materials for your sample shoes or a small production run. If you have a large production run, the material supplier will be happy to help you place an order directly with the factory.

The material market in Houjie is a great place to find shoe leather. There are many different suppliers with various types of leather. You will find leather in every color of the rainbow, from thick to thin, and in many different finishes. You can buy leather by the hide, or a dozen hides at once. Of course, if you have a production order, someone is available to help you with that too.

Textiles for shoes are also plentiful in the local market. You can buy swatch cuttings or 100-meter rolls. You will see mesh for shoe uppers, shoe-lining materials, 4K knitting factories and entire stores with reinforcing fabrics and strobel bottoms for shoes.

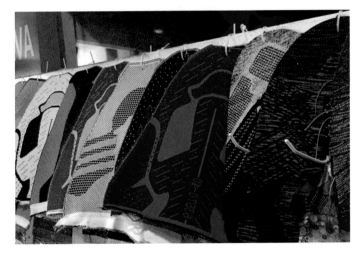

Shoe outsoles are also available in the local market. You will find dealers with hundreds of outsole models on display. These are "open" mold outsole units. Every type of outsole for every type of shoe will be available. You can find soles for sport shoes, dress shoes, boots, flat treads, platform heels for women's shoes, soccer cleats, or casual and running shoe bottoms. In the local market, you will find "copy" bottoms of the latest shoe designs (without logos).

You cannot buy a 'single' outsole but, you can order small runs of 5 to 10 units to make samples. The only issue with the local market outsole is that the last bottom is already set. This may or may not work for your market. You can buy the last with the outsoles, or you can have a local last maker help you model the last to fit the outsoles.

The material markets are a great place to find all sorts of shoe accessories. Shoelaces, decorative hardware, reinforcements, embellishments, footbeds and anything else you may need can be purchased in small qualities to make samples.

You must be careful when purchasing shoe materials from the local market. The supply factory's contact information may not always be available, and there may not be material physical test data reports ready.

Before you use any local shoe material in your production, you need to get lab tests done to make sure the material is suitable for your shoes.

The material markets are a great place to find new ideas, track down new vendors, and explore options you may not have seen before. There is no other place where you can see so many different shoe materials and vendors all at once.

CHAPTER 21
MATERIAL VENDOR RELATIONS

A supply of high-quality shoe materials and sub-components are essential to great looking and long lasting shoes. Your shoe material suppliers can be your best partners as you design and develop your shoe lines. A good relationship with your material suppliers has many benefits. They can help recommend materials for your shoes, and they can also help you make or find new and unique materials. A supply factory with steady material orders from you can move your production to the head of the line and may be more accommodating to your situation if there is ever a problem.

Building relationships directly with the material suppliers can be time-consuming but is definitely well worth the effort. The big shoe brands will often have employees dedicated full time to sourcing and developing new materials. For small shoe companies it will be the traveling designers and developers that lay the groundwork for vendor relations.

Finding shoe material suppliers
A great place to start is with your shoe factory's existing material supply partners. Ask your shoe factory development department to order swatch books and sample cards for your study. They will have many leather, textile, PU leather, and plastic swatch books. Don't forget to ask for the price sheets! If they can't get you material books, snap a photo of the contact information on the book so you can communicate with them yourself. If you don't see anything you like, don't be afraid to strike out on your own to find new suppliers! There are great material shows full of vendors looking for new customers. The Material Show and Alibaba.com are great tools for finding materials close to your shoe factory.

Suppliers will come to you
Once you get started, the material suppliers will be coming to you. If you work for a major brand, you may need to turn suppliers away! Long-term relationships with material supply reps are also a great way to get some "inside" information. You may hear your material rep say, "Oh yeah, we are making tons of this material for .... and ...." Your material rep is also a great source of industry gossip. "Did you hear that so and so has moved to the new shoe company in Portland?" Keep your eyes and ears open!

Visiting your material suppliers
When traveling overseas, make time to visit your existing material suppliers to see how they make their products. Supplier visits are always a worthwhile use of your time. You will gain insights as to the vendor's capabilities and processes. You may see something that peeks your imagination. A new machine, a new process, an old machine, a competitors material in production, there is so much to see if you are there and being mindful of your surroundings.

Take a few minutes and drink some tea, you may just find something new.

Nominating suppliers: pros and cons
While the shoe factory is responsible for buying the raw materials for the shoes, you can select or nominate the supplier you want them to buy from. For specific or exotic materials there may only be one supplier, but for most materials there are many suppliers. The shoe factory will most likely have an existing relationship with a supplier and may prefer not to follow your nomination.

Why nominate a material supplier?
As a shoe brand, you may nominate a supplier to maintain consistency between your various shoe factories. Your packing box and leather suppliers are the first vendors you should consider nominating. This ensures the consistency of your packing boxes and that your shoes will have the same quality of leather.

You may also choose to nominate a supplier so that you can control the material price negotiations. If the material vendor has a close relationship with the shoe factory, you may never see the "real" price the shoe factory pays for the materials. You will have to trust that the factory is always telling you the truth about the material costs.

When you have a nominated supplier, you can also negotiate a lower price based on bulk material purchases. Large shoe brands with production in several factories will often sign contracts with material suppliers committing to a sales volume at a discounted price.

Material development
A close relationship with a material supplier will often give you the first look at any new materials they have in development. The big shoe brands can also demand, or are given, exclusive rights to a new materials if they agree to purchase large quantities. Material vendors will also offer reduced development costs for good customers. Many material suppliers do not offer new material development services to small customers, but if you have a good relationship, you may be able to get help with new materials even if you are a small brand.

Special treatment
Shoe material suppliers will also give good customers special treatment. If you agree to make high volume, bulk purchases of commodity materials or agree to buy a material type exclusively from one supplier, they will return the favor by offering lower MOQs for special items. You may also get rush or priority shipping for your materials. If you negotiate a volume purchase agreement, the factory may agree to hold a stock of finished goods for you. This can reduce your material lead-time and potentially reduce your production time.

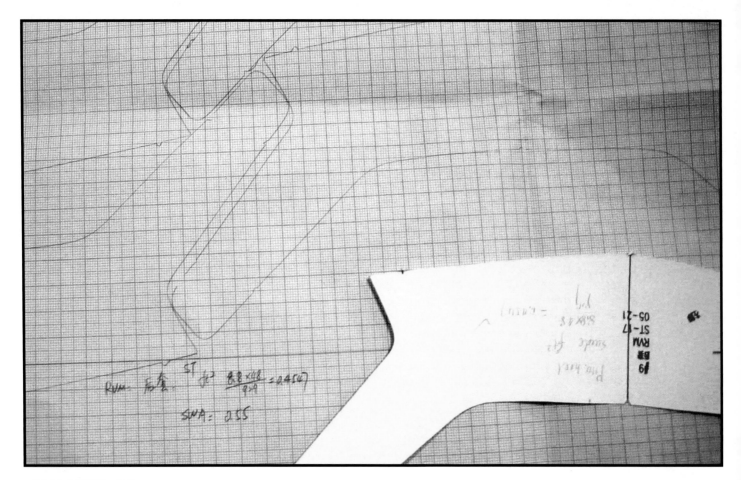

CHAPTER 22
MATERIAL COSTING AND CONSUMPTION

The total cost of a shoe is based on the unit price of its materials, the consumption of the pattern, and the labor, profit, and overhead requirements of the factory. When cost engineering a new shoe it is important to make sure the materials you select are appropriate to the targeted price point and that the pattern design uses materials efficiently.

How is the cost of a shoe calculated?
Once the design is confirmed, the factory will take the shoe specification and itemize the cost of each item. This document is called the costing sheet. The costing sheet will include EVERY part of the shoe, including the glue, thread, stuffing paper, silica gel pack, hang-tags, etc. Everything that goes into the shoe box (including the shoe box and carton case) will be listed. The costing sheet lists each component, the component's material, the consumption amount, and the unit price of the material. With this information, the unit price for each component is calculated.

Pattern consumption
Cutting loss
LOP labor, overhead, and profit
Currency conversion

These costing calculations are done on a men's size 9 and the women's size 7 shoe. The shoe factory will quote the same price for all sizes. The size 6 will use less material while the size 13 will use more. The labor to assemble the small or large shoe is nearly the same. While there are fewer total stitches in the smaller shoe, the total number of cutting and sewing operations and workers required will be the same.

Pattern consumption

Every component part will be listed with its cost per unit and the consumption needed to make that part. A cutting waste percentage will also be added. The cutting waste percentage, cutting loss, or interlock loss, is the amount of scrap material left over after the parts have been cut from the bulk material. Yes, the shoe price will include the cost of the scrap material that is thrown away! A very efficient pattern with low material consumption and low cutting waste will cost less than a pattern that wastes material. A shoe designed with high-end materials can be less expensive if the parts are designed for tight nesting and minimal material waste.

Cutting loss for each material type

Roll materials such as fabric may have very little cutting loss, less than 5%. PU synthetic and coated leather will also have a relatively low cutting loss. If the material has a directional pattern and is required to be cut in a specific stretch direction, the cutting loss may increase.

In the case of fine leather for an expensive shoe, the factory cannot use any leather with cuts or scars from the animal. The cutting loss can be as high as 25%! Expensive materials with high cutting loss will make for high priced shoes.

The size and shape of the raw material can also affect the cutting yield. A 64" wide roll of mesh, fabric, or PU synthetic is easy to cut. A cowhide, with its curving shape and shifting grain direction cannot be cut as efficiently as man-made materials. Calf, goat, pig, and snake hides are quite small thus using the same pattern pieces as used on rolled material will lead to a higher cutting loss.

The profit margin for a shoe factory is often less than 10% of the shoes' selling price. The cutting loss must be carefully calculated or the factory can lose out. You should be checking the waste and consumption values carefully to ensure the factory is not adding a little extra in their favor.

The larger shoe brands will have costing technicians to check the material price for each material from the supplier and measure the material usage.

Both the factory and the brand will make the same study and compare results. This is time-consuming work, but if the production run is 500,000 pairs, the cost savings can add up fast. A diligent costing technician with helpful computer software can save a company many thousands of dollars.

LOP: labor, overhead, and profit

After the factory has calculated the material costs they will add on the expense of operating the factory. What is the cost of the labor, overhead, and profit? The shoe factory may calculate the LOP in many ways. The most common calculation is a flat rate per shoe. The material cost, plus $3.50 LOP, may be the final price for a simple sneaker. For a complicated snowboarding boot, the LOP may be $10.00 per pair. Some factories will start with the material cost, then add a fixed percentage for LOP of approximately 15% to 20%.

Many factors drive the LOP. Is the factory located in an expensive area such as South China or Italy? You may find a lower LOP in Western China or Poland for example. Is the factory space owned by the factory or rented? What is the cost to borrow money? What is the condition of the local labor market around the factory? These expenses all contribute to the LOP.

Currency conversions

After all the material expenses are combined with the LOP expenses, you will have the final cost of the shoe. It is likely the price will be calculated in the local currency of the factory such as Chinese RMB or Euros. You and the shoe factory will need to agree on precisely what currency conversion rate will be used. Double check the conversion rate with your bank and local banks in the country to make sure you have a fair rate for you and your partner factory. If you are not careful, you may give the factory a bonus of a few percent!

Cost breakdown of materials

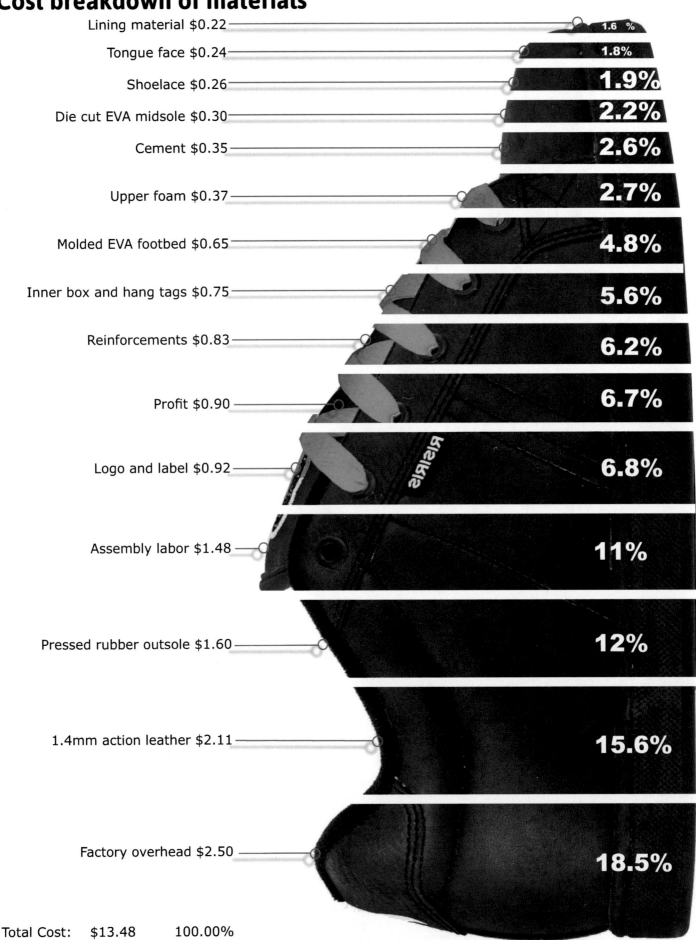

Lining material $0.22 ——————————————— 1.6 %

Tongue face $0.24 ——————————————— 1.8%

Shoelace $0.26 ——————————————— 1.9%

Die cut EVA midsole $0.30 ——————————————— 2.2%

Cement $0.35 ——————————————— 2.6%

Upper foam $0.37 ——————————————— 2.7%

Molded EVA footbed $0.65 ——————————————— 4.8%

Inner box and hang tags $0.75 ——————————————— 5.6%

Reinforcements $0.83 ——————————————— 6.2%

Profit $0.90 ——————————————— 6.7%

Logo and label $0.92 ——————————————— 6.8%

Assembly labor $1.48 ——————————————— 11%

Pressed rubber outsole $1.60 ——————————————— 12%

1.4mm action leather $2.11 ——————————————— 15.6%

Factory overhead $2.50 ——————————————— 18.5%

Total Cost: $13.48   100.00%

Project Name:	Sneaker Factory Jogger							
Factory:	Houjie #1							
Prototype ID:	MSK069							
Season:	Spring 2018							
Division:	Running							
Color Description:	WHITE / GREY / BLACK							
Country of Origin:	China							
Construction:	Cold Cement Cement							
Gender/Size:	M'S9#							
SizeRun:	5-14							
Last Code:	SUX-6000							
O/S Code:	LF_204							
Status:	PHOTO							

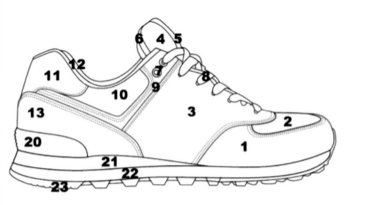

	Component Type	Component Specification	Supplier	Units	Unit Price	Net Usage	Gross Usage	Pair Price
	UPPER							
1	Toe Top / Mudguard	1.2mm PU Duratec (WR) Emboss#BS1	Nan-Ya	44"/Y	1.250	0.595	0.607	0.7583
2	Vamp	MESH + 4MMKF329+24GT/C	Cosmo HK	44"/Y	3.560	0.043	0.044	0.1569
	Vamp Lining	Cambrelle	Local	44"/Y	1.250	0.927	0.946	1.1824
3	Quarter/Eyerow	1.2mm PU Duratec (WR) Emboss#BS1	Nan-Ya	44"/Y	0.150	1.000	1.000	0.1500
	Quarter logo	TPR Logo Stiched on	Local	44"/Y	3.560	0.056	0.057	0.2044
4	Tongue	MESH+4MMKF329+24GT/C	Cosmo HK	44"/Y	1.250	0.504	0.514	0.6426
5	Tongue Logo	Embroidery "text" logo	Local	2.000	0.150	1.000	1.000	0.1500
6	Tongue Lining	Visa Terry + 4MMKF329+24GT/C	Local	44"/Y	3.560	0.040	0.041	0.1452
	Tongue Foam	20mm KFF PU foam	Local	44"/Y	2.940	0.040	0.041	0.1200
7	Lace Eyelet	8mm Steel	Dae-Sung	8.000	2.940	0.095	0.097	0.2849
8	Shoe Lace	8mm Oval	Pahio	2.000	2.955	0.042	0.043	0.1257
9	Collar Underlay	1.2mm PU Duratec (WR) Emboss#BS1	Cosmo HK	36"/Y	2.955	0.044	0.045	0.1338
10	Collar Panel	MESH+4MMKF329+24GT/C	Cosmo HK	44"/Y	0.870	0.138	0.140	0.1220
11	Heel Logo	Embroidery "text" logo	Local	2.000	0.850	0.029	0.030	0.0255
12	Heel Lining	Visa Terry + 4MMKF329+24GT/C	Cosmo HK	pair	0.102	1.000	1.020	0.1040
13	Heel Counter	1.2mm PU Duratec (WR) Emboss#BS1	Nan-Ya	54"/Y	1.670	0.020	0.020	0.0334
	Internal Heel Counter	Texon .4mm	Texon	2.000	0.353	0.361	0.368	0.1298
	Internal Toe Puff	Texon .2mm	Texon	2.000	0.030	1.000	1.020	0.0306
	Eyerow Reinforcement	Super Tuff	Local	2.000	0.060	1.115	1.137	0.0682
	Upper Thread	bonded nylon 6 250D 3 Ply	Coats or A&E	Each	0.080	1.000	1.000	0.0800
								4.6478
	OUTSOLE UNIT							
20	Heel Counter	Injection Plastic Red	Xie-Xie Injection	Pair	2.000	1.000	1.000	0.6500
21	Midsole Wedge Top	Hot Press EVA Asker "C" 45-50	Local	Pair	2.000	1.000	1.000	0.7000
22	Midsole Wedge Bottom	Hot Press EVA Asker "C" 55-60	Local	Pair	0.500	1.000	1.000	0.5000
23	Outsole	#1-44 NBS400 Shore "A" 65 +or-3 SG 1.1 +1.4	CW Pressing	pair	0.850	1.000	1.000	1.5000
	Insole Strobal	Texon T28	Texon	54"/Y	0.850	1.000	1.000	0.8500
	Footbed	Cold Pressed EVA Asker "C" 45 Standard Open Mold	Local	2	1.600	0.055	0.056	0.0898
	Foobed Skin	SAMPLE MESH+4MMKF329+24GT/C	Cosmo HK	54"/Y	0.500	1.000	1.000	0.5000
	Foobed Logo	Screen Print Logo "Text" 45mm x 25MM	Local	Pair				4.7898
	Cement	Water based PU	Nom-Pou	1.000				
	PACKING			PRS	0.100	1.000	1.000	0.7000
	Inner Box	2016 Box art E-Flue - White Back PVC skin		PRS	0.040	1.000	1.000	0.0400
	Out Carton	Brown	Lai-Wah	PRS	0.005	1.000	1.000	0.0050
	Tongue label	3cm x 3cm White + Black Screen + Weld	Local	PRS	0.020	1.000	1.000	0.0200
	EEC label	2cm x 2cm White + Black Print	Local	PRS	0.060	1.000	1.000	0.0600
	HangTag	4-Color Print	Local	PRS	0.005	1.000	1.000	0.0050
	Tag pin	White	Lai-Wah	PRS	0.020	1.000	1.000	0.0200
	Poly bag		Local	PRS	0.010	1.000	1.000	0.0100
	Wrap Tissue	10 gram 2 sheets	Local	PRS	0.010	1.000	1.000	0.0100
	Toe Tissue	10 gram 2 sheets	Local	PRS	0.010	1.000	1.000	0.0100
								0.8800
	1. Material Cost total:							10.3176
	2. Labor Total:							2.0000
	a. Cut:							
	4. OTHERS	TPR mold US$400.00	Based on:					0.0040
	5. Profit:	7.00%						
	6. Tooling:							0.0000
	a. Cutting Die:	$0.00	Based on:					
	b. Last:	$0.00	Based on:					
	c. Outsole Mould:	$25,000.00	Based on:					0.2500
						Grand Total FOB US$		14.5716
						Confirmed Price FOB US$		

CHAPTER 23

SHOE MATERIAL SUPPLY CHAIN

Thus far we have studied many factors that will help to determine the correct materials for your shoes. We have looked at the performance, price, and testing standards of each material and component. Now we will look at how a material arrives at the shoe factory in time for your production. This is called the material supply chain.

The material supply chain is made up of all the steps it takes to get your chosen shoe material or component moving from your product specification sheet to final assembly. The material supply chain is sometimes complex and the process of having each specific material available for production in the right place and at the right time can often get convoluted.

Hey! I am the shoe designer, why do I care about the material supply chain? This is someone else's problem, right? Wrong. As a professional designer, you need to take responsibility for ensuring your product is successful. Ignoring your material supply chain can cause schedule delays, quality problems, pricing mishaps, unintended substitutions, and other production disasters. Having a basic understanding of how the material supply chain functions can save you time and trouble.

When looking at the supply chain for a specific material, there are four main factors to consider. These four factors will be different for every material you specify. Remember, even a simple shoe can have materials from over a dozen different suppliers.

Material production lead-time
Minimum order quantity
Country of origin
Vendor purchase terms

Material production lead-time

The lead-time for a material is how long it takes for a material vendor to deliver the specified material to the shoe factory once the order is placed. Just like the factory must schedule the shoe assembly, the material supplier must gather raw materials and schedule the material production. When a shoe factory quotes a delivery date of 90 days to make your order, you can assume that almost 45 days are consumed with the ordering and delivery of the required materials.

When a shoe factory receives your order the material purchasing department swings into action checking your orders' material requirements. Shoe factories may keep some basic materials in stock, but they cannot afford to have production quantities of shoe materials sitting in a storehouse waiting for orders.

Lead-times for shoe materials vary depending on quantity, material type, supplier backlog, and tooling requirements. All production materials are "made to order," the material supplier does not have vast stockpiles of finished goods waiting for factory orders. Shoe material suppliers know that order lead-time must be less than 60 days, so they have adapted their processes. A lining material vendor will have white material in stock waiting for your color instructions to make the dye lots. Leather tanneries will have a steady supply of hides coming into the factory in a partially tanned state waiting for your color and embossing specifications.

Molded parts such as midsoles and outsoles are ordered from pressing factories. The pressing factories will have the raw materials for rubber and EVA in stock, they only need to be mixed, and color matched before they can start production. The lead-time of molded parts will depend on the productivity of the mold. Injection parts can be made at a rate of 60 parts per hour, while a compression molded EVA midsole may be produced at a rate of only 6 per hour. Tooling and back-up tooling may be required to produce large orders. The gut sizes of EVA midsoles, 9 to 11, often require extra "B" molds to speed up production. For high volume orders, a dozen extra molds may be required!

Materials sourced outside of the factory's home country will require longer lead-times. A special material with a long-lead time will need to be forecasted and stocked inside the shoe factory ahead of the production orders. The shoe factory may increase the unit price of a material if they are required to buy it in advance. You may also be responsible to pay for any unused materials if your forecast is wrong. If a material requires air shipping in order to meet the production deadline, you will need to pay the extra cost for that service.

Long lead-time materials: exotic materials, overseas materials.
Short lead-time materials: stock or commodity items.

Minimum order quantity or MOQ

MOQ is the smallest amount of a material you can purchase. The MOQ will vary depending on the material, the vendor, and your relationship with the vendor. A custom weave of a new mesh pattern may have an MOQ of 5000 yards, while a color match for a stock mesh may require only 500 yards. The MOQ for fabric colors is usually based on the size of the dyeing tanks.

For leather, the MOQ will also be based on the size of the dyeing drum. You can expect 500 square feet or 25 hides, roughly enough to make 250 pairs of shoes. The MOQ for PU trims can be as low as 25 yards. These small runs are made in the factory's sample line and may cost 50% more than a standard 500-yard run.

Many materials have very low or no MOQ's. Common reinforcing materials such as Super-Tuff, strobel sock materials, and heel counter materials are held in stock by the supply factory and can be delivered on demand. These materials are not dyed to match so the supplier will have production quantities on hand.

It is important to provide your partner shoe factories with a production forecast for a new model or SKU. The factory can plan the material purchase systematically. The factory will receive better prices and better service if they can place fewer, larger material orders. With appropriate forecasts, the shoe factory can usually meet the MOQ for an item even if the first order is below

the MOQ. Shoe factories will often complain about material MOQ's for special items. You will need to be flexible and work with them to get your shoe made how you want it. Extra material left over at the end of a production season can be a huge headache.

Country of origin

It is critical to know where each particular shoe material is made. If you are making shoes in Europe, do your best to specify locally made materials whenever you can. For shoes made in China, materials can be sourced locally or from Korea, Taiwan, or Japan without any trouble.

Items such as outsoles, midsoles, and injection parts should be sourced locally. The fitting of these parts must be supervised by the shoe factory as they are responsible for the assembly. It is a shoe-making nightmare to have components arrive from a foreign country that do not fit as planned.

For commodity materials, do your best to specify a local vendor in the same country as your shoe factory. Unique or rare materials critical to your design are worthy of air shipping, forecasting, or pre-positioning. Do not waste your time selecting foreign materials for hidden internal components unless you have an exotic performance requirement. Ask your factory to provide samples of local options if you cannot find one yourself.

Materials that must be imported may be subject to fees, taxes or import duties. Some factories have a "bonded" warehouse. The bonded warehouse allows the factory to import material duty-free if they plan to export the materials as finished goods.

Material vendor purchase terms

High-value exotic materials or specialized single source materials may come with extraordinary purchase terms. For example, overseas suppliers may demand payment in full before shipment to China. In this case, the shoe factory will have to pay for the material many months before they ship the goods and can invoice you for the final product.

The required cash flow for material purchases may cause the factory to insist on a 30% to 50% payment from you upon order placement. Almost all shoe factories borrow money to buy raw materials so do not be surprised. A shoe factory may also insist upon an extra markup for the specific material based on the purchase terms of the supplier and the interest rates they incur to borrow money for the material purchases.

CHAPTER 24

EXOTIC AND ILLEGAL MATERIALS

Exotic animal hides like snake, ostrich, alligator, and even elephant are used in footwear to create drama, luxury, mystique and a feeling of exclusivity. While these exotic materials may be hard to find, difficult to use, shockingly expensive, or just plain illegal to import; they each have their individual look and feel that make them unique and very desirable for use in footwear.

Can I use exotic hides?
Yes, you can use exotic hides! While we may think of ostrich, alligator, and python as rare, exotic, or threatened animals they are in fact plentiful, not threatened, and commercially farmed according to international regulations. Captive breeding, farming, and regulated culling are legal sources for exotic hides. Endangered and threatened species, or animals hunted in the wild, cannot be legally traded.

Working with exotic materials
Working with exotic materials requires special knowledge in order to use the materials effectively and understand how to legally source and resell products containing these special materials.

Aligator skins are available in hornback and smooth bellies, each has a unique use in footwear. Due to the high value of the exotic hides, mistakes can be very costly. Check your pattern twice before you start cutting!

How do you know if a material is legal?

When working with exotic materials, you should first look up the animal or material on the CITES website.

The Convention on International Trade in Endangered Species of Wild Fauna and Flora, CITES, is an international agreement between governments. The goal of CITES is to ensure that international trade in specimens of wild animals and plants does not threaten their survival. Roughly 5,600 species of animals are protected by CITES against over-exploitation through international trade. They are listed in the three CITES appendices. The species are grouped in the appendices according to how threatened they are by international trade. The CITES agreement covers live animals and product derived from them.

In addition to the CITES regulations, the U.S. Fish and Wildlife Department has its own regulations as does the HM Revenue & Customs in the U.K., and the state of California in the USA.

You will need to consult your home country's wildlife and customs departments to make sure you can legally handle and import these materials.

Here are some helpful links:

http://checklist.cites.org/#/en

https://www.gov.uk/guidance/importing-animal-furs-skins-and-fish

Avoiding legal complications

The best way to avoid any legal complications while working with exotic animal hides is to only purchase materials from reputable and regulated suppliers. The top suppliers work hard to comply with the CITES regulations, US regulations, and can supply you with the proper documentation to import, export, and re-import both raw materials and finished goods.

In the USA, Rojé Leathers is a top supplier for all types of exotic animal hides. They have a huge selection of legally sourced and tagged hides from many exotic animals.

Alligator leather: $400 to $700 per skin
1.1mm to 2.1mm

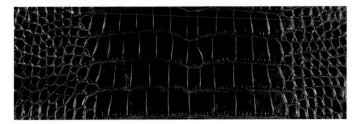

Caiman leather: $200 to $250 per skin
1.2mm to 1.8mm

Nile crocodile leather: $500 to $900 per skin
.7mm to2.1mm

Ostrich leather: $30.00 per square foot
.5mm to 1.9mm

Lizard skin: $65.00 per square foot
.4mm to .9mm

Python skin: $245.00 per hide
1/2 - 1 oz.

CHAPTER 25

BUILDING A SHOE MATERIAL LIBRARY

Having a well-stocked material library is an important tool for any shoe design office. For shoe designers and footwear developers, it is critical to build a library of relevant material swatches and sample books. If you are designing running shoes, mesh books and footbed samples are key. If you are designing hiking boots, a selection of leather and lasting board swatches will be useful. Having materials on hand allows you to communicate what the new design will look like to product managers, sales managers, or customers.

Sample books

Sample books are available for all types of footwear material. Mesh, leathers, synthetics, hardware, thread, reinforcements, foams, rubber, plastic, mold texture, everything a designer will need is out there. Swatches for footwear materials come in all different shapes and sizes. Fabric swatches can be organized into 3-ring binders, glued to cards, or strung together on a string. Leather swatches are often cut into small squares and stacked in boxes. Metal parts and rubber logos may be glued into binders or vacuum-sealed to card stock.

The top suppliers will have material collections organized into years and seasons with new books for Spring/Summer and Autumn/Winter. A proper book will be a 3-ring binder and will have a cutting of each material type shown in a few colors. One edge of the cutting will be secured so you can pull back the swatch and see the backing layers. The best vendors will have the physical test data, roll size, and material MOQ listed. These books may or may not have prices listed. The price is never on the swatch card itself but will be listed on a separate page in the front or back of the book. If you get a book without any costing information, make sure to ask for it.

So how do you get the swatch book from a Chinese mesh factory?

Just ask! Material vendors provide swatch books free of charge to shoe factories, shoe brands, and shoe designers. Designers working for large brands will have no trouble getting updated sample books. The material factories know that if a Nike designer has their swatch book that could mean big orders in the future. Independent designers, or designers working for smaller brands, may have to be a little more creative in getting their swatch books.

Material sales reps

Get to know the shoe material factories' local sales representatives. The large material vendors will have sales reps in Asia, Europe, and the Americas. The local rep will make a sales commission on any materials you buy if they secure the factory introduction. If you look promising, they will visit with you or send you a material book. If you work for a large shoe company, make sure you maintain personal contacts with material vendors, you may need these contacts later.

Preferred vendors

If you are already working with some shoe factories, make sure to ask them for material books of their preferred vendors. Don't be afraid to ask your shoe factory if you can take their sample books. They can get new ones. Make sure to ask for new sample books on the first day of your visit so the factory has time to get books for you.

What is in the shoe factory?

Ask your shoe factory to make a swatch book of material they have in their warehouse. The shoe factory will be more than happy to make a swatch book of their existing material stock with the hope that you can design a shoe to help use it up! You may also be able to negotiate a discount on any old material you can use up.

Plan factory tours

When you travel, try to arrange tours of your top material suppliers. It's always good to see exactly how the materials are made so you can understand the design possibilities and limitations of the production process. The end of a tour is a great time to get your sample books refreshed and to get a look at any new developments.

Make sure to visit outsole and hardware factories to see how these parts are made. Don't be afraid to ask for samples of anything you see in production. Suppliers will often let you have scrap parts to help inspire you. Just ask, if they say "no," then keep moving. They may let you take a photo.

If you can't make it to the material factory, don't worry. If you are close by, the material factory can send a local sales rep to meet with you at your shoe factory.

Visit shoe material shows

In the USA and Europe, there are several small trade shows dedicated to shoe materials. The local sales reps and factory salespeople will be available to meet with you. Bring your business cards and catalogs so the material suppliers can see what you are working on. They will be eager to help. Bring an extra bag, or even an extra suitcase, for material books!

Dedicated to footwear, The Material Show is held in two locations every year. The NW Material Show in Portland, OR and the NE Material Show in Wilmington, MA. Shoe designers from across the country visit this show to catch up on what's new. https://americanevents.com

Local material markets

When traveling to shoe and clothing production areas, make sure to visit the local material markets. Material markets are a great place to pick up swatch books and materials for development samples. In China, there are towns with hundreds of material sellers with goods on display. In just a few days you can see dozens of suppliers making all types of footwear components.

Just ask

Don't be afraid to make cold calls or send emails to material suppliers. The worst that can happen is they say "no," or ask you to pay for samples and shipping.

DIY - make it yourself!

Make your own swatch cards. Don't be afraid to buy competitors shoes to get material swatches. Cut swatches from anything you see in the market. Jackets, backpacks or anything that has a material you like.

Find old books

If you have friends in the shoe trades, don't be afraid to ask them for their old books. An old book is better than none.

CHAPTER 26

SUSTAINABLE SHOE PRODUCTION

The hard fact

The modern mass produced shoe, made of textiles, leather, plastic, and rubber parts glued and sewn together is not environmentally sustainable. The modern shoe is very difficult to recycle. With stitching securing the upper parts together and the outsole firmly bonded with PU cement; it's almost impossible to cost effectively break down used shoes into useful components for recycling. The manufacturing of these components themselves consumes vast amounts of water and energy while creating mountains of post-industrial and post-consumer waste.

Your choices

With that qualification said, footwear designers, shoe developers, product managers, and factories can make choices to help lessen the negative environmental and social impacts of shoe production. There are no magic shoe materials or production techniques that can make a shoe entirely green, sustainable, or ethical, but depending on your own environmental and social priorities, there are available options.

We will consider different aspects of shoe production that can make your shoes more or less environmentally sustainable:

Sustainable shoe material selection
Environmentally friendly footwear production processes
Waste reduction in footwear manufacturing
Sustainable shoe material selection

Organic vs man-made textiles

If your priority is drinking water preservation, then using man-made textiles is a better choice over cotton and other natural textiles. While both cotton and man-made fibers require large quantities of water for dyeing processes, this water is used in an industrial facility allowing the water to be recovered, recycled, and reused in a closed loop system. In southern China, local governments have forced textile dyeing houses to relocate into industrial estates with controlled water purification facilities.

The process of growing cotton, especially organic cotton, consumes enormous quantities of water that is not reused in a closed loop. Some studies estimate that more than 700 gallons (2,700 liters) of water are required to make the cotton alone for one cotton t-shirt! Yes, once this water is used in the cotton fields it does return to nature, but it is no longer available to drink or grow food crops.

On the flip side of cotton and natural fibers, is the production of man-made polymer based fabrics such and nylon or polyester. The amount of water required to make these fibers is radically less but the energy requirement is higher, and there is a greater danger of water contamination from petrochemicals.

Natural vs. man-made "leather"

Natural leather from animal hides also requires large amounts of water. According to studies done by a major leather producer, raising animals and processing their hides requires over 264 gallons (1,000 liters) of water to produce two square feet of leather. Two square feet of leather is enough to make just one pair of shoes. Raising animals and then processing leather into hides has a two-fold effect on the environment with its harmful agricultural run-off plus water which has been contaminated with hazardous tanning byproducts. Water aside, the treatment of animals is a major concern for vegan customers while the production of man-made imitation leather is not regularly considered a moral hazard.

As with fabrics, the man-made alternatives to natural leather have their individual environmental costs. Man-made synthetic materials are very often layers of polyester fabric, foams, and fibers that are fused together and quite impossible to separate once the shoe has reached the end of its lifespan. Producing synthetic materials also consumes energy, and the danger of water contamination from petrochemicals is high.

Natural vs. synthetic rubber

Again, the choice of rubber compounds comes down to a choice of your environmental priorities. Natural rubber production leads to increased deforestation in Southeast Asia and reduces the amount of land being used for food cultivation. Synthetic rubber is produced with a combination of Styrene and Butadiene, and both are petrochemicals refined from crude oil. The production of these compounds requires significant energy inputs, and both are byproducts of oil production.

Although there are many material options, each comes with either an environmental or a social cost. You need to decide according to where your priorities lie.

Materials with recycled content

Another way to reduce the overall environmental impact of footwear production is to specify some of the many footwear materials made with recycled content. When reviewing materials, it is important to understand the difference between post-consumer and post-industrial waste. Many industrial processes create waste or scrap inside the factories. These materials can often be recovered and reprocessed easily into the finished materials. Injection plastic and foam can be reground and re-molded, while textile fibers can be chopped and re-purposed. For many factories, this is simply efficient processing and a smart way to save money. Other post-industrial waste is sent out for reprocessing into various other products.

Post-consumer recycled content is produced when the raw materials are recovered from the waste stream after use. These products may cost more, as the materials may require complicated sorting, cleaning, and reprocessing. The amount of post-consumer content in a product depends on the physical properties required. Usually, higher physical test standards will demand lower post-consumer content. Fabrics are now available with 10% to 70% recycled content.

Woven and knit fabrics are now commonly made with post-consumer recycled PET plastic fibers. Shoe lasting boards and strobel materials are now produced with both post-industrial and post-consumer waste. Paper fiber based lasting boards are very commonly made from over 50% post-consumer waste.

Foam products for shoe footbeds and linings are also being made with post-consumer and post-industrial recycled foam materials. New biodegradable additives are available that allow plastic to degrade in decades rather than centuries.

Environmentally friendly production processes

Aside from material choices, many of the processes in shoe manufacturing can be adapted to be more environmentally friendly.

Footwear production is transitioning away from solvent-based bonding cements to water-based cements. Water-based cement has significantly fewer volatile organic compounds (VOCs), but does require more heat energy to be applied in the factory and may not be as strong as the solvent based cement it replaces. Printing inks are also moving to water-based processes, but as with cements, the performance of water-based ink is inferior.

These water-based products do have some side effects. They commonly require more heat and longer cycle times to process. To the factory, this can mean higher energy bills and slower assembly lines. Thus, these products cost more and may reduce factory efficiency.

Waste reduction in footwear manufacturing

Waste reduction in the footwear assembly process is a good business practice regardless of any environmental goals. Reducing scrap material translates into improved profit margins.

The shoe factory can tackle the issue of waste reduction in the cutting department with advanced worker training and improved operations. The shoe designer also has a major role in waste reduction. A shoe design with very few large cut parts will create more waste, while the modern 4K CNC knit upper can be constructed with almost no waste.

EVA midsole production has been transformed by the introduction of injected or expanded per-formed blanks. The new molded blanks replace die cut EVA and reduce waste by almost 50%. Other midsole materials such as Adidas Boost™ foam are formed "in-mold" in a single operation with very little waste. 3D printing is also a new technology that has the potential to reduce or even eliminate waste in midsole production.

Design simplification

When considering sustainable shoe design and production, the concept of less can be your guide. The simplification your shoe design can lead to fewer materials, less waste and less energy to produce.

There are many ways to simplify a shoe design. The conventional shoe is made by assembling many parts, similar effects can be made by laser etching the pattern design, welding the design, printing the design or weaving the design. You can even mold a shoe from one piece of foam. Simplification does not mean a shoe will be boring or inexpensive.

Product lifespan

Footwear products with a long life span will help keep shoes out of landfills. Your design and material choices are the deciding factors for your products' lifespan.

With any design choice there are trade-offs. A thicker sole will last longer but will cost more and be heavier. Darker colors are less likely to soil and stain, but what kind of world would we have if everyone wore black shoes?

High quality leather shoes can last for many years if they have replaceable soles. But not every one can afford this kind of shoe. The modern light weight running shoe is lucky to last 500 miles. For a dedicated runner even a high quality running shoes will be spent after only a few months of use. Yes, thicker rubber and harder EVA may last longer but few serious athletes will sacrifice performance for extended durability.

Ethical shoe production?

We could write an entire book or an entire library of books on the subject of ethics in shoes. This is another case where you will have to decide what ethical shoe production means to you. Is the production and sale of five inch stiletto heels ethical when you consider the pain inflicted to women's feet?

If you look in the market you can find many companies offering "ethically" produced shoes. Here is a list of the features you can consider for your shoes.

Artisan-made
Direct partnerships with factories
Ethically-sourced, not marked-up production prices
Female artisan-made in Peru
Fair labor practices
Made in USA
Vegan
Ethical and low-impact production
Made from recycled materials
Made of recyclable materials
Employment and scholarships for women
Organic materials
Zero or low waste production
Ecologically friendly production
Material from fair trade family farms in Brazil
Respecting fair trade standards
Worker's rights in Sub-Saharan Africa
Eco-Friendly production and design
Chrome-free shoes
Ending tire waste one pair of shoes at a time
Eco-conscious and up-cycled materials
Ethically-made sandals from Haiti
Cruelty-free shoes
Shoes made in ethical working conditions
Middleman-free

What should you do?

You can see there are options available when it comes to producing a more environmentally responsible footwear product. The designer has choices to make as far as the environmental impact caused by the production of the materials selected and the manufacturer has laws to follow as far as reusing water and water pollution regulations.

New materials are being created everyday which reuse post-consumer waste. Also, adaptations to manufacturing processes are being introduced to cut down on waste products, be it scrap materials or harmful chemicals, in an effort to make production processes more environmentally friendly.

126

CHAPTER 27

SHOE DISSECTION

The best way to understand how materials are used is to see for yourself! As a designer or developer, it is important to see with your own eyes exactly how a particular type of shoe is constructed. With just a few careful cuts you can see exactly what Nike™ puts inside the new Air Max or how Adidas™ makes its soccer cleats.

This type of exploration does not have to be expensive. Nike classics can be found on Ebay™ or Craigslist™ for just a few dollars. A well used second-hand pair of sneakers can provide you with priceless insights.

We have saved you some time, effort, and money by collecting 35 different shoe models for you to study. Each shoe has been opened up to review its internal construction.

While we do not have access to the top secret product specifications of these shoes, we can easily measure and compare the materials we find inside.

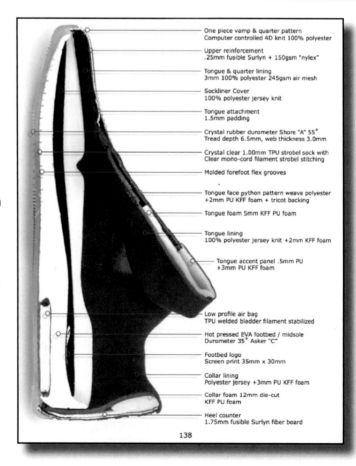

One piece vamp & quarter pattern
Computer controlled 4D knit 100% polyester

Upper reinforcement
.25mm fusible Surlyn + 150gsm "nylex"

Tongue & quarter lining
3mm 100% polyester 245gsm air mesh

Sockliner Cover
100% polyester jersey knit

Tongue attachment
1.5mm padding

Crystal rubber durometer Shore "A" 55°
Tread depth 6.5mm, web thickness 3.0mm

Crystal clear 1.00mm TPU strobel sock with
Clear mono-cord filament strobel stitching

Molded forefoot flex grooves

Tongue face python pattern weave polyester
+2mm PU KFF foam + tricot backing

Tongue foam 5mm KFF PU foam

Tongue lining
100% polyester jersey knit +2mm KFF foam

Tongue accent panel .5mm PU
+3mm PU KFF foam

Low profile air bag
TPU welded bladder filament stabilized

Hot pressed EVA footbed / midsole
Durometer 35° Asker "C"

Footbed logo
Screen print 35mm x 30mm

Collar lining
Polyester jersey +3mm PU KFF foam

Collar foam 12mm die-cut
KFF PU foam

Heel counter
1.75mm fusible Surlyn fiber board

138

127

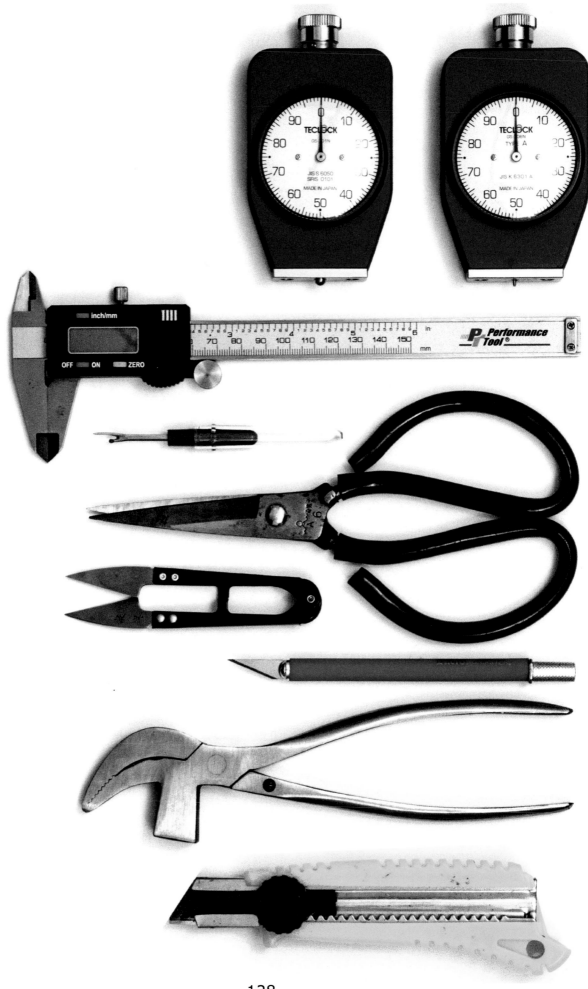

Shell toe casual sneaker

Released in 1969, the shell toe was marketed as a pro model volleyball shoe and a low top basketball shoe. Made famous by NBA superstar Kareem Abdul-Jabbar, the shell toe became the shoe of choice for NBA players in the 70's. Later worn by rap music pioneers Run DMC, the shell toe went on to be a sneaker culture classic.

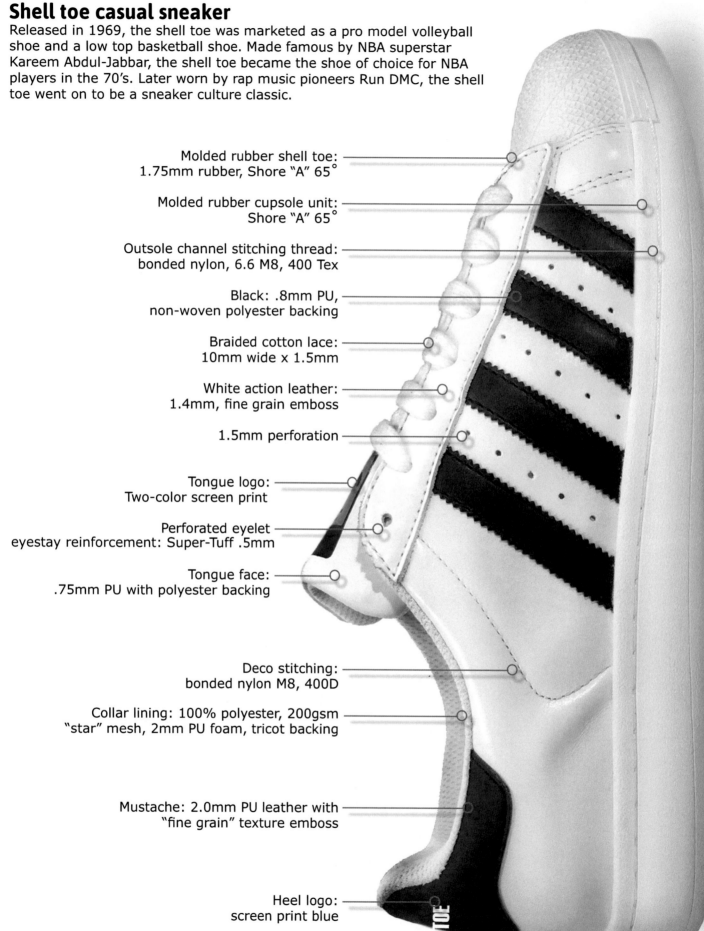

Molded rubber shell toe:
1.75mm rubber, Shore "A" 65°

Molded rubber cupsole unit:
Shore "A" 65°

Outsole channel stitching thread:
bonded nylon, 6.6 M8, 400 Tex

Black: .8mm PU,
non-woven polyester backing

Braided cotton lace:
10mm wide x 1.5mm

White action leather:
1.4mm, fine grain emboss

1.5mm perforation

Tongue logo:
Two-color screen print

Perforated eyelet
eyestay reinforcement: Super-Tuff .5mm

Tongue face:
.75mm PU with polyester backing

Deco stitching:
bonded nylon M8, 400D

Collar lining: 100% polyester, 200gsm
"star" mesh, 2mm PU foam, tricot backing

Mustache: 2.0mm PU leather with
"fine grain" texture emboss

Heel logo:
screen print blue

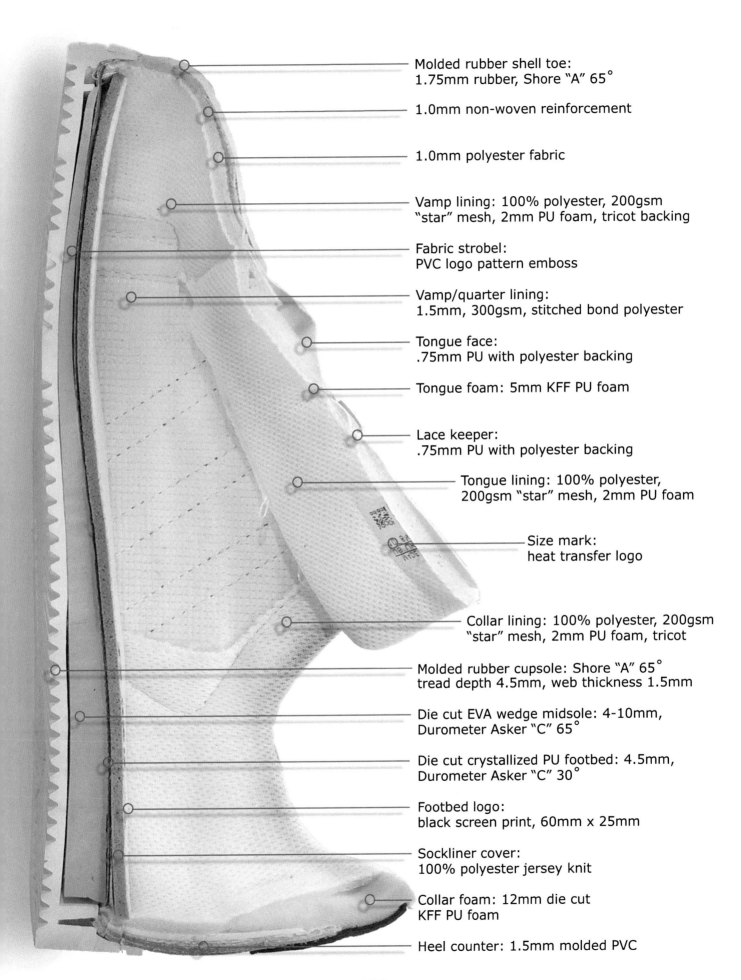

Molded rubber shell toe:
1.75mm rubber, Shore "A" 65°

1.0mm non-woven reinforcement

1.0mm polyester fabric

Vamp lining: 100% polyester, 200gsm
"star" mesh, 2mm PU foam, tricot backing

Fabric strobel:
PVC logo pattern emboss

Vamp/quarter lining:
1.5mm, 300gsm, stitched bond polyester

Tongue face:
.75mm PU with polyester backing

Tongue foam: 5mm KFF PU foam

Lace keeper:
.75mm PU with polyester backing

Tongue lining: 100% polyester,
200gsm "star" mesh, 2mm PU foam

Size mark:
heat transfer logo

Collar lining: 100% polyester, 200gsm
"star" mesh, 2mm PU foam, tricot

Molded rubber cupsole: Shore "A" 65°
tread depth 4.5mm, web thickness 1.5mm

Die cut EVA wedge midsole: 4-10mm,
Durometer Asker "C" 65°

Die cut crystallized PU footbed: 4.5mm,
Durometer Asker "C" 30°

Footbed logo:
black screen print, 60mm x 25mm

Sockliner cover:
100% polyester jersey knit

Collar foam: 12mm die cut
KFF PU foam

Heel counter: 1.5mm molded PVC

Track spike

Designed for its ultra lightweight and traction, the track spike is a sleek and simple running machine. The upper has a minimalist welded mesh design, the midsole is very thin, and the outsole has been replaced with an injection molded plastic spike plate. Built for speed, there are no extra reinforcements to slow you down.

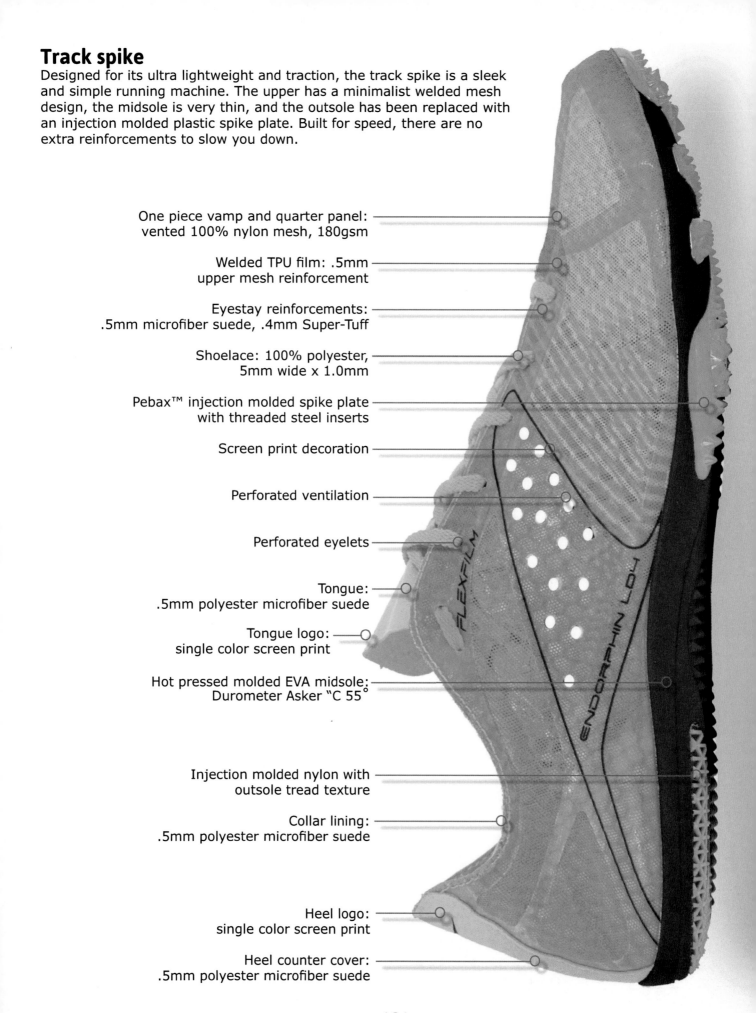

One piece vamp and quarter panel:
vented 100% nylon mesh, 180gsm

Welded TPU film: .5mm
upper mesh reinforcement

Eyestay reinforcements:
.5mm microfiber suede, .4mm Super-Tuff

Shoelace: 100% polyester,
5mm wide x 1.0mm

Pebax™ injection molded spike plate
with threaded steel inserts

Screen print decoration

Perforated ventilation

Perforated eyelets

Tongue:
.5mm polyester microfiber suede

Tongue logo:
single color screen print

Hot pressed molded EVA midsole:
Durometer Asker "C 55°

Injection molded nylon with
outsole tread texture

Collar lining:
.5mm polyester microfiber suede

Heel logo:
single color screen print

Heel counter cover:
.5mm polyester microfiber suede

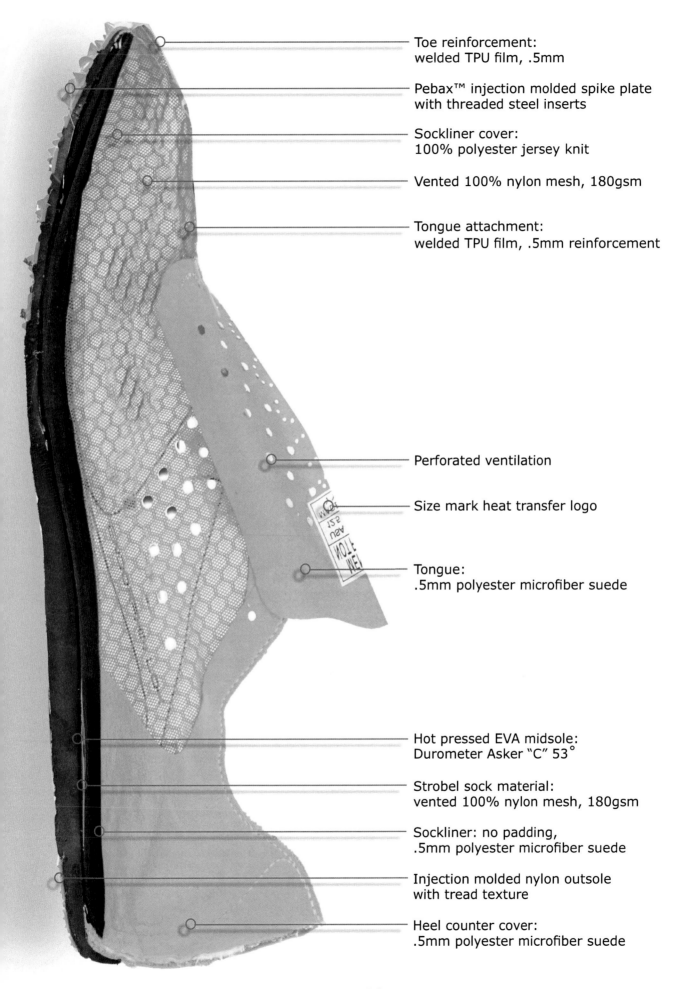

Toe reinforcement:
welded TPU film, .5mm

Pebax™ injection molded spike plate
with threaded steel inserts

Sockliner cover:
100% polyester jersey knit

Vented 100% nylon mesh, 180gsm

Tongue attachment:
welded TPU film, .5mm reinforcement

Perforated ventilation

Size mark heat transfer logo

Tongue:
.5mm polyester microfiber suede

Hot pressed EVA midsole:
Durometer Asker "C" 53°

Strobel sock material:
vented 100% nylon mesh, 180gsm

Sockliner: no padding,
.5mm polyester microfiber suede

Injection molded nylon outsole
with tread texture

Heel counter cover:
.5mm polyester microfiber suede

Full-length airbag running shoe

This training shoe features a full-length EVA midsole bonded to a blow molded TPU airbag. The upper is a one-piece 4k knit upper. Add the airbrush fade and minimalist lacing system and this high technology modern design becomes a visual sports marketing masterpiece.

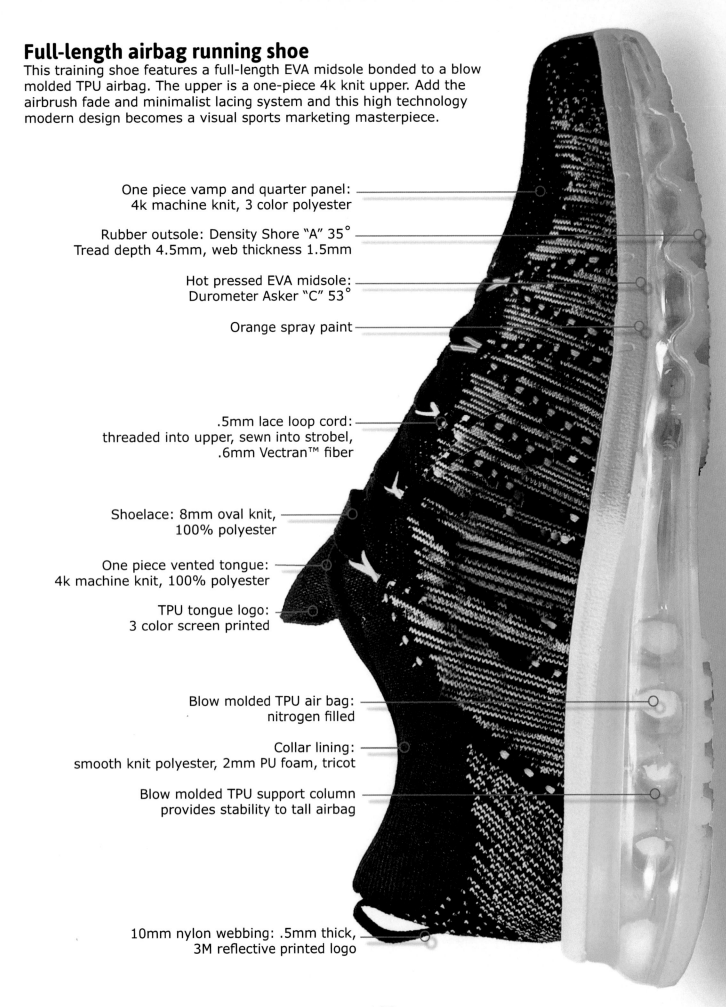

One piece vamp and quarter panel:
4k machine knit, 3 color polyester

Rubber outsole: Density Shore "A" 35°
Tread depth 4.5mm, web thickness 1.5mm

Hot pressed EVA midsole:
Durometer Asker "C" 53°

Orange spray paint

.5mm lace loop cord:
threaded into upper, sewn into strobel,
.6mm Vectran™ fiber

Shoelace: 8mm oval knit,
100% polyester

One piece vented tongue:
4k machine knit, 100% polyester

TPU tongue logo:
3 color screen printed

Blow molded TPU air bag:
nitrogen filled

Collar lining:
smooth knit polyester, 2mm PU foam, tricot

Blow molded TPU support column
provides stability to tall airbag

10mm nylon webbing: .5mm thick,
3M reflective printed logo

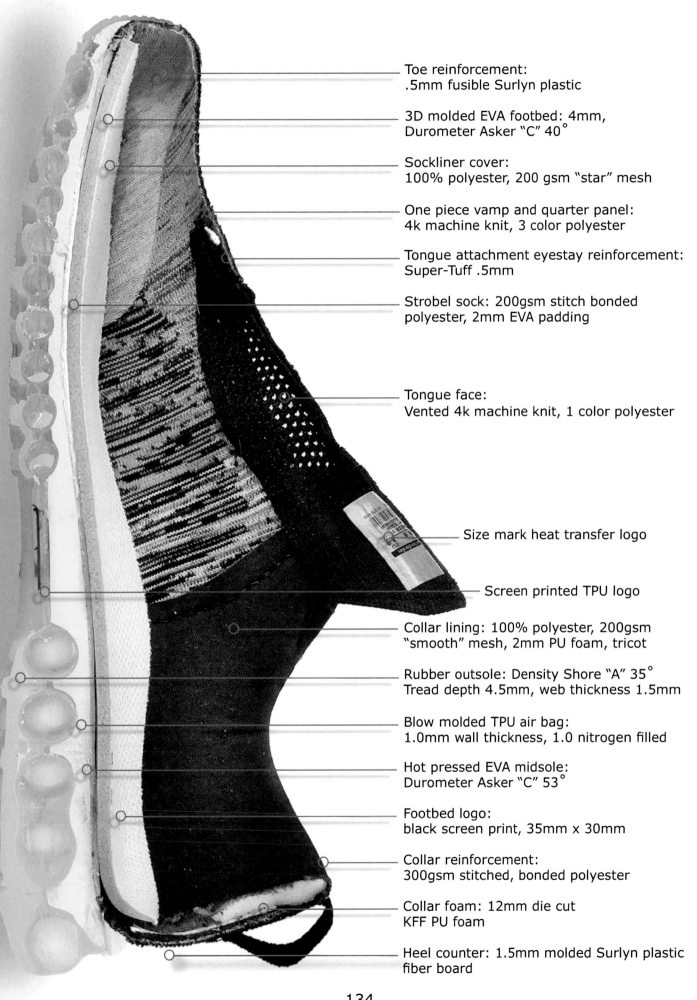

Toe reinforcement:
.5mm fusible Surlyn plastic

3D molded EVA footbed: 4mm,
Durometer Asker "C" 40°

Sockliner cover:
100% polyester, 200 gsm "star" mesh

One piece vamp and quarter panel:
4k machine knit, 3 color polyester

Tongue attachment eyestay reinforcement:
Super-Tuff .5mm

Strobel sock: 200gsm stitch bonded
polyester, 2mm EVA padding

Tongue face:
Vented 4k machine knit, 1 color polyester

Size mark heat transfer logo

Screen printed TPU logo

Collar lining: 100% polyester, 200gsm
"smooth" mesh, 2mm PU foam, tricot

Rubber outsole: Density Shore "A" 35°
Tread depth 4.5mm, web thickness 1.5mm

Blow molded TPU air bag:
1.0mm wall thickness, 1.0 nitrogen filled

Hot pressed EVA midsole:
Durometer Asker "C" 53°

Footbed logo:
black screen print, 35mm x 30mm

Collar reinforcement:
300gsm stitched, bonded polyester

Collar foam: 12mm die cut
KFF PU foam

Heel counter: 1.5mm molded Surlyn plastic
fiber board

134

Ultra modern running shoe

This running shoe has a very complicated full-length airbag but its unique feature is the upper construction. This shoe is made with very little stitching. The upper is 4k computer knit, while all the reinforcements and logos are welded in place.

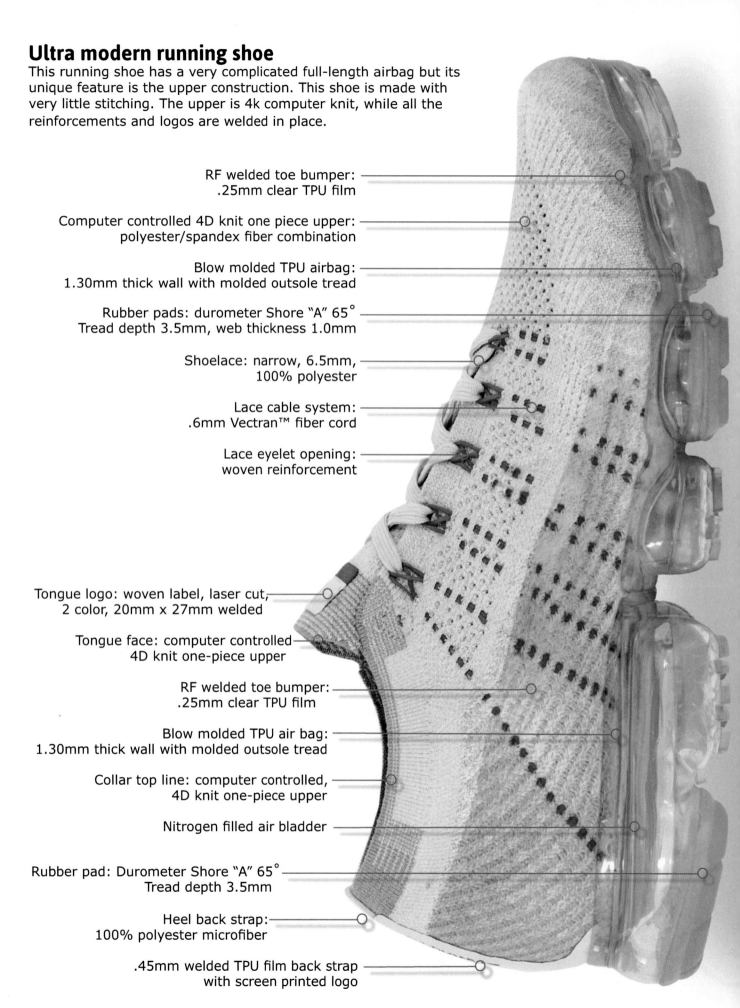

RF welded toe bumper:
.25mm clear TPU film

Computer controlled 4D knit one piece upper:
polyester/spandex fiber combination

Blow molded TPU airbag:
1.30mm thick wall with molded outsole tread

Rubber pads: durometer Shore "A" 65°
Tread depth 3.5mm, web thickness 1.0mm

Shoelace: narrow, 6.5mm,
100% polyester

Lace cable system:
.6mm Vectran™ fiber cord

Lace eyelet opening:
woven reinforcement

Tongue logo: woven label, laser cut,
2 color, 20mm x 27mm welded

Tongue face: computer controlled
4D knit one-piece upper

RF welded toe bumper:
.25mm clear TPU film

Blow molded TPU air bag:
1.30mm thick wall with molded outsole tread

Collar top line: computer controlled,
4D knit one-piece upper

Nitrogen filled air bladder

Rubber pad: Durometer Shore "A" 65°
Tread depth 3.5mm

Heel back strap:
100% polyester microfiber

.45mm welded TPU film back strap
with screen printed logo

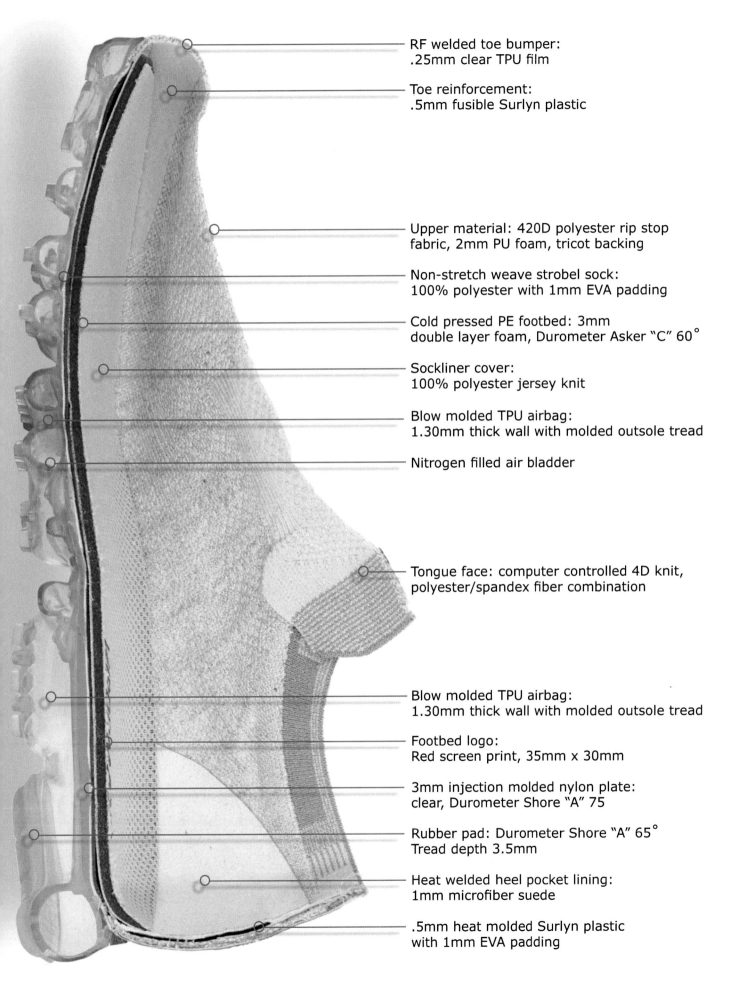

RF welded toe bumper:
.25mm clear TPU film

Toe reinforcement:
.5mm fusible Surlyn plastic

Upper material: 420D polyester rip stop
fabric, 2mm PU foam, tricot backing

Non-stretch weave strobel sock:
100% polyester with 1mm EVA padding

Cold pressed PE footbed: 3mm
double layer foam, Durometer Asker "C" 60°

Sockliner cover:
100% polyester jersey knit

Blow molded TPU airbag:
1.30mm thick wall with molded outsole tread

Nitrogen filled air bladder

Tongue face: computer controlled 4D knit,
polyester/spandex fiber combination

Blow molded TPU airbag:
1.30mm thick wall with molded outsole tread

Footbed logo:
Red screen print, 35mm x 30mm

3mm injection molded nylon plate:
clear, Durometer Shore "A" 75

Rubber pad: Durometer Shore "A" 65°
Tread depth 3.5mm

Heat welded heel pocket lining:
1mm microfiber suede

.5mm heat molded Surlyn plastic
with 1mm EVA padding

Modern low cut basketball shoe

This is a pro model for a top NBA star, this low cut basketball shoe features a molded EVA "drop-in" footbed/midsole combination. Extra cushioning is provided by a low profile airbag fitted to the midsole. The crystal rubber sole is complemented by a unique crystal clear strobel sock.

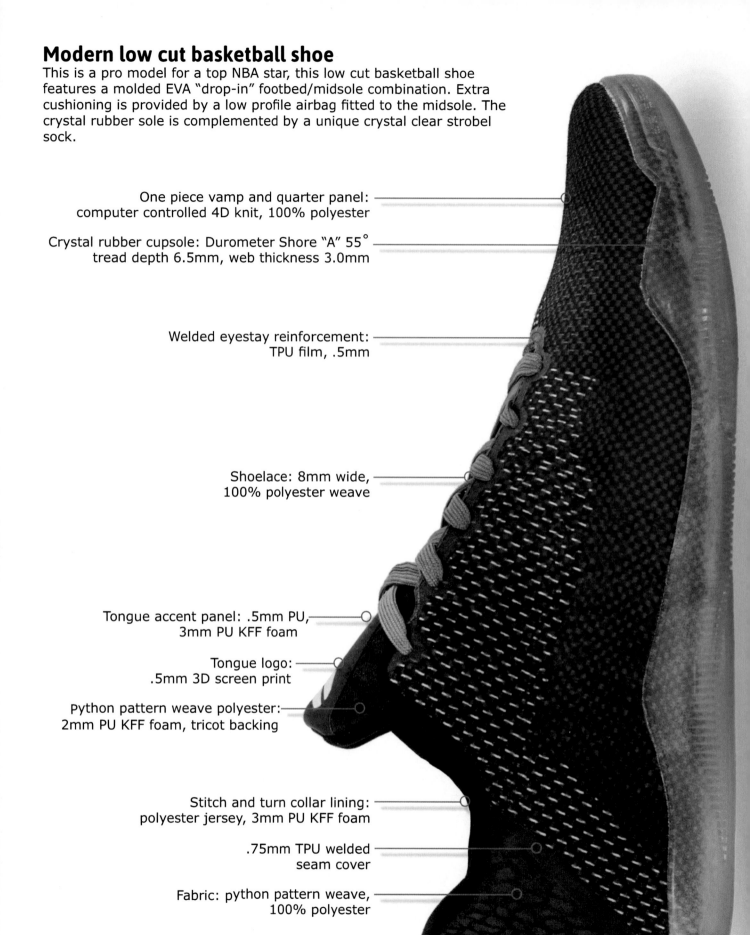

One piece vamp and quarter panel: computer controlled 4D knit, 100% polyester

Crystal rubber cupsole: Durometer Shore "A" 55° tread depth 6.5mm, web thickness 3.0mm

Welded eyestay reinforcement: TPU film, .5mm

Shoelace: 8mm wide, 100% polyester weave

Tongue accent panel: .5mm PU, 3mm PU KFF foam

Tongue logo: .5mm 3D screen print

Python pattern weave polyester: 2mm PU KFF foam, tricot backing

Stitch and turn collar lining: polyester jersey, 3mm PU KFF foam

.75mm TPU welded seam cover

Fabric: python pattern weave, 100% polyester

Heel logo embroidery

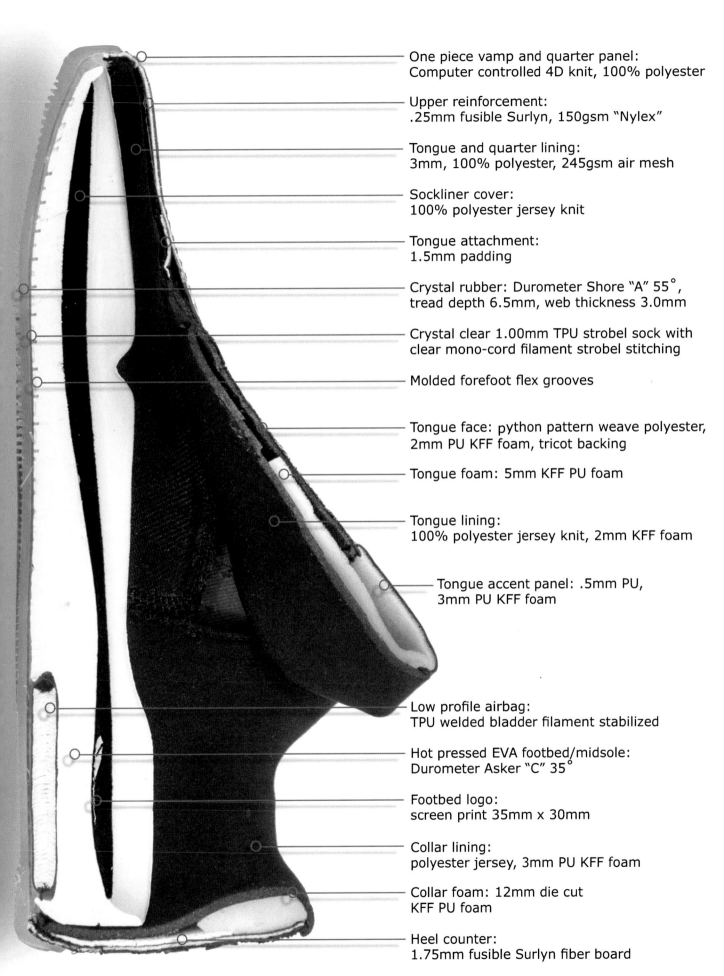

One piece vamp and quarter panel:
Computer controlled 4D knit, 100% polyester

Upper reinforcement:
.25mm fusible Surlyn, 150gsm "Nylex"

Tongue and quarter lining:
3mm, 100% polyester, 245gsm air mesh

Sockliner cover:
100% polyester jersey knit

Tongue attachment:
1.5mm padding

Crystal rubber: Durometer Shore "A" 55°,
tread depth 6.5mm, web thickness 3.0mm

Crystal clear 1.00mm TPU strobel sock with
clear mono-cord filament strobel stitching

Molded forefoot flex grooves

Tongue face: python pattern weave polyester,
2mm PU KFF foam, tricot backing

Tongue foam: 5mm KFF PU foam

Tongue lining:
100% polyester jersey knit, 2mm KFF foam

Tongue accent panel: .5mm PU,
3mm PU KFF foam

Low profile airbag:
TPU welded bladder filament stabilized

Hot pressed EVA footbed/midsole:
Durometer Asker "C" 35°

Footbed logo:
screen print 35mm x 30mm

Collar lining:
polyester jersey, 3mm PU KFF foam

Collar foam: 12mm die cut
KFF PU foam

Heel counter:
1.75mm fusible Surlyn fiber board

Modern high top basketball shoe

This shoe features a printed textile upper with over-molded plastic reinforcements. The outsole has an extra thick midsole with an injection molded support frame. The inside of this shoe could not be more different than the outside, the complicated upper gives way to an ultra clean and nearly seamless inner lining.

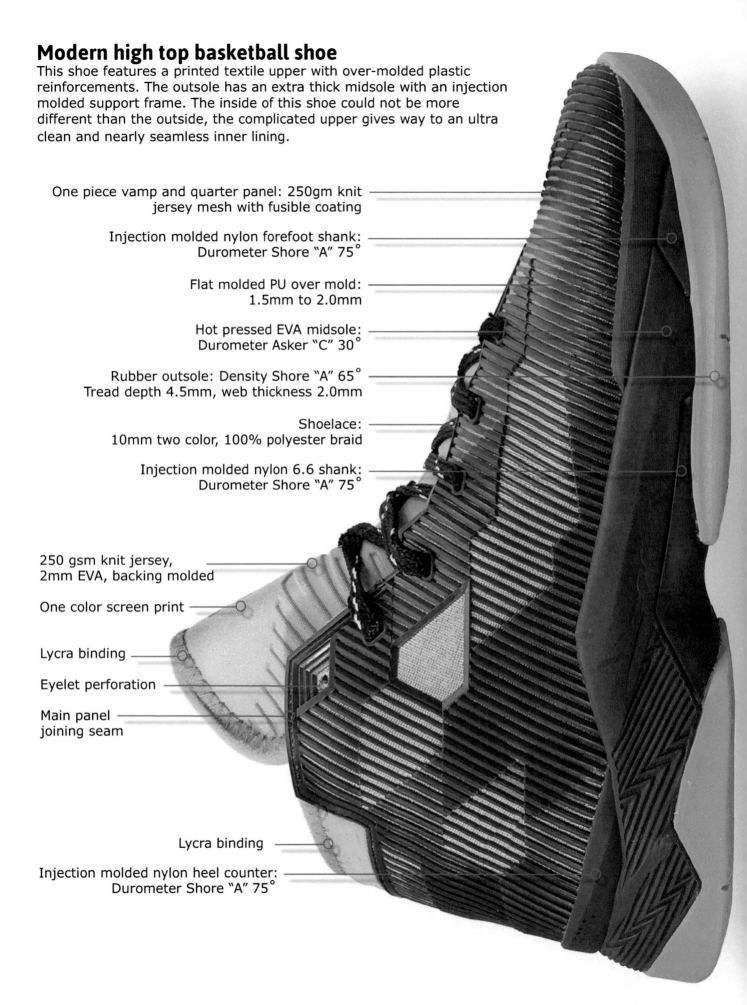

One piece vamp and quarter panel: 250gm knit jersey mesh with fusible coating

Injection molded nylon forefoot shank: Durometer Shore "A" 75°

Flat molded PU over mold: 1.5mm to 2.0mm

Hot pressed EVA midsole: Durometer Asker "C" 30°

Rubber outsole: Density Shore "A" 65° Tread depth 4.5mm, web thickness 2.0mm

Shoelace: 10mm two color, 100% polyester braid

Injection molded nylon 6.6 shank: Durometer Shore "A" 75°

250 gsm knit jersey, 2mm EVA, backing molded

One color screen print

Lycra binding

Eyelet perforation

Main panel joining seam

Lycra binding

Injection molded nylon heel counter: Durometer Shore "A" 75°

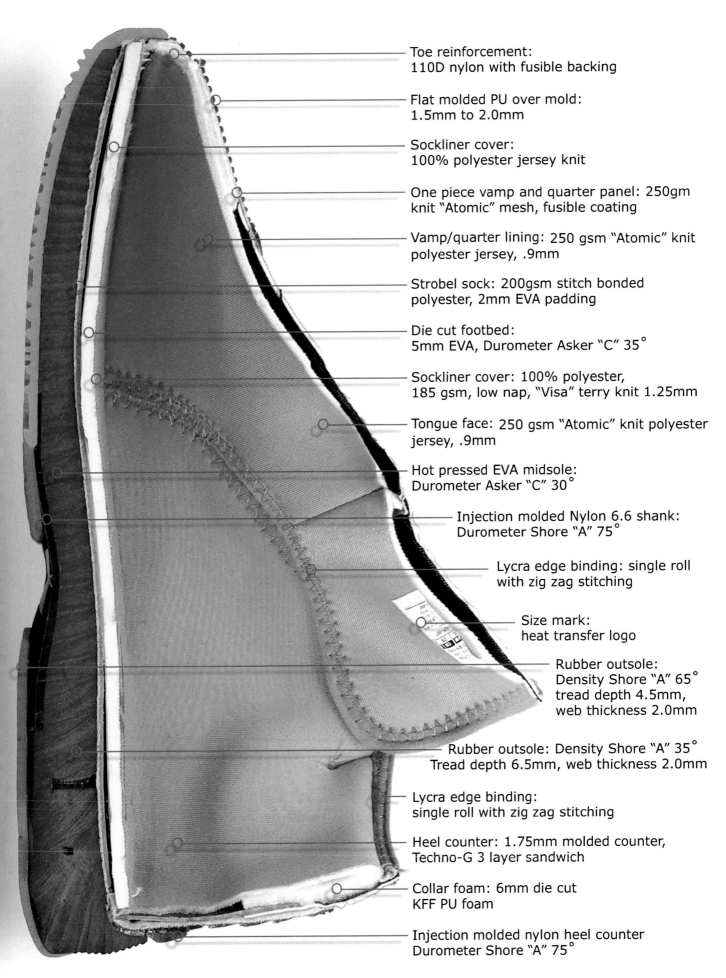

Toe reinforcement:
110D nylon with fusible backing

Flat molded PU over mold:
1.5mm to 2.0mm

Sockliner cover:
100% polyester jersey knit

One piece vamp and quarter panel: 250gm
knit "Atomic" mesh, fusible coating

Vamp/quarter lining: 250 gsm "Atomic" knit
polyester jersey, .9mm

Strobel sock: 200gsm stitch bonded
polyester, 2mm EVA padding

Die cut footbed:
5mm EVA, Durometer Asker "C" 35°

Sockliner cover: 100% polyester,
185 gsm, low nap, "Visa" terry knit 1.25mm

Tongue face: 250 gsm "Atomic" knit polyester
jersey, .9mm

Hot pressed EVA midsole:
Durometer Asker "C" 30°

Injection molded Nylon 6.6 shank:
Durometer Shore "A" 75°

Lycra edge binding: single roll
with zig zag stitching

Size mark:
heat transfer logo

Rubber outsole:
Density Shore "A" 65°
tread depth 4.5mm,
web thickness 2.0mm

Rubber outsole: Density Shore "A" 35°
Tread depth 6.5mm, web thickness 2.0mm

Lycra edge binding:
single roll with zig zag stitching

Heel counter: 1.75mm molded counter,
Techno-G 3 layer sandwich

Collar foam: 6mm die cut
KFF PU foam

Injection molded nylon heel counter
Durometer Shore "A" 75°

90's air running shoe

This shoe was one of a long line of air sole sneakers, but its pure 90's styling proved timeless. Rebooted in the 2000's, this classic design continues to be manufactured today. A simple upper with lots of lacing options is paired with a visually striking air bag, encapsulated by a retro style PU midsole.

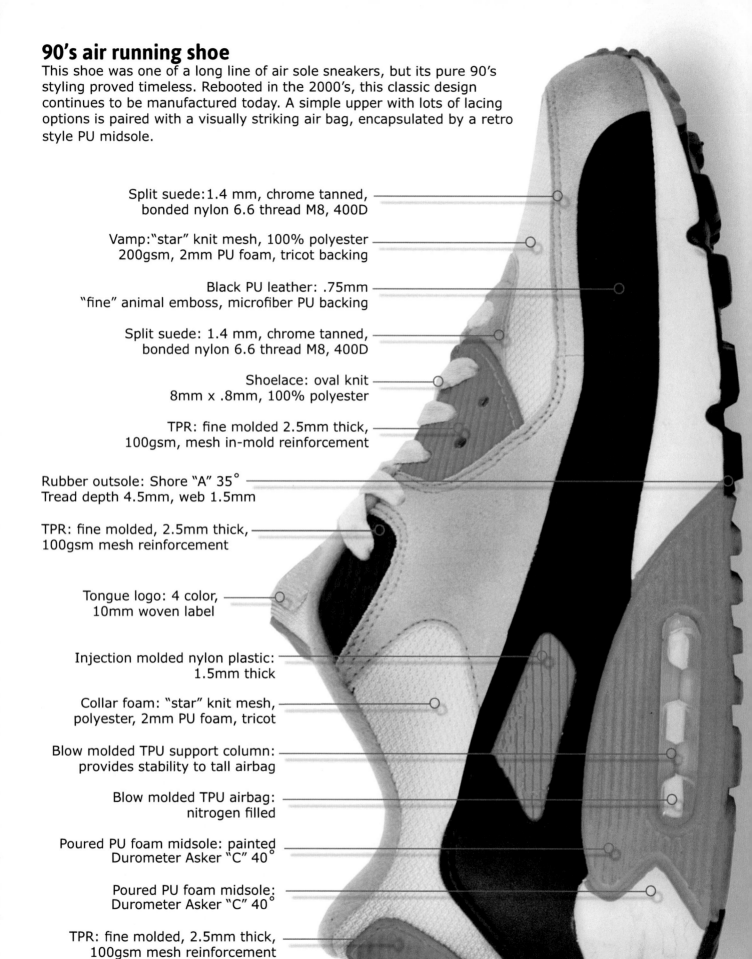

Split suede:1.4 mm, chrome tanned, bonded nylon 6.6 thread M8, 400D

Vamp:"star" knit mesh, 100% polyester 200gsm, 2mm PU foam, tricot backing

Black PU leather: .75mm "fine" animal emboss, microfiber PU backing

Split suede: 1.4 mm, chrome tanned, bonded nylon 6.6 thread M8, 400D

Shoelace: oval knit 8mm x .8mm, 100% polyester

TPR: fine molded 2.5mm thick, 100gsm, mesh in-mold reinforcement

Rubber outsole: Shore "A" 35° Tread depth 4.5mm, web 1.5mm

TPR: fine molded, 2.5mm thick, 100gsm mesh reinforcement

Tongue logo: 4 color, 10mm woven label

Injection molded nylon plastic: 1.5mm thick

Collar foam: "star" knit mesh, polyester, 2mm PU foam, tricot

Blow molded TPU support column: provides stability to tall airbag

Blow molded TPU airbag: nitrogen filled

Poured PU foam midsole: painted Durometer Asker "C" 40°

Poured PU foam midsole: Durometer Asker "C" 40°

TPR: fine molded, 2.5mm thick, 100gsm mesh reinforcement

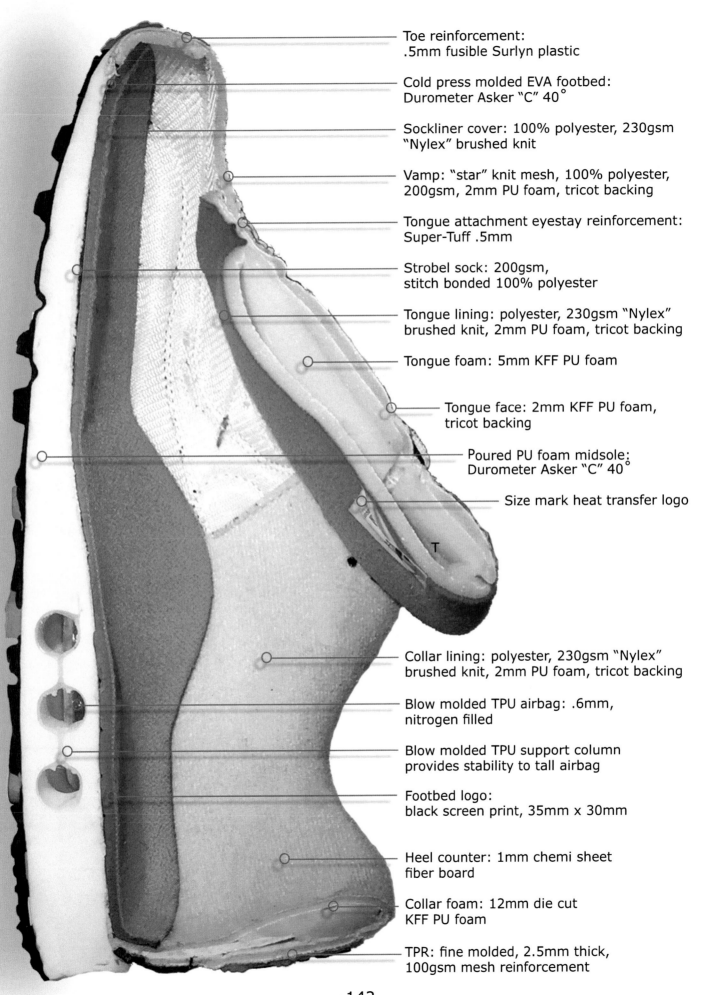

Toe reinforcement:
.5mm fusible Surlyn plastic

Cold press molded EVA footbed:
Durometer Asker "C" 40°

Sockliner cover: 100% polyester, 230gsm
"Nylex" brushed knit

Vamp: "star" knit mesh, 100% polyester,
200gsm, 2mm PU foam, tricot backing

Tongue attachment eyestay reinforcement:
Super-Tuff .5mm

Strobel sock: 200gsm,
stitch bonded 100% polyester

Tongue lining: polyester, 230gsm "Nylex"
brushed knit, 2mm PU foam, tricot backing

Tongue foam: 5mm KFF PU foam

Tongue face: 2mm KFF PU foam,
tricot backing

Poured PU foam midsole:
Durometer Asker "C" 40°

Size mark heat transfer logo

Collar lining: polyester, 230gsm "Nylex"
brushed knit, 2mm PU foam, tricot backing

Blow molded TPU airbag: .6mm,
nitrogen filled

Blow molded TPU support column
provides stability to tall airbag

Footbed logo:
black screen print, 35mm x 30mm

Heel counter: 1mm chemi sheet
fiber board

Collar foam: 12mm die cut
KFF PU foam

TPR: fine molded, 2.5mm thick,
100gsm mesh reinforcement

Waffle jogger

This classic running shoe design traces its lineage directly to the simple shoe that transformed an upstart shoe company into a global footwear empire. Designed in the late 1970's, this shoe features a waffle bottom outsole with a die cut EVA midsole wedge design. Made of suede and mesh, the upper is bonded to an EVA wedge with a simple waffle bottom.

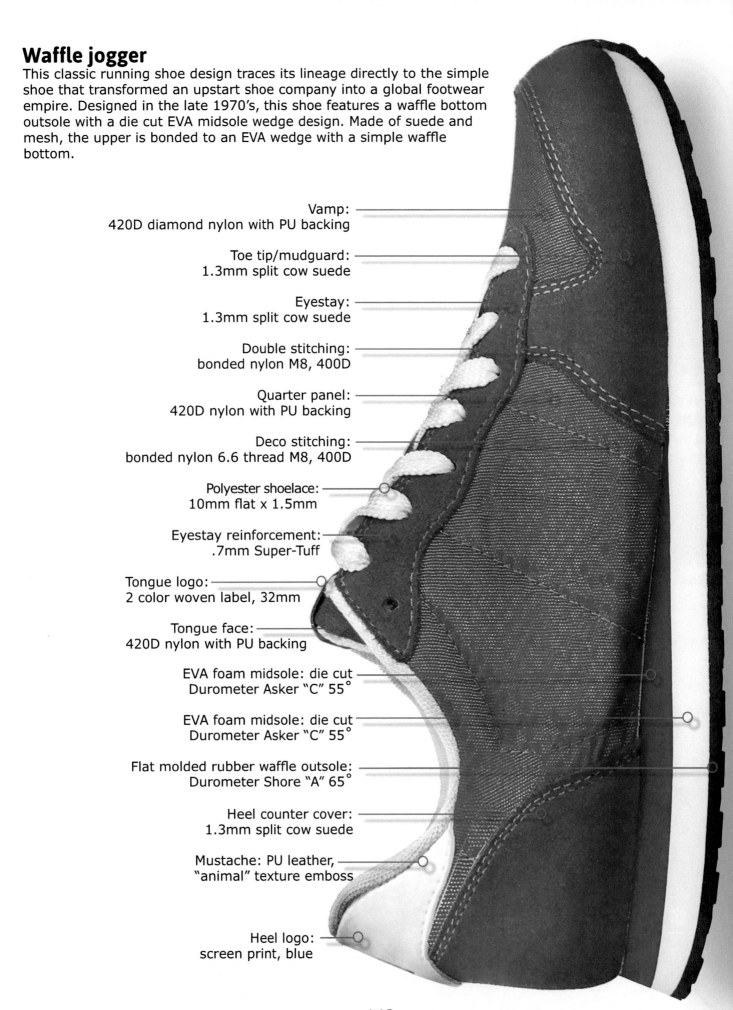

Vamp:
420D diamond nylon with PU backing

Toe tip/mudguard:
1.3mm split cow suede

Eyestay:
1.3mm split cow suede

Double stitching:
bonded nylon M8, 400D

Quarter panel:
420D nylon with PU backing

Deco stitching:
bonded nylon 6.6 thread M8, 400D

Polyester shoelace:
10mm flat x 1.5mm

Eyestay reinforcement:
.7mm Super-Tuff

Tongue logo:
2 color woven label, 32mm

Tongue face:
420D nylon with PU backing

EVA foam midsole: die cut
Durometer Asker "C" 55°

EVA foam midsole: die cut
Durometer Asker "C" 55°

Flat molded rubber waffle outsole:
Durometer Shore "A" 65°

Heel counter cover:
1.3mm split cow suede

Mustache: PU leather,
"animal" texture emboss

Heel logo:
screen print, blue

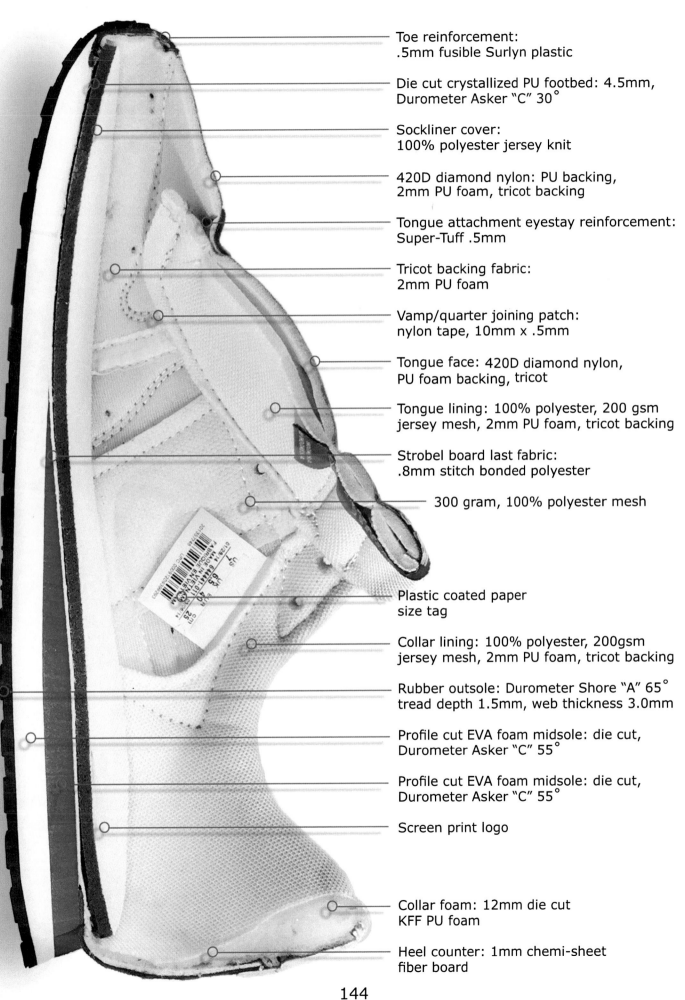

Toe reinforcement:
.5mm fusible Surlyn plastic

Die cut crystallized PU footbed: 4.5mm,
Durometer Asker "C" 30°

Sockliner cover:
100% polyester jersey knit

420D diamond nylon: PU backing,
2mm PU foam, tricot backing

Tongue attachment eyestay reinforcement:
Super-Tuff .5mm

Tricot backing fabric:
2mm PU foam

Vamp/quarter joining patch:
nylon tape, 10mm x .5mm

Tongue face: 420D diamond nylon,
PU foam backing, tricot

Tongue lining: 100% polyester, 200 gsm
jersey mesh, 2mm PU foam, tricot backing

Strobel board last fabric:
.8mm stitch bonded polyester

300 gram, 100% polyester mesh

Plastic coated paper
size tag

Collar lining: 100% polyester, 200gsm
jersey mesh, 2mm PU foam, tricot backing

Rubber outsole: Durometer Shore "A" 65°
tread depth 1.5mm, web thickness 3.0mm

Profile cut EVA foam midsole: die cut,
Durometer Asker "C" 55°

Profile cut EVA foam midsole: die cut,
Durometer Asker "C" 55°

Screen print logo

Collar foam: 12mm die cut
KFF PU foam

Heel counter: 1mm chemi-sheet
fiber board

144

Trail running shoe

This is a lightweight shoe designed for off-road use. It features a one-piece rip-stop textile upper with welded TPU reinforcements and board lasted construction. The faux double lasted outsole design requires an extra thick footbed/midsole.

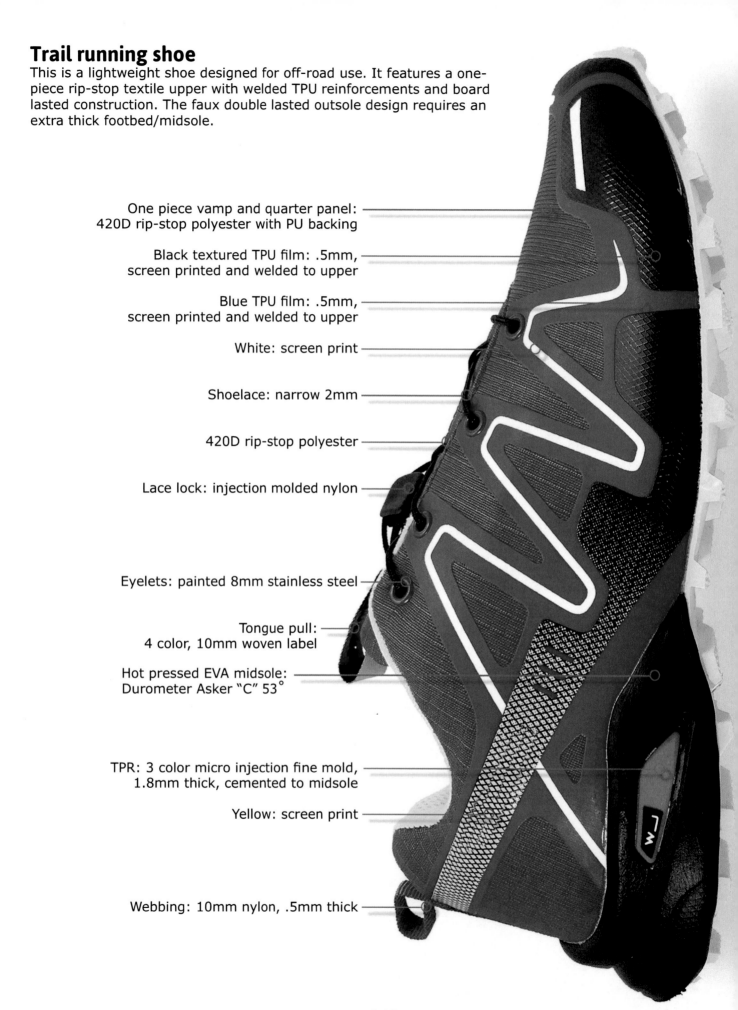

One piece vamp and quarter panel: 420D rip-stop polyester with PU backing

Black textured TPU film: .5mm, screen printed and welded to upper

Blue TPU film: .5mm, screen printed and welded to upper

White: screen print

Shoelace: narrow 2mm

420D rip-stop polyester

Lace lock: injection molded nylon

Eyelets: painted 8mm stainless steel

Tongue pull: 4 color, 10mm woven label

Hot pressed EVA midsole: Durometer Asker "C" 53°

TPR: 3 color micro injection fine mold, 1.8mm thick, cemented to midsole

Yellow: screen print

Webbing: 10mm nylon, .5mm thick

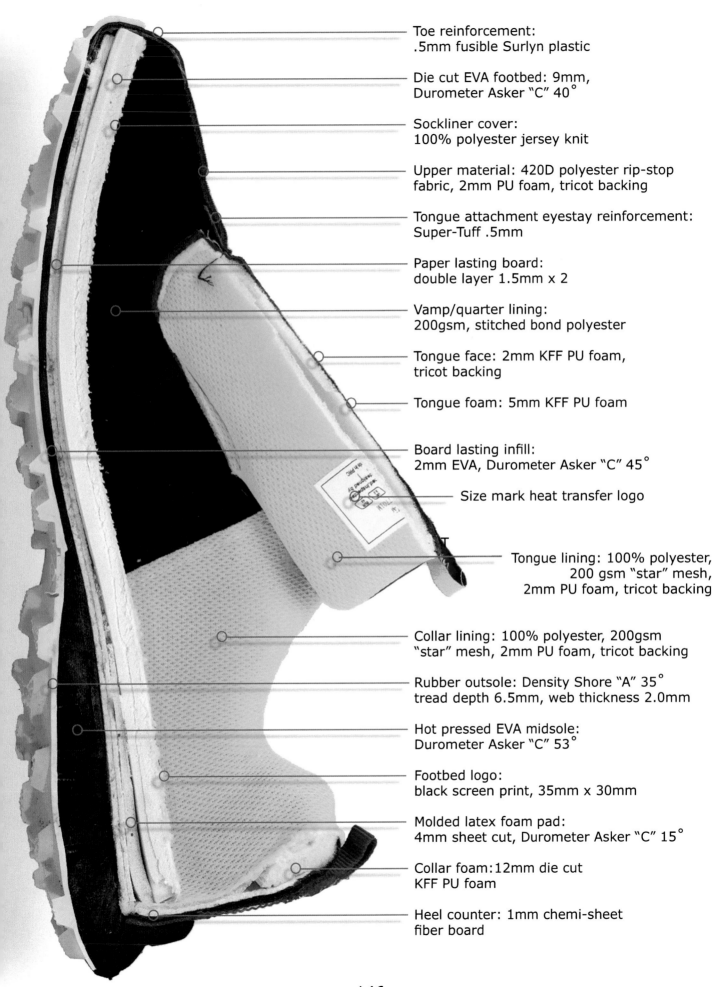

Toe reinforcement:
.5mm fusible Surlyn plastic

Die cut EVA footbed: 9mm,
Durometer Asker "C" 40°

Sockliner cover:
100% polyester jersey knit

Upper material: 420D polyester rip-stop
fabric, 2mm PU foam, tricot backing

Tongue attachment eyestay reinforcement:
Super-Tuff .5mm

Paper lasting board:
double layer 1.5mm x 2

Vamp/quarter lining:
200gsm, stitched bond polyester

Tongue face: 2mm KFF PU foam,
tricot backing

Tongue foam: 5mm KFF PU foam

Board lasting infill:
2mm EVA, Durometer Asker "C" 45°

Size mark heat transfer logo

Tongue lining: 100% polyester,
200 gsm "star" mesh,
2mm PU foam, tricot backing

Collar lining: 100% polyester, 200gsm
"star" mesh, 2mm PU foam, tricot backing

Rubber outsole: Density Shore "A" 35°
tread depth 6.5mm, web thickness 2.0mm

Hot pressed EVA midsole:
Durometer Asker "C" 53°

Footbed logo:
black screen print, 35mm x 30mm

Molded latex foam pad:
4mm sheet cut, Durometer Asker "C" 15°

Collar foam:12mm die cut
KFF PU foam

Heel counter: 1mm chemi-sheet
fiber board

146

Faux vulcanized cupsole skate shoe

Real vulcanized shoes can be heavy, labor intensive to make, and require a specialized vulcanizing shoe factory to produce. These problems can be avoided by using a cupsole designed to look like the traditional vulcanized shoe. The use of vulcanization safe suede and canvas complete the illusion.

Vamp: split suede, 1.3mm, low nap, chrome tanned

Molded rubber cupsole: Durometer Shore "A" 65°, micro diamond texture

Faux vulcanized stripe painted after molding

Deco stitching: bonded nylon 6.6 thread M8, 400D

Eyestay: 1.3mm, low nap, split suede, .5mm Super-Tuff

Shoelace: 10mm x 1.5 mm 100% polyester, flat braided

Quarter panel: cotton canvas, 8oz. weight, 1mm SBR foam backing

Tongue face: cotton canvas 8oz., 1mm SBR foam backing

Punched eyelets: 4mm x .5mm, Super-Tuff reinforcements

Tongue binding: knit polyester jersey, single stitch, single fold, double rolled

Collar line: deco stitching, bonded nylon 6.6 thread M8, 400D

Heel counter cover: 1.3mm, low nap, chrome tanned, split suede

Heel logo: "license plate," 1.5mm, screen printed die cut rubber

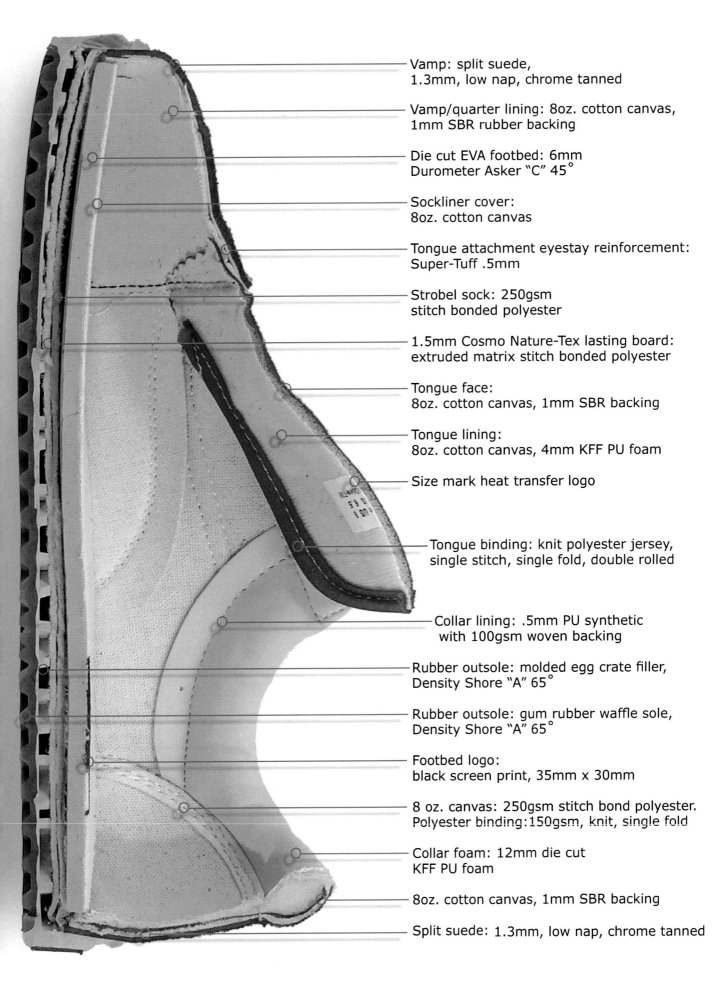

Vamp: split suede,
1.3mm, low nap, chrome tanned

Vamp/quarter lining: 8oz. cotton canvas,
1mm SBR rubber backing

Die cut EVA footbed: 6mm
Durometer Asker "C" 45°

Sockliner cover:
8oz. cotton canvas

Tongue attachment eyestay reinforcement:
Super-Tuff .5mm

Strobel sock: 250gsm
stitch bonded polyester

1.5mm Cosmo Nature-Tex lasting board:
extruded matrix stitch bonded polyester

Tongue face:
8oz. cotton canvas, 1mm SBR backing

Tongue lining:
8oz. cotton canvas, 4mm KFF PU foam

Size mark heat transfer logo

Tongue binding: knit polyester jersey,
single stitch, single fold, double rolled

Collar lining: .5mm PU synthetic
with 100gsm woven backing

Rubber outsole: molded egg crate filler,
Density Shore "A" 65°

Rubber outsole: gum rubber waffle sole,
Density Shore "A" 65°

Footbed logo:
black screen print, 35mm x 30mm

8 oz. canvas: 250gsm stitch bond polyester.
Polyester binding:150gsm, knit, single fold

Collar foam: 12mm die cut
KFF PU foam

8oz. cotton canvas, 1mm SBR backing

Split suede: 1.3mm, low nap, chrome tanned

Rock climbing shoe

This shoe is purpose-built for one thing only: climbing. Not suitable for walking, and not designed for comfort, climbing shoes have a unique shape not found in any other type of footwear. Stripped of almost all functional components found in normal footwear, the modern climbing shoe is a form dedicated purely to function.

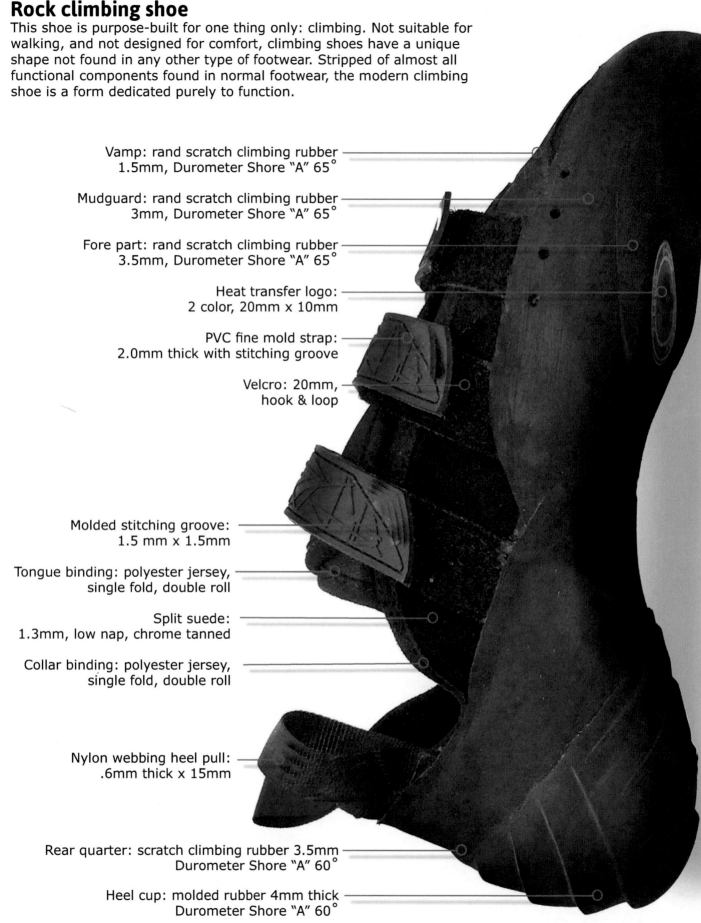

Vamp: rand scratch climbing rubber
1.5mm, Durometer Shore "A" 65°

Mudguard: rand scratch climbing rubber
3mm, Durometer Shore "A" 65°

Fore part: rand scratch climbing rubber
3.5mm, Durometer Shore "A" 65°

Heat transfer logo:
2 color, 20mm x 10mm

PVC fine mold strap:
2.0mm thick with stitching groove

Velcro: 20mm,
hook & loop

Molded stitching groove:
1.5 mm x 1.5mm

Tongue binding: polyester jersey,
single fold, double roll

Split suede:
1.3mm, low nap, chrome tanned

Collar binding: polyester jersey,
single fold, double roll

Nylon webbing heel pull:
.6mm thick x 15mm

Rear quarter: scratch climbing rubber 3.5mm
Durometer Shore "A" 60°

Heel cup: molded rubber 4mm thick
Durometer Shore "A" 60°

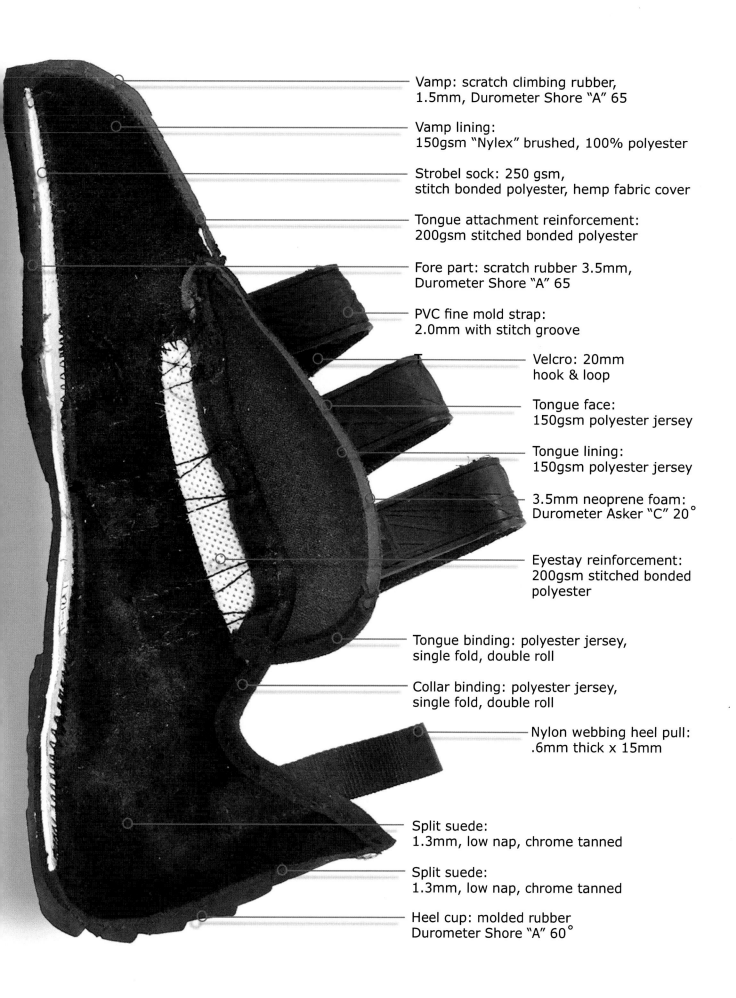

Vamp: scratch climbing rubber,
1.5mm, Durometer Shore "A" 65

Vamp lining:
150gsm "Nylex" brushed, 100% polyester

Strobel sock: 250 gsm,
stitch bonded polyester, hemp fabric cover

Tongue attachment reinforcement:
200gsm stitched bonded polyester

Fore part: scratch rubber 3.5mm,
Durometer Shore "A" 65

PVC fine mold strap:
2.0mm with stitch groove

Velcro: 20mm
hook & loop

Tongue face:
150gsm polyester jersey

Tongue lining:
150gsm polyester jersey

3.5mm neoprene foam:
Durometer Asker "C" 20°

Eyestay reinforcement:
200gsm stitched bonded
polyester

Tongue binding: polyester jersey,
single fold, double roll

Collar binding: polyester jersey,
single fold, double roll

Nylon webbing heel pull:
.6mm thick x 15mm

Split suede:
1.3mm, low nap, chrome tanned

Split suede:
1.3mm, low nap, chrome tanned

Heel cup: molded rubber
Durometer Shore "A" 60°

Football cleat

Designed for support, traction, and protection the modern football cleat features an injection molded outsole and molded midsole. The upper features firm heel counters, extra padding, and a velcro support strap. The shoe is board lasted with a 3mm nylon plate.

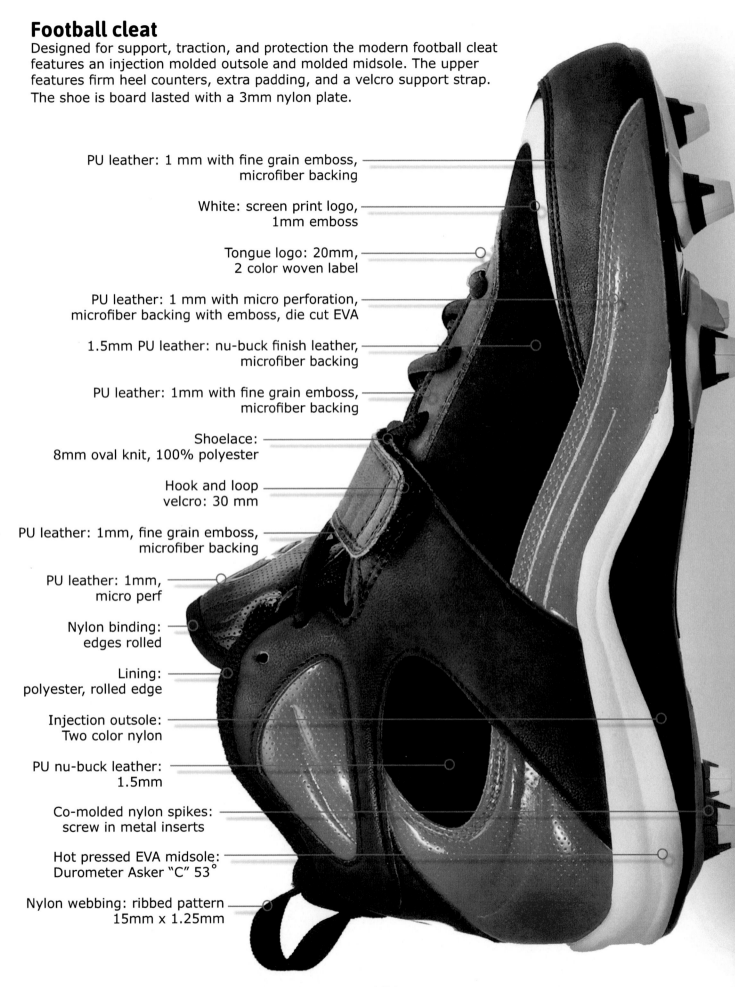

PU leather: 1 mm with fine grain emboss, microfiber backing

White: screen print logo, 1mm emboss

Tongue logo: 20mm, 2 color woven label

PU leather: 1 mm with micro perforation, microfiber backing with emboss, die cut EVA

1.5mm PU leather: nu-buck finish leather, microfiber backing

PU leather: 1mm with fine grain emboss, microfiber backing

Shoelace: 8mm oval knit, 100% polyester

Hook and loop velcro: 30 mm

PU leather: 1mm, fine grain emboss, microfiber backing

PU leather: 1mm, micro perf

Nylon binding: edges rolled

Lining: polyester, rolled edge

Injection outsole: Two color nylon

PU nu-buck leather: 1.5mm

Co-molded nylon spikes: screw in metal inserts

Hot pressed EVA midsole: Durometer Asker "C" 53°

Nylon webbing: ribbed pattern 15mm x 1.25mm

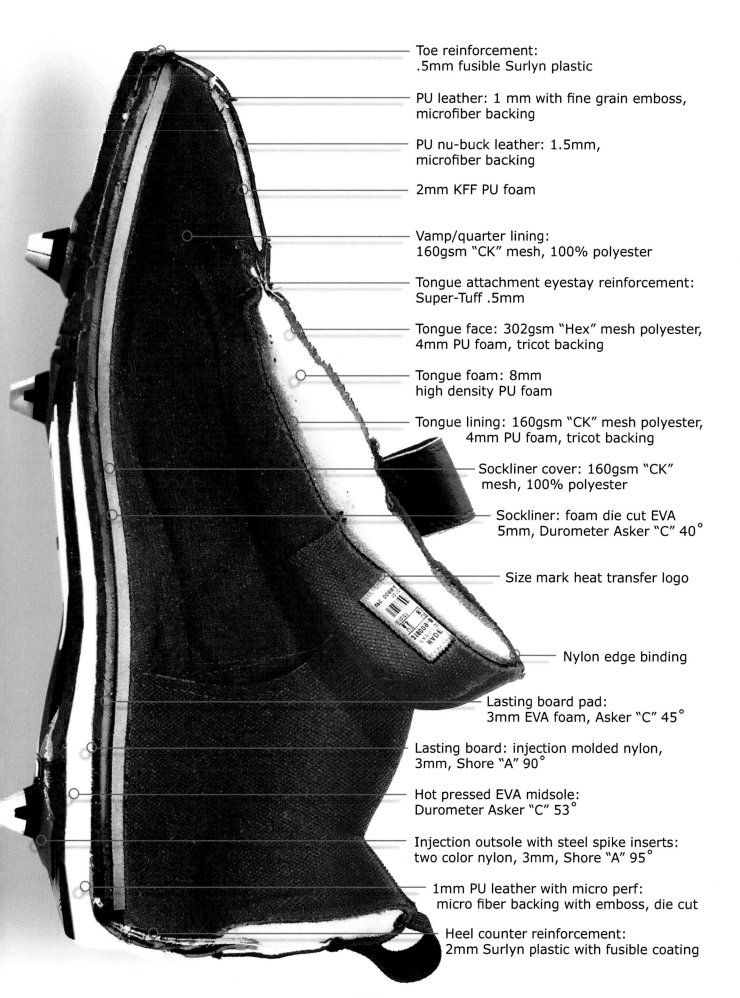

Toe reinforcement:
.5mm fusible Surlyn plastic

PU leather: 1 mm with fine grain emboss,
microfiber backing

PU nu-buck leather: 1.5mm,
microfiber backing

2mm KFF PU foam

Vamp/quarter lining:
160gsm "CK" mesh, 100% polyester

Tongue attachment eyestay reinforcement:
Super-Tuff .5mm

Tongue face: 302gsm "Hex" mesh polyester,
4mm PU foam, tricot backing

Tongue foam: 8mm
high density PU foam

Tongue lining: 160gsm "CK" mesh polyester,
4mm PU foam, tricot backing

Sockliner cover: 160gsm "CK"
mesh, 100% polyester

Sockliner: foam die cut EVA
5mm, Durometer Asker "C" 40°

Size mark heat transfer logo

Nylon edge binding

Lasting board pad:
3mm EVA foam, Asker "C" 45°

Lasting board: injection molded nylon,
3mm, Shore "A" 90°

Hot pressed EVA midsole:
Durometer Asker "C" 53°

Injection outsole with steel spike inserts:
two color nylon, 3mm, Shore "A" 95°

1mm PU leather with micro perf:
micro fiber backing with emboss, die cut

Heel counter reinforcement:
2mm Surlyn plastic with fusible coating

Soccer cleat

The soccer cleat is designed for a sleek, snug fit with minimal tongue padding. The heel counter, designed for stability, is made of sturdy injection molded plastic. The collar is well padded, while the midsole padding is non-existent. The tongue is laced on the side making for a smooth kicking surface.

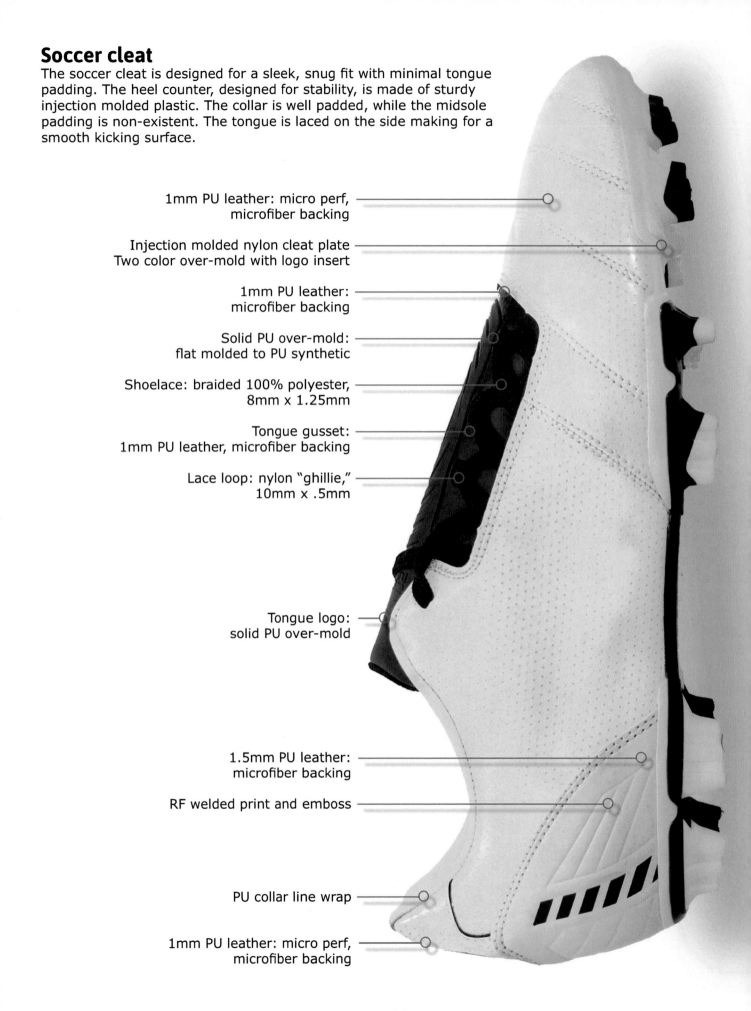

1mm PU leather: micro perf, microfiber backing

Injection molded nylon cleat plate
Two color over-mold with logo insert

1mm PU leather:
microfiber backing

Solid PU over-mold:
flat molded to PU synthetic

Shoelace: braided 100% polyester,
8mm x 1.25mm

Tongue gusset:
1mm PU leather, microfiber backing

Lace loop: nylon "ghillie,"
10mm x .5mm

Tongue logo:
solid PU over-mold

1.5mm PU leather:
microfiber backing

RF welded print and emboss

PU collar line wrap

1mm PU leather: micro perf,
microfiber backing

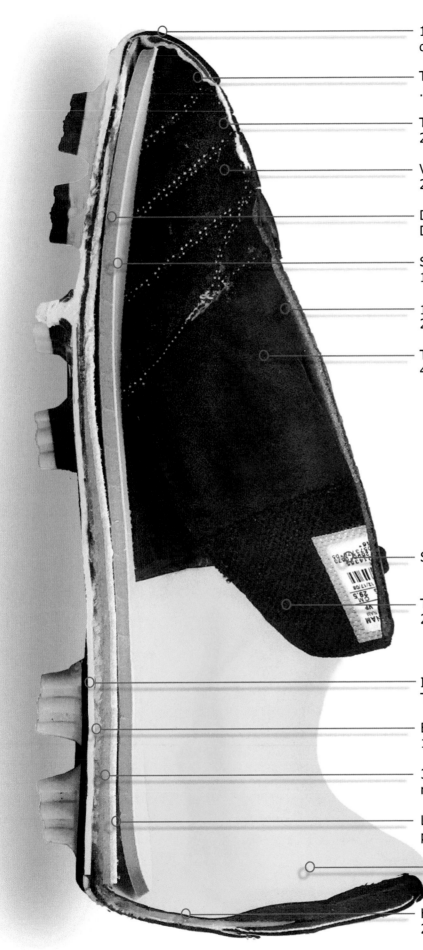

1mm PU leather: micro perf,
custom black dyed microfiber backing

Toe reinforcement:
.5mm fusible Surlyn plastic

Toe box backing fabric:
200gsm stitched bonded polyester

Vamp lining: 110D nylon,
2mm KFF PU foam, tricot backing

Die cut EVA footbed: 8mm,
Durometer Asker "C" 40°

Sockliner cover:
100% polyester jersey knit

1mm PU leather: microfiber backing,
2mm KFF pu foam, tricot backing

Tongue lining: 110D nylon,
4mm KFF PU foam, tricot backing

Size mark heat transfer logo

Tongue lining: 100% polyester,
200gsm "star" mesh, 2mm PU foam

Injection molded nylon cleat plate:
Two color over-mold with logo insert

Board lasting infill:
1.5mm paper lasting board

3mm lasting board:
resin impregnated fiber board

Lasting board:1mm stitched bonded
polyester, resin impregnated

Collar lining: 1.0mm PU leather,
8mm high density KFF collar foam

Heel counter:
2.25mm injection molded Surlyn plastic

154

The classic vulcanized basketball shoe

With a design dating back to the 1920's, this canvas high top dominated sports footwear until the 1970's. Its simple design and robust construction were once state of the art. Now largely replaced by the modern cold cement sneaker in performance markets, this footwear icon is a fashion and counter-culture favorite.

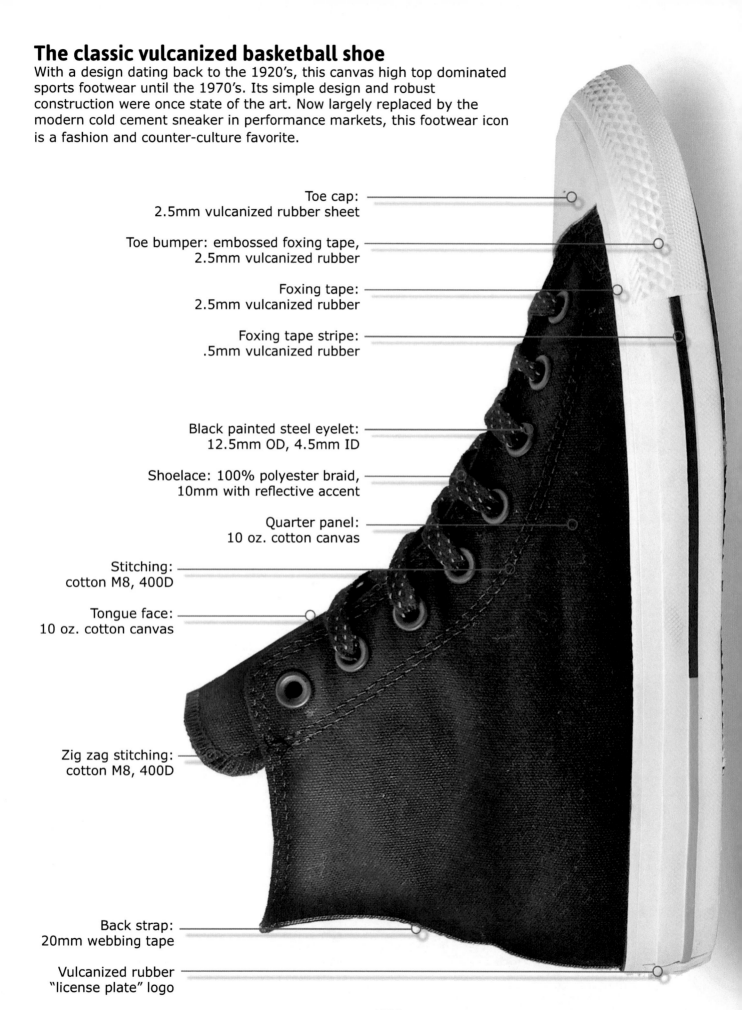

Toe cap:
2.5mm vulcanized rubber sheet

Toe bumper: embossed foxing tape,
2.5mm vulcanized rubber

Foxing tape:
2.5mm vulcanized rubber

Foxing tape stripe:
.5mm vulcanized rubber

Black painted steel eyelet:
12.5mm OD, 4.5mm ID

Shoelace: 100% polyester braid,
10mm with reflective accent

Quarter panel:
10 oz. cotton canvas

Stitching:
cotton M8, 400D

Tongue face:
10 oz. cotton canvas

Zig zag stitching:
cotton M8, 400D

Back strap:
20mm webbing tape

Vulcanized rubber
"license plate" logo

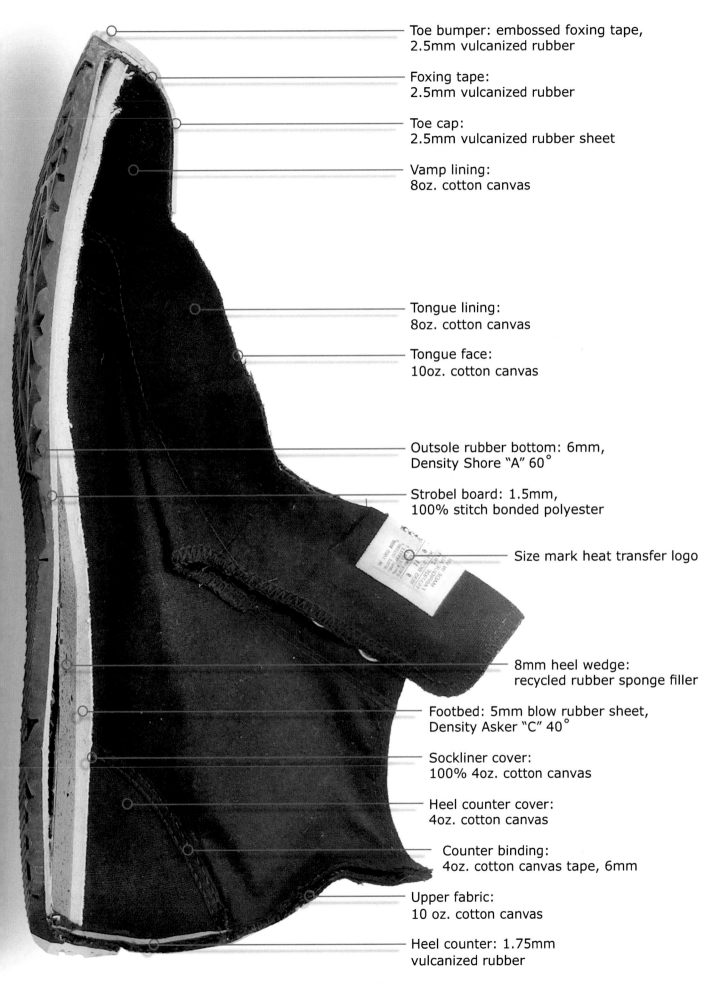

Toe bumper: embossed foxing tape, 2.5mm vulcanized rubber

Foxing tape: 2.5mm vulcanized rubber

Toe cap: 2.5mm vulcanized rubber sheet

Vamp lining: 8oz. cotton canvas

Tongue lining: 8oz. cotton canvas

Tongue face: 10oz. cotton canvas

Outsole rubber bottom: 6mm, Density Shore "A" 60°

Strobel board: 1.5mm, 100% stitch bonded polyester

Size mark heat transfer logo

8mm heel wedge: recycled rubber sponge filler

Footbed: 5mm blow rubber sheet, Density Asker "C" 40°

Sockliner cover: 100% 4oz. cotton canvas

Heel counter cover: 4oz. cotton canvas

Counter binding: 4oz. cotton canvas tape, 6mm

Upper fabric: 10 oz. cotton canvas

Heel counter: 1.75mm vulcanized rubber

Cycling shoes

The cycling shoe is designed to hold the foot securely and efficiently in order to transmit the rider's energy to the pedal. The injection molded outsole anchors the pedal cleating system and distributes the pedaling force across the foot without flexing.

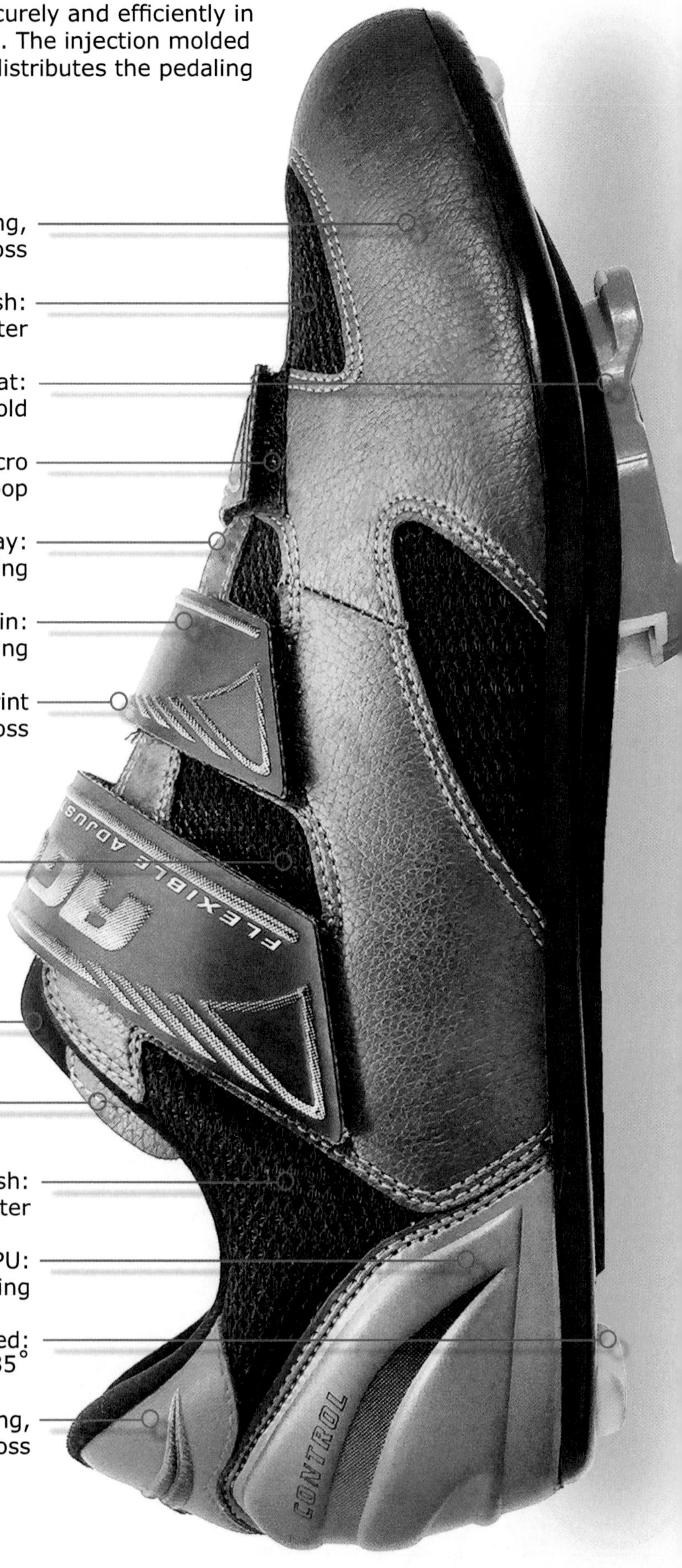

1.25mm PU: polyester backing, fine grain leather emboss

Knit mesh: 260gsm, 100% polyester

Nylon speed cleat: two color plastic over-mold

30mm Velcro hook & loop

Eyestay: 1.25mm PU with polyester backing

.5mm PVC skin: woven 220D polyester backing

Screen print and emboss

Knit mesh: 260gsm, 100% polyester

Tongue padding: 120gsm, 100% polyester jersey

1.25mm PU: polyester backing, fine grain leather emboss

Knit mesh: 260gsm, 100% polyester

.5mm metallic PU: embossed 3mm PVC, sponge foam backing

Nylon insert over-molded: Durometer Shore "A" 85°

1.0mm PU: polyester backing, screen print, emboss

1.25mm PU: polyester backing, fine grain leather emboss

Nylon insert overmolded: Durometer Shore "A" 85°

Toe reinforcement: .5mm fusible Surlyn plastic

Knit mesh: 260gsm, 100% polyester

Nylon speed cleat: two color plastic over-mold

Glass and carbon fiber reinforced nylon plastic injection: Shore "A" 95°

Tongue attachment eyestay reinforcement: Super-Tuff .5mm

Stamped steel cleat attachment insert: Black rust proof plating

Tongue lining: 120gsm, 100% polyester jersey

Tongue face: 1.25mm PU with polyester backing

Tongue insert foam: 5mm high density SBR foam

Tongue foam: 5mm KFF PU foam

Phenolic resin lasting board: 2.0mm, 3/4 length

PE plastic lasting board: 2.0mm, full length

Collar lining: 100% polyester, 160gsm, jersey mesh, 2mm PU foam, tricot backing

Sockliner cover: 100% polyester jersey knit

Hot pressed PE foam midsole: Durometer Asker "C" 55°

Collar foam: 6mm die cut KFF PU foam

Heel counter: 1.0mm fusible Surlyn plastic

Baseball cleat

The modern baseball cleat is designed for superior traction and fast cuts on both grass and gravel. This shoe is built for straight line speed but needs support for cornering the bases.

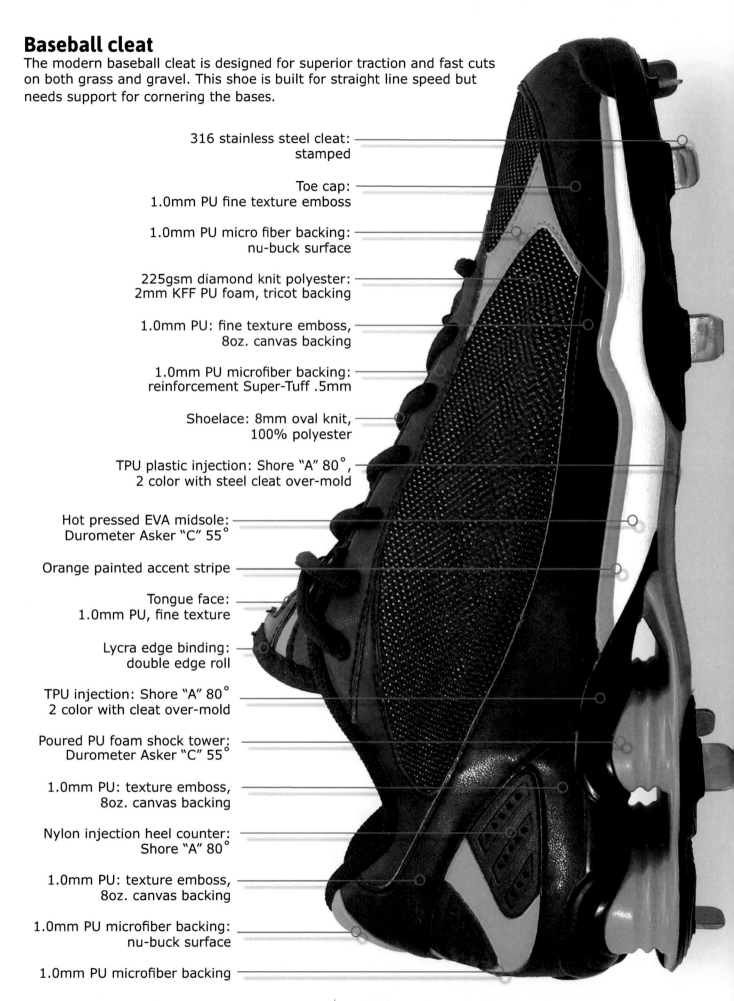

316 stainless steel cleat: stamped

Toe cap: 1.0mm PU fine texture emboss

1.0mm PU micro fiber backing: nu-buck surface

225gsm diamond knit polyester: 2mm KFF PU foam, tricot backing

1.0mm PU: fine texture emboss, 8oz. canvas backing

1.0mm PU microfiber backing: reinforcement Super-Tuff .5mm

Shoelace: 8mm oval knit, 100% polyester

TPU plastic injection: Shore "A" 80°, 2 color with steel cleat over-mold

Hot pressed EVA midsole: Durometer Asker "C" 55°

Orange painted accent stripe

Tongue face: 1.0mm PU, fine texture

Lycra edge binding: double edge roll

TPU injection: Shore "A" 80° 2 color with cleat over-mold

Poured PU foam shock tower: Durometer Asker "C" 55°

1.0mm PU: texture emboss, 8oz. canvas backing

Nylon injection heel counter: Shore "A" 80°

1.0mm PU: texture emboss, 8oz. canvas backing

1.0mm PU microfiber backing: nu-buck surface

1.0mm PU microfiber backing

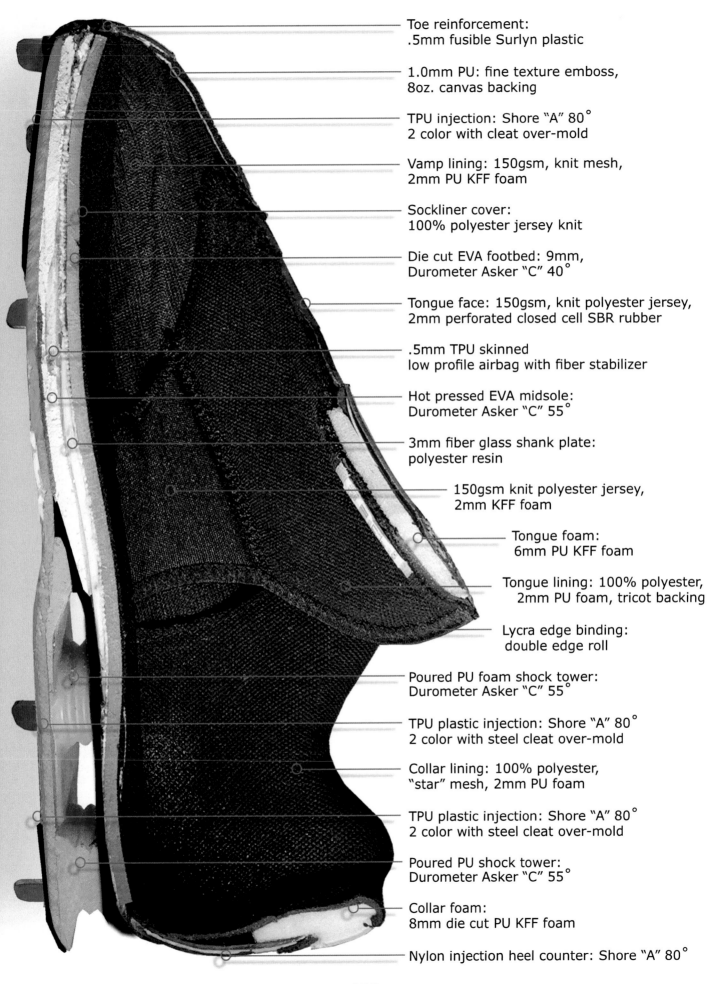

Toe reinforcement:
.5mm fusible Surlyn plastic

1.0mm PU: fine texture emboss,
8oz. canvas backing

TPU injection: Shore "A" 80°
2 color with cleat over-mold

Vamp lining: 150gsm, knit mesh,
2mm PU KFF foam

Sockliner cover:
100% polyester jersey knit

Die cut EVA footbed: 9mm,
Durometer Asker "C" 40°

Tongue face: 150gsm, knit polyester jersey,
2mm perforated closed cell SBR rubber

.5mm TPU skinned
low profile airbag with fiber stabilizer

Hot pressed EVA midsole:
Durometer Asker "C" 55°

3mm fiber glass shank plate:
polyester resin

150gsm knit polyester jersey,
2mm KFF foam

Tongue foam:
6mm PU KFF foam

Tongue lining: 100% polyester,
2mm PU foam, tricot backing

Lycra edge binding:
double edge roll

Poured PU foam shock tower:
Durometer Asker "C" 55°

TPU plastic injection: Shore "A" 80°
2 color with steel cleat over-mold

Collar lining: 100% polyester,
"star" mesh, 2mm PU foam

TPU plastic injection: Shore "A" 80°
2 color with steel cleat over-mold

Poured PU shock tower:
Durometer Asker "C" 55°

Collar foam:
8mm die cut PU KFF foam

Nylon injection heel counter: Shore "A" 80°

Wrestling shoes

The modern wrestling shoe is designed for lightweight, mobility, and traction. The upper is thin and flexible with maximum ventilation. The outsole keeps the wrestler low to the ground, cushioning is not required. This shoe is board lasted with a thin, flexible fiberboard.

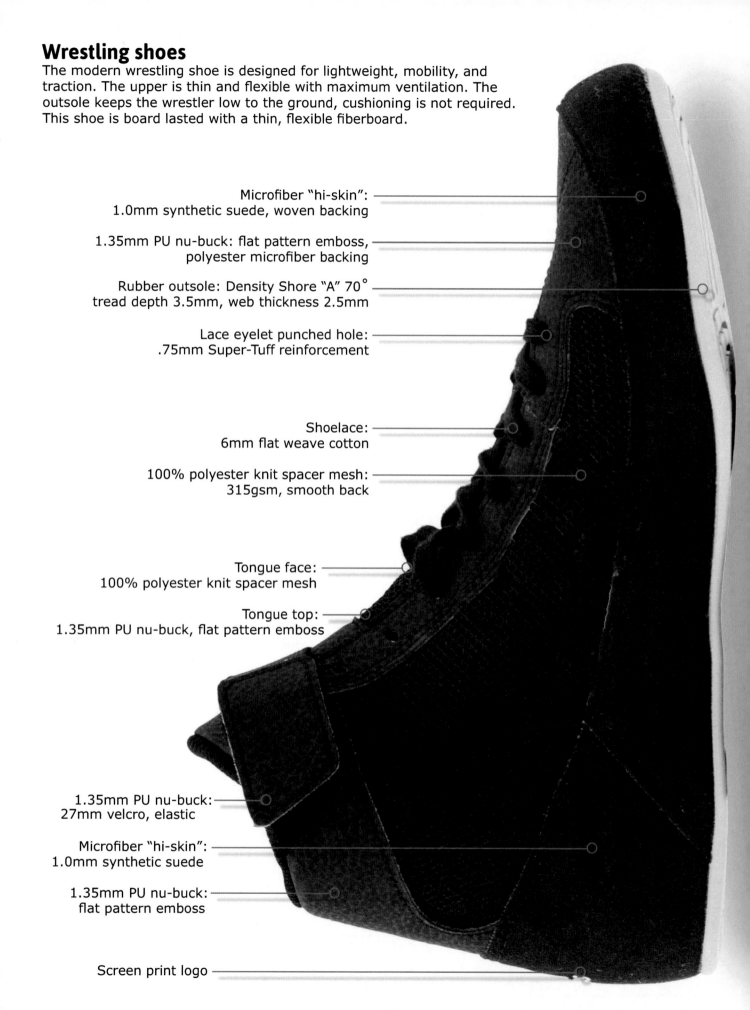

Microfiber "hi-skin":
1.0mm synthetic suede, woven backing

1.35mm PU nu-buck: flat pattern emboss,
polyester microfiber backing

Rubber outsole: Density Shore "A" 70°
tread depth 3.5mm, web thickness 2.5mm

Lace eyelet punched hole:
.75mm Super-Tuff reinforcement

Shoelace:
6mm flat weave cotton

100% polyester knit spacer mesh:
315gsm, smooth back

Tongue face:
100% polyester knit spacer mesh

Tongue top:
1.35mm PU nu-buck, flat pattern emboss

1.35mm PU nu-buck:
27mm velcro, elastic

Microfiber "hi-skin":
1.0mm synthetic suede

1.35mm PU nu-buck:
flat pattern emboss

Screen print logo

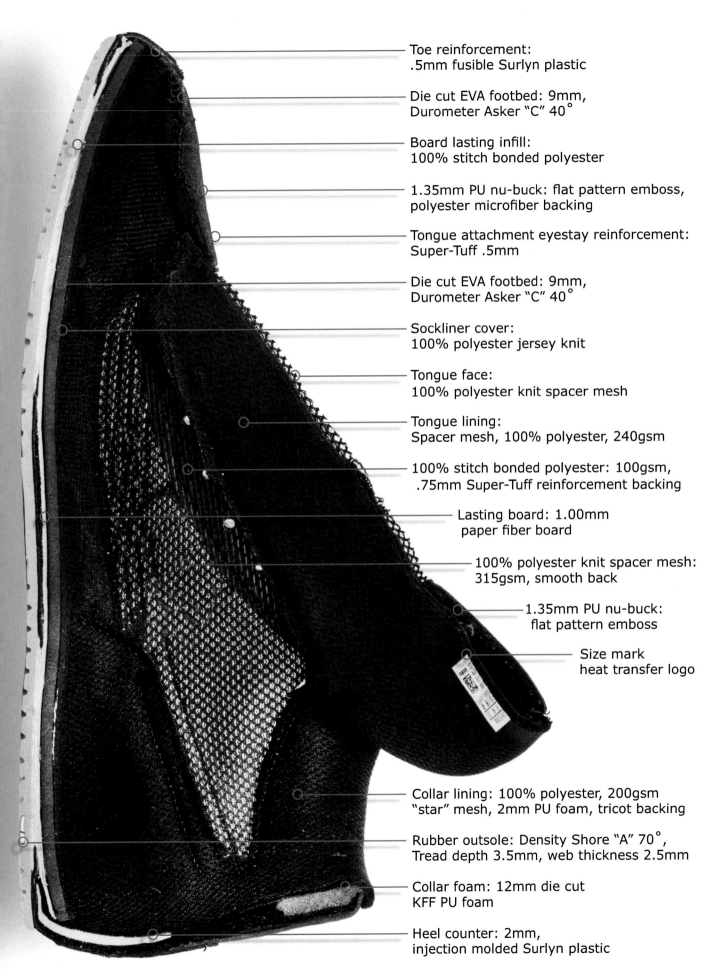

Toe reinforcement:
.5mm fusible Surlyn plastic

Die cut EVA footbed: 9mm,
Durometer Asker "C" 40°

Board lasting infill:
100% stitch bonded polyester

1.35mm PU nu-buck: flat pattern emboss,
polyester microfiber backing

Tongue attachment eyestay reinforcement:
Super-Tuff .5mm

Die cut EVA footbed: 9mm,
Durometer Asker "C" 40°

Sockliner cover:
100% polyester jersey knit

Tongue face:
100% polyester knit spacer mesh

Tongue lining:
Spacer mesh, 100% polyester, 240gsm

100% stitch bonded polyester: 100gsm,
.75mm Super-Tuff reinforcement backing

Lasting board: 1.00mm
paper fiber board

100% polyester knit spacer mesh:
315gsm, smooth back

1.35mm PU nu-buck:
flat pattern emboss

Size mark
heat transfer logo

Collar lining: 100% polyester, 200gsm
"star" mesh, 2mm PU foam, tricot backing

Rubber outsole: Density Shore "A" 70°,
Tread depth 3.5mm, web thickness 2.5mm

Collar foam: 12mm die cut
KFF PU foam

Heel counter: 2mm,
injection molded Surlyn plastic

Skateboarding shoe

The classic skate shoe from the early 2000's has a low profile cupsole, outrageously fat tongue, and smooth action leather upper. This example features an elastic band to hold the tongue in place, and a PVC gel insert to reduce heel bruising.

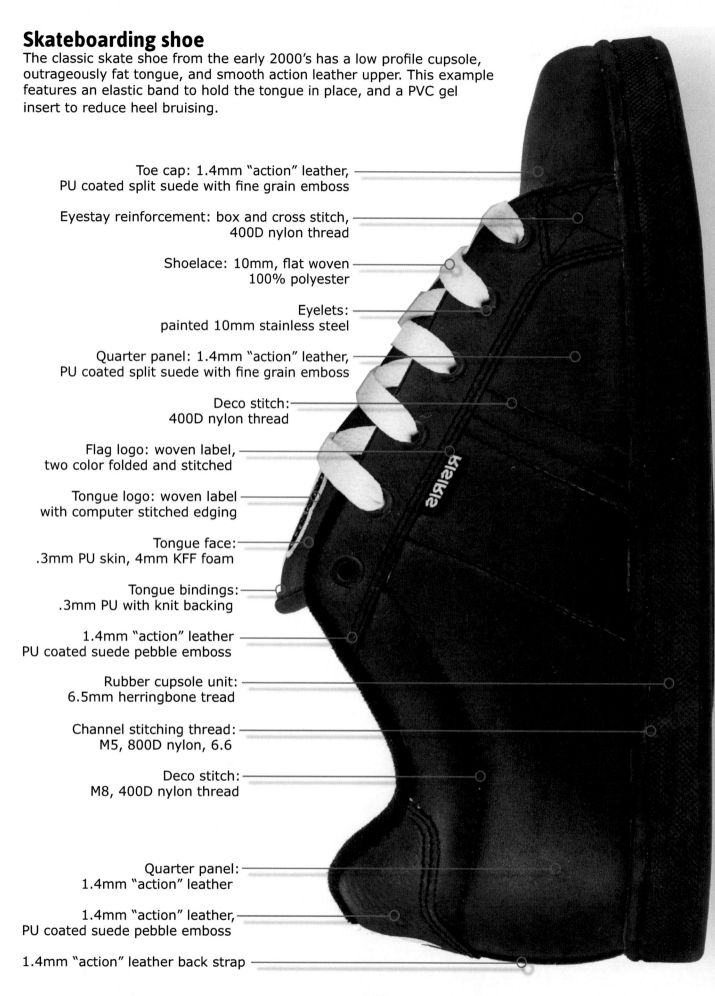

Toe cap: 1.4mm "action" leather, PU coated split suede with fine grain emboss

Eyestay reinforcement: box and cross stitch, 400D nylon thread

Shoelace: 10mm, flat woven 100% polyester

Eyelets: painted 10mm stainless steel

Quarter panel: 1.4mm "action" leather, PU coated split suede with fine grain emboss

Deco stitch: 400D nylon thread

Flag logo: woven label, two color folded and stitched

Tongue logo: woven label with computer stitched edging

Tongue face: .3mm PU skin, 4mm KFF foam

Tongue bindings: .3mm PU with knit backing

1.4mm "action" leather PU coated suede pebble emboss

Rubber cupsole unit: 6.5mm herringbone tread

Channel stitching thread: M5, 800D nylon, 6.6

Deco stitch: M8, 400D nylon thread

Quarter panel: 1.4mm "action" leather

1.4mm "action" leather, PU coated suede pebble emboss

1.4mm "action" leather back strap

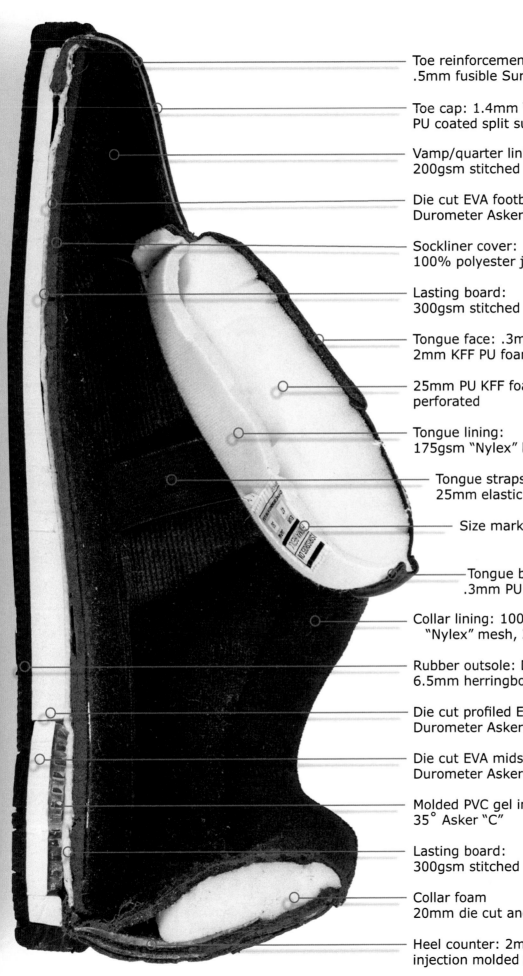

Toe reinforcement:
.5mm fusible Surlyn plastic

Toe cap: 1.4mm "action" leather
PU coated split suede with fine grain emboss

Vamp/quarter lining:
200gsm stitched bonded polyester

Die cut EVA footbed: 9mm,
Durometer Asker "C" 40°

Sockliner cover:
100% polyester jersey knit

Lasting board:
300gsm stitched bonded polyester

Tongue face: .3mm PU skin,
2mm KFF PU foam

25mm PU KFF foam
perforated

Tongue lining:
175gsm "Nylex" knit 100% polyester

Tongue straps:
25mm elastic band

Size mark sewn on tag

Tongue bindings:
.3mm PU with knit backing

Collar lining: 100% polyester, 175gsm
"Nylex" mesh, 2mm PU foam, tricot backing

Rubber outsole: Density Shore "A" 65°
6.5mm herringbone tread

Die cut profiled EVA midsole:
Durometer Asker "C" 53°

Die cut EVA midsole:
Durometer Asker "C" 53°

Molded PVC gel insert:
35° Asker "C"

Lasting board:
300gsm stitched bonded polyester

Collar foam
20mm die cut and shaved KFF PU foam

Heel counter: 2mm,
injection molded Surlyn

164

Topside boat shoe

The boat shoe features a flat outsole with cut rubber sipes for gripping wet decking. The rawhide laces, moccasin toe, and slip on pattern are all about style. A truly casual shoe, this topsider has no reinforcements and little cushioning. This example is strobel stitched then stitched down to the outsole.

Shoelace: 3mm x 3mm, full grain

Moccasin stitching: M5, 600D nylon 6.6 tread

2.25mm full grain natural leather: pebble embossed

Rubber outsole: Density Shore "A" 60° tread depth 5.0mm

1.0mm full grain natural leather: 8oz. canvas reinforcement

10mm brass eyelets: custom logo embossed

Shoelace: 3mm x 3mm, full grain

1.0mm full grain natural leather: 8oz. canvas reinforcement

2.25mm full grain natural leather: pebble embossed

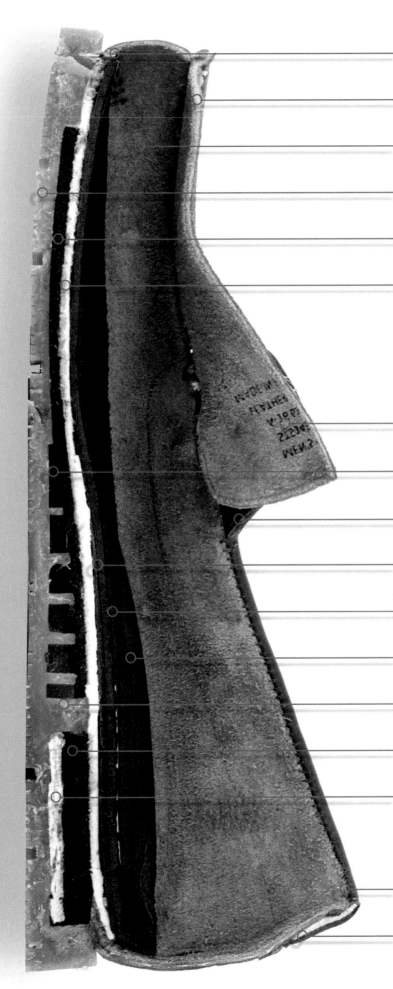

Outsole stitch down:
M5, 600D nylon 6.6 thread

2.25mm full grain natural leather:
pebble embossed, suede back side lining

Suede back side lining

Rubber outsole: Density Shore "A" 60°,
Tread depth 5.0mm

Die cut EVA midsole: 4mm,
Durometer Asker "C" 40°

Strobel sock:
250gsm stitch bonded polyester

Screen printed size mark

Molded egg-crate midsole

1.0mm full grain natural leather:
8oz. canvas reinforcement

Die cut EVA footbed: 9mm,
Durometer Asker "C" 40°

Sockliner cover:
100% polyester jersey knit

Molded EVA footbed: heel cup 9mm,
Durometer Asker "C" 50°

Rubber outsole: Tread depth 4.5mm,
Density Shore "A" 65°

Die cut EVA midsole: 7.5mm,
Durometer Asker "C" 53°

Heel filler:
2.0mm paper lasting board

Collar seam: turned out,
top line reinforcement 350gsm polyester

Heel seam reinforcement:
6oz. canvas

River sandal

The modern river sandal has a grippy rubber outsole with built in toe protection and a compression molded EVA midsole. The upper is constructed using variable width webbing and padded with neoprene rubber foam. The neoprene rubber foam is laminated to elastic polyester knit fabric. With the upper firmly secured under the midsole, this shoe can stand up to the roughest rivers.

Rubber outsole: Density Shore "A" 65°
Tread depth 5.5mm, web thickness 3.0mm

.75mm PU nu-buck leather:
polyester fiber backing

1.25 mm nylon webbing:
variable width 13mm to 17mm

Injection molded lace end

2 color TPR micro injection fine mold:
1.5mm thick sewn into edge

Locking lace toggle:
spring loaded, injection molded nylon

3mm round elastic cord:
polyester jacket with rubber core

Polyester knit jersey fabric,
2mm neoprene backing

Lycra edge binding with zig zag stitching

Nylon webbing loop 12mm x 1mm:
2 color with reflective accent

Rubber outsole: Tread depth 5.5mm
web thickness 3.0mm, Density Shore "A" 65°

Painted accent

Hot pressed EVA midsole
Durometer Asker "C" 48°

.75mm PU nu-buck leather:
polyester fiber backing

Lycra edge binding with zig zag stitching

Nylon webbing loop: 12mm x 1mm,
2 color with reflective accent

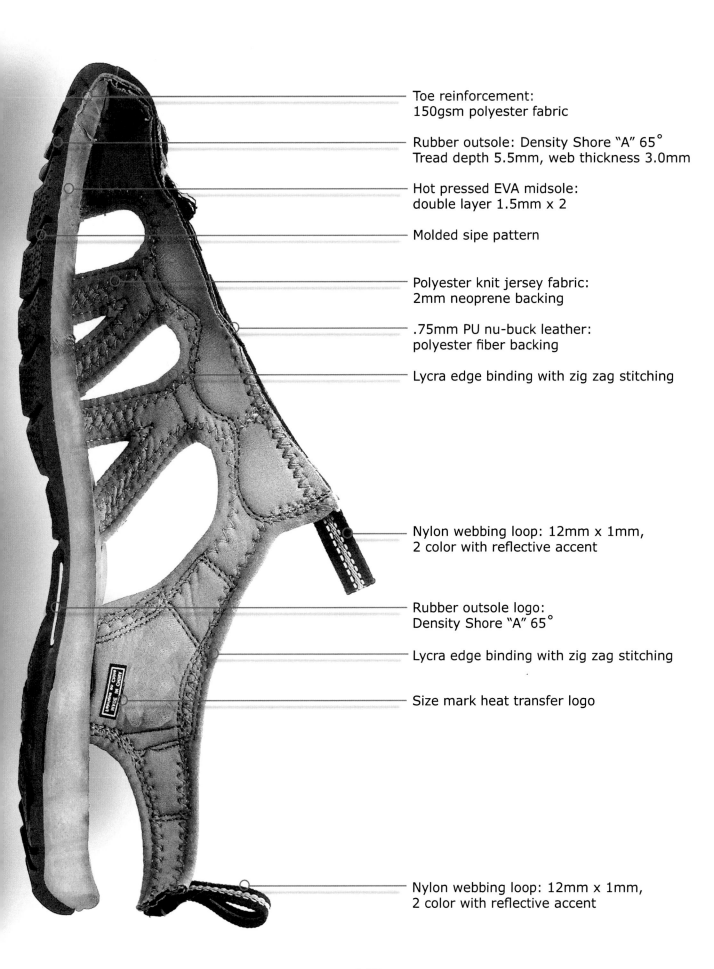

Toe reinforcement:
150gsm polyester fabric

Rubber outsole: Density Shore "A" 65°
Tread depth 5.5mm, web thickness 3.0mm

Hot pressed EVA midsole:
double layer 1.5mm x 2

Molded sipe pattern

Polyester knit jersey fabric:
2mm neoprene backing

.75mm PU nu-buck leather:
polyester fiber backing

Lycra edge binding with zig zag stitching

Nylon webbing loop: 12mm x 1mm,
2 color with reflective accent

Rubber outsole logo:
Density Shore "A" 65°

Lycra edge binding with zig zag stitching

Size mark heat transfer logo

Nylon webbing loop: 12mm x 1mm,
2 color with reflective accent

The 80's basketball shoe

This style was produced for the basketball legend Michael Jordan. The prototype was banned by the NBA commissioner because it did not have enough white on the upper. The ban was used as a marketing tool and Michael Jordan never looked back.

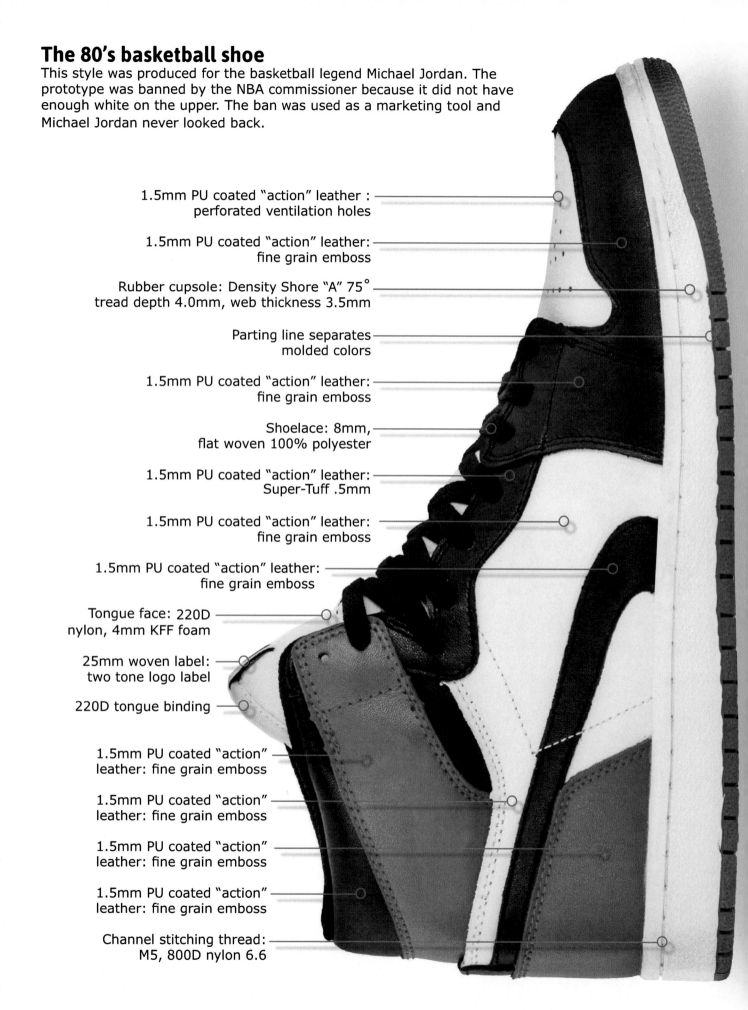

1.5mm PU coated "action" leather : perforated ventilation holes

1.5mm PU coated "action" leather: fine grain emboss

Rubber cupsole: Density Shore "A" 75° tread depth 4.0mm, web thickness 3.5mm

Parting line separates molded colors

1.5mm PU coated "action" leather: fine grain emboss

Shoelace: 8mm, flat woven 100% polyester

1.5mm PU coated "action" leather: Super-Tuff .5mm

1.5mm PU coated "action" leather: fine grain emboss

1.5mm PU coated "action" leather: fine grain emboss

Tongue face: 220D nylon, 4mm KFF foam

25mm woven label: two tone logo label

220D tongue binding

1.5mm PU coated "action" leather: fine grain emboss

1.5mm PU coated "action" leather: fine grain emboss

1.5mm PU coated "action" leather: fine grain emboss

1.5mm PU coated "action" leather: fine grain emboss

Channel stitching thread: M5, 800D nylon 6.6

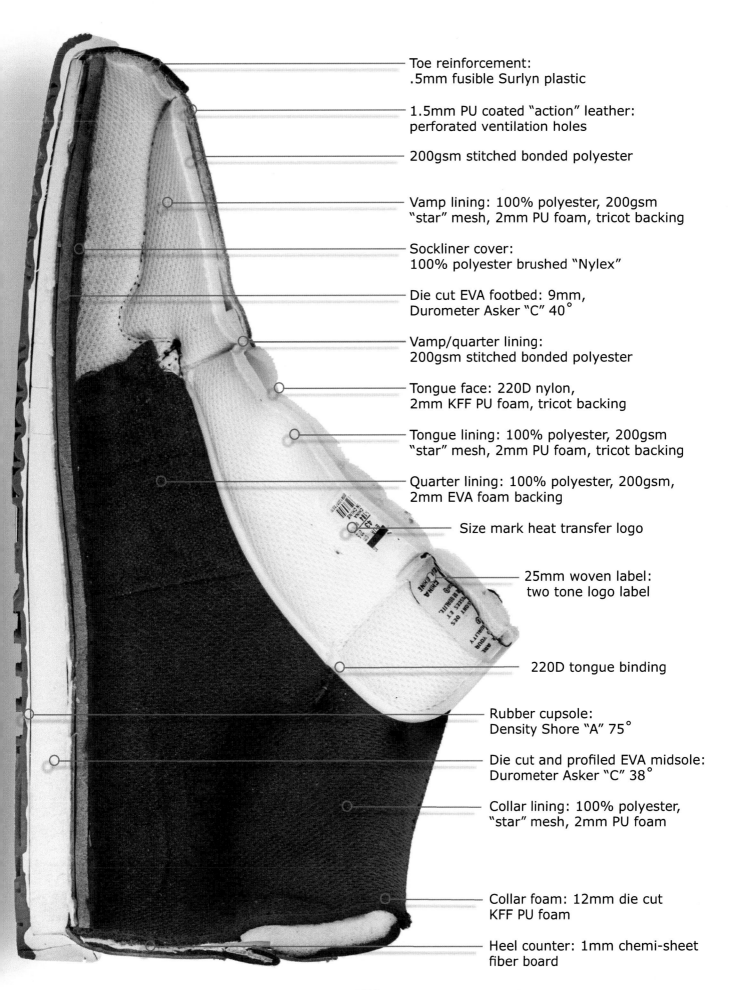

Toe reinforcement:
.5mm fusible Surlyn plastic

1.5mm PU coated "action" leather:
perforated ventilation holes

200gsm stitched bonded polyester

Vamp lining: 100% polyester, 200gsm
"star" mesh, 2mm PU foam, tricot backing

Sockliner cover:
100% polyester brushed "Nylex"

Die cut EVA footbed: 9mm,
Durometer Asker "C" 40°

Vamp/quarter lining:
200gsm stitched bonded polyester

Tongue face: 220D nylon,
2mm KFF PU foam, tricot backing

Tongue lining: 100% polyester, 200gsm
"star" mesh, 2mm PU foam, tricot backing

Quarter lining: 100% polyester, 200gsm,
2mm EVA foam backing

Size mark heat transfer logo

25mm woven label:
two tone logo label

220D tongue binding

Rubber cupsole:
Density Shore "A" 75°

Die cut and profiled EVA midsole:
Durometer Asker "C" 38°

Collar lining: 100% polyester,
"star" mesh, 2mm PU foam

Collar foam: 12mm die cut
KFF PU foam

Heel counter: 1mm chemi-sheet
fiber board

Inexpensive dress shoe

This men's dress shoe has a hidden secret. It is very cheap. Produced with 100% man-made materials, the upper is PU and the outsole is injection molded TPR with a faux stacked leather paint job. The lining inside is similar to sports shoe. An expensive leather dress shoe will have a full leather lining.

1.1mm PU with leather emboss: perforated with woven polyester backing

Injection TPR outsole with faux leather painted sidewall

Extruded PVC with faux stitched down welt

Faux channel stitching thread: M5, 800D nylon 6.6

1.1mm PU with leather emboss: perforated with woven polyester backing

Full-brogue wing tip decoration

Shoelace: 2mm waxed cotton

Injection TPR outsole: faux stacked leather heel

1.1mm PU with leather emboss: perforated with woven polyester backing

1.1mm PU with leather emboss: perforated with woven polyester backing

Extruded PVC:
Faux stitched down welt

Vamp reinforcement:
.5mm chemi-sheet

1.1mm PU with leather emboss:
perforated with woven polyester backing

Vamp lining:
150gsm jersey lining, 2mm PU foam

2.0mm paper fiber
lasting board

Die cut EVA footbed: 9mm,
Durometer Asker "C" 40°

Sockliner cover:
100% polyester jersey knit

Injection TPR outsole:
egg-crate cushioning

Tongue lining: 100% polyester,
150gsm jersey lining, 2mm PU foam

Tongue lining:
.5mm PU with leather emboss

Size mark heat transfer logo

Tongue face:
1.1mm PU with leather emboss

Lasting board: 3/4 length
2.0mm hard board

Collar lining:
.5mm PU with leather emboss

Egg crate heel lift

Footbed:
heat transfer logo

Outsole mold injection port
hidden inside

Heel lining:
faux pigskin PU with stitched bonded backing

Heel counter:
1.3mm chemi-sheet

Driving moccasin

This sleek shoe is designed for close fitting comfort. The moccasin construction wraps the foot with unbacked nu-buck leather. The outsole bottom is attached through the leather for a flexible low profile feeling. The large heel radius allows the shoe to roll while the rubber texture grips the floor mat.

Flat molded rubber outsole:
Durometer Shore "A" 65°

2.0mm nu-buck brushed leather:
tumbled, suede back finish

Hand-sewn moccasin toe:
M5, 800D nylon 6.6 waxed thread

Outsole attachment stitching:
M20, 135D nylon 6.6 thread

2.0mm nu-buck brushed leather:
tumbled, suede back finish

Tongue edge stitching:
M20, 135D nylon 6.6 thread

Leather lace:
2.0mm nu-buck brushed leather

2.0mm nu-buck brushed leather:
tumbled, suede back finish

Stitch and turn seam

Double stitching:
M20, 135D nylon 6.6 thread

Hand sewn:
M5, 800D nylon 6.6 waxed thread

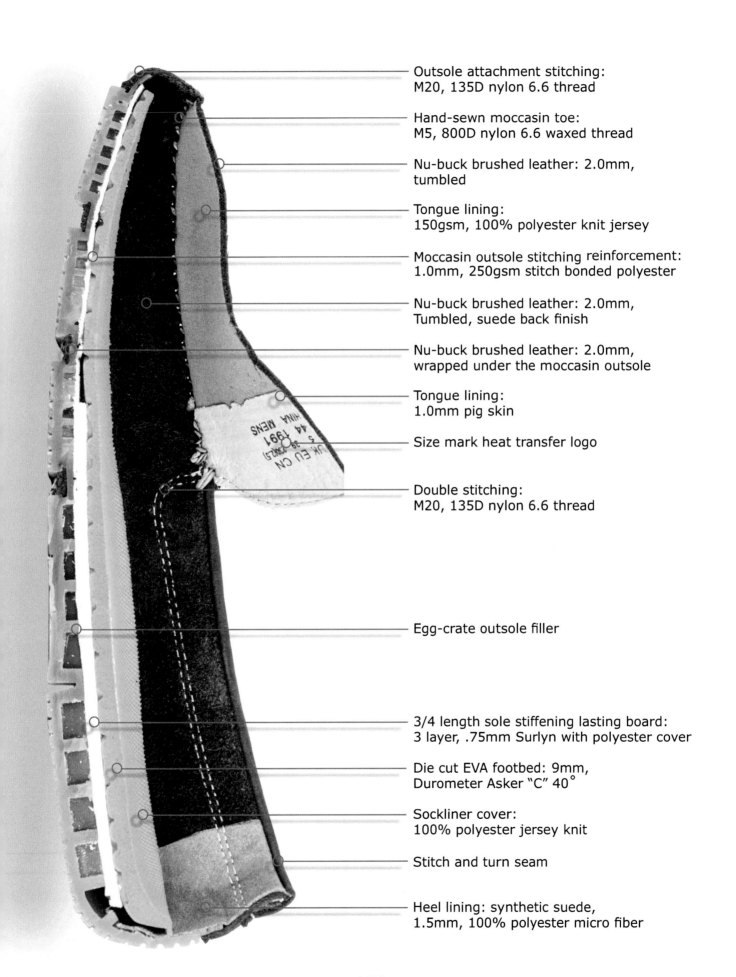

Outsole attachment stitching:
M20, 135D nylon 6.6 thread

Hand-sewn moccasin toe:
M5, 800D nylon 6.6 waxed thread

Nu-buck brushed leather: 2.0mm,
tumbled

Tongue lining:
150gsm, 100% polyester knit jersey

Moccasin outsole stitching reinforcement:
1.0mm, 250gsm stitch bonded polyester

Nu-buck brushed leather: 2.0mm,
Tumbled, suede back finish

Nu-buck brushed leather: 2.0mm,
wrapped under the moccasin outsole

Tongue lining:
1.0mm pig skin

Size mark heat transfer logo

Double stitching:
M20, 135D nylon 6.6 thread

Egg-crate outsole filler

3/4 length sole stiffening lasting board:
3 layer, .75mm Surlyn with polyester cover

Die cut EVA footbed: 9mm,
Durometer Asker "C" 40°

Sockliner cover:
100% polyester jersey knit

Stitch and turn seam

Heel lining: synthetic suede,
1.5mm, 100% polyester micro fiber

Lightweight hiker

This shoe is a light hiker designed for off-road use. It has a rugged suede upper with breathable mesh panels. The outsole has a rubber toe bumper and a full length EVA midsole. The midsole has a stiffening shank located just under the lasting board.

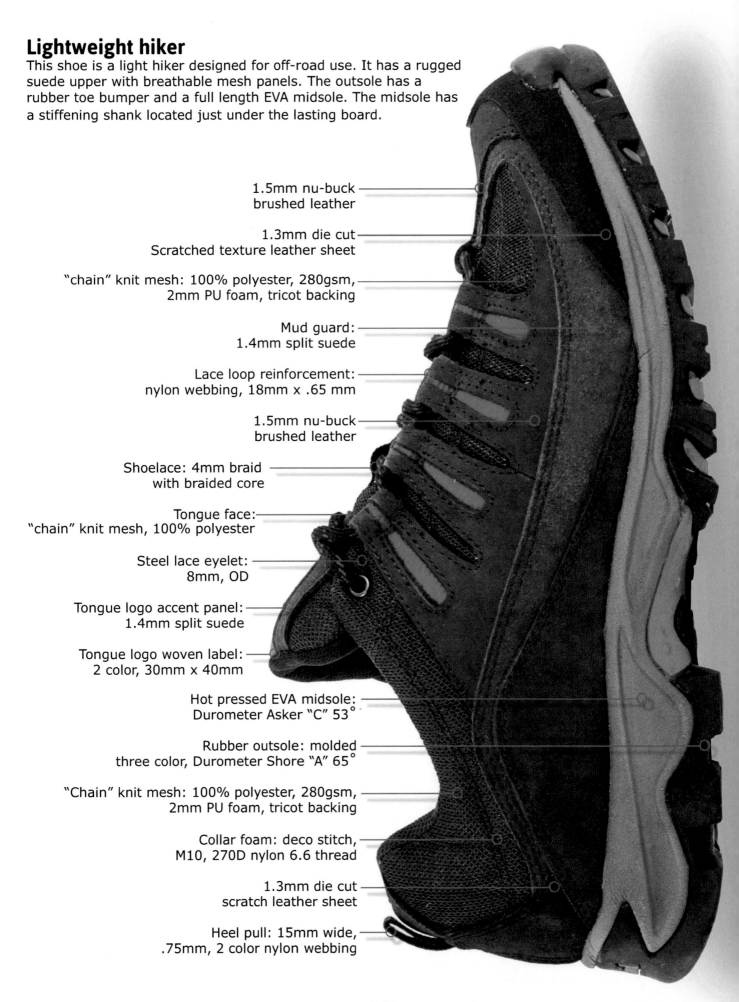

1.5mm nu-buck brushed leather

1.3mm die cut Scratched texture leather sheet

"chain" knit mesh: 100% polyester, 280gsm, 2mm PU foam, tricot backing

Mud guard: 1.4mm split suede

Lace loop reinforcement: nylon webbing, 18mm x .65 mm

1.5mm nu-buck brushed leather

Shoelace: 4mm braid with braided core

Tongue face: "chain" knit mesh, 100% polyester

Steel lace eyelet: 8mm, OD

Tongue logo accent panel: 1.4mm split suede

Tongue logo woven label: 2 color, 30mm x 40mm

Hot pressed EVA midsole: Durometer Asker "C" 53°

Rubber outsole: molded three color, Durometer Shore "A" 65°

"Chain" knit mesh: 100% polyester, 280gsm, 2mm PU foam, tricot backing

Collar foam: deco stitch, M10, 270D nylon 6.6 thread

1.3mm die cut scratch leather sheet

Heel pull: 15mm wide, .75mm, 2 color nylon webbing

1.3mm die cut
scratch leather sheet

Toe reinforcement:
1mm chemi sheet

1.5mm nu-buck
brushed leather

Vamp lining: 200 gsm "square" mesh,
2mm PU foam, tricot backing

Tongue bottom lace loop:
1.5mm nu-buck brushed leather

Vamp lining: 200 gsm "square" mesh,
2mm PU foam, tricot backing

Tongue foam:
10mm KFF PU foam

Tongue face: "chain" knit mesh,
100% polyester, 280gsm, 2mm PU foam

Hot pressed EVA midsole:
Durometer Asker "C" 53°

Plastic shank: 3mm thick,
co-molded with EVA midsole

Rubber outsole: molded,
three color, Durometer Shore "A" 65°

Size mark heat transfer logo

Tongue logo: woven label,
2 color, 30mm x 40mm

Collar lining: 100% polyester, 200gsm,
"star" mesh, 2mm PU foam, tricot

Sockliner cover:
100% polyester jersey knit

Cold pressed EVA footbed: 9mm,
Durometer Asker "C" 40°

Sockliner logo:
screen printing

Heel lining synthetic suede:
1.5mm, 100% polyester microfiber

Collar foam: 12mm die cut
KFF PU foam

Heel counter: 1mm chemi-sheet
fiber board

Waterproof off-trail hiking boot

This hiking boot is designed for rough terrain and wet weather. The mid-cut boot has a waterproof lining inside, tough rubber toe rand, and Italian designed high-end rubber outsole. With its full-length plastic lasting board acting as a shank, and its high-density EVA midsole, this boot is suitable for trekking with a light pack in the wild.

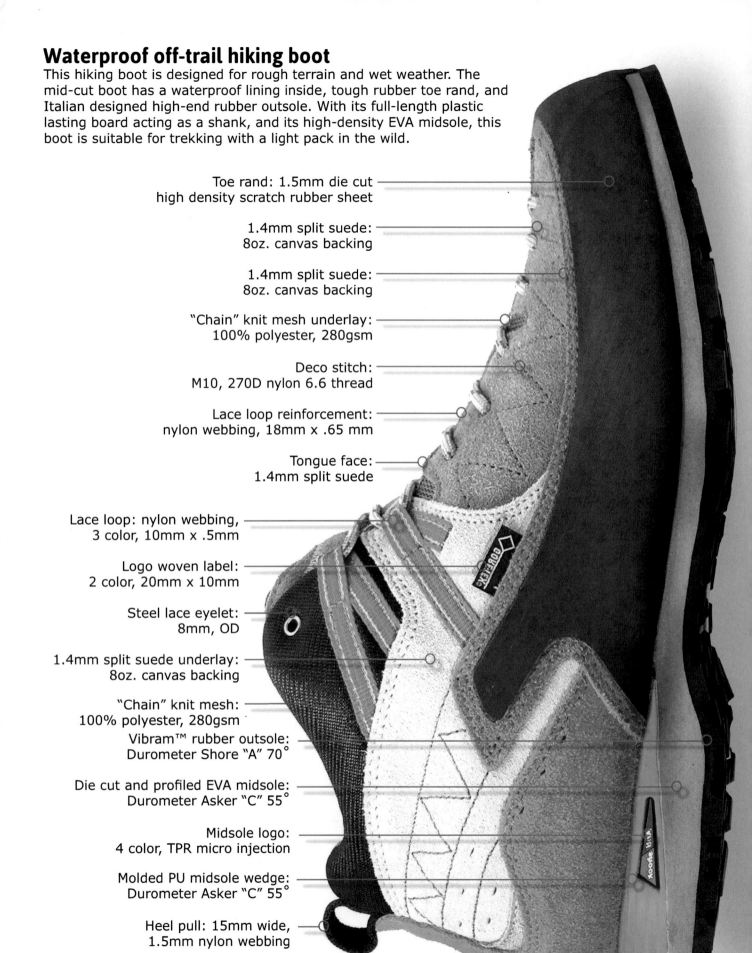

Toe rand: 1.5mm die cut high density scratch rubber sheet

1.4mm split suede: 8oz. canvas backing

1.4mm split suede: 8oz. canvas backing

"Chain" knit mesh underlay: 100% polyester, 280gsm

Deco stitch: M10, 270D nylon 6.6 thread

Lace loop reinforcement: nylon webbing, 18mm x .65 mm

Tongue face: 1.4mm split suede

Lace loop: nylon webbing, 3 color, 10mm x .5mm

Logo woven label: 2 color, 20mm x 10mm

Steel lace eyelet: 8mm, OD

1.4mm split suede underlay: 8oz. canvas backing

"Chain" knit mesh: 100% polyester, 280gsm

Vibram™ rubber outsole: Durometer Shore "A" 70°

Die cut and profiled EVA midsole: Durometer Asker "C" 55°

Midsole logo: 4 color, TPR micro injection

Molded PU midsole wedge: Durometer Asker "C" 55°

Heel pull: 15mm wide, 1.5mm nylon webbing

Counter cover: 1.4mm split suede

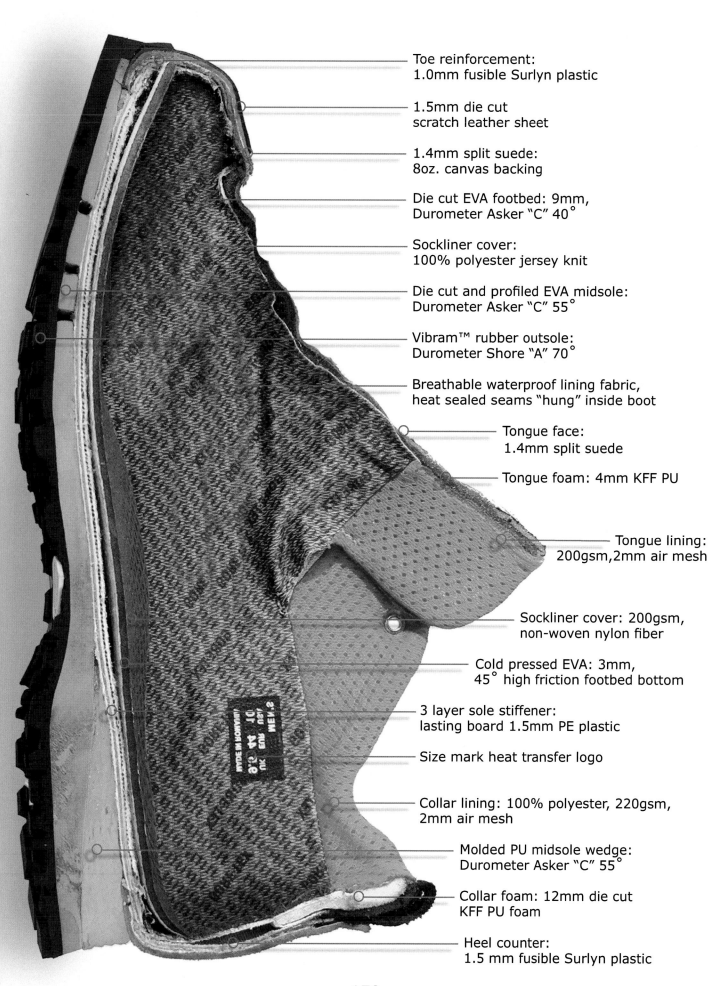

Toe reinforcement:
1.0mm fusible Surlyn plastic

1.5mm die cut
scratch leather sheet

1.4mm split suede:
8oz. canvas backing

Die cut EVA footbed: 9mm,
Durometer Asker "C" 40°

Sockliner cover:
100% polyester jersey knit

Die cut and profiled EVA midsole:
Durometer Asker "C" 55°

Vibram™ rubber outsole:
Durometer Shore "A" 70°

Breathable waterproof lining fabric,
heat sealed seams "hung" inside boot

Tongue face:
1.4mm split suede

Tongue foam: 4mm KFF PU

Tongue lining:
200gsm,2mm air mesh

Sockliner cover: 200gsm,
non-woven nylon fiber

Cold pressed EVA: 3mm,
45° high friction footbed bottom

3 layer sole stiffener:
lasting board 1.5mm PE plastic

Size mark heat transfer logo

Collar lining: 100% polyester, 220gsm,
2mm air mesh

Molded PU midsole wedge:
Durometer Asker "C" 55°

Collar foam: 12mm die cut
KFF PU foam

Heel counter:
1.5 mm fusible Surlyn plastic

Steel toe biker boots

This classic biker boot is designed for comfort, safety, and style. With its tough leather hide, steel toe, and steel ring, this boot is road ready. Inside you will find a high-end poured PU footbed and durable insulating lining. The outsole is a combination of rubber, EVA, and molded TPR.

Full-grain leather: 2.2mm, chrome tanned

Steel ring: 45mm OD, welded, 5mm stainless

Steel rivet: 9mm, OD

Double layer leather harness: 2.2mm full-grain leather

Goodyear welted outsole and dual density PU midsole

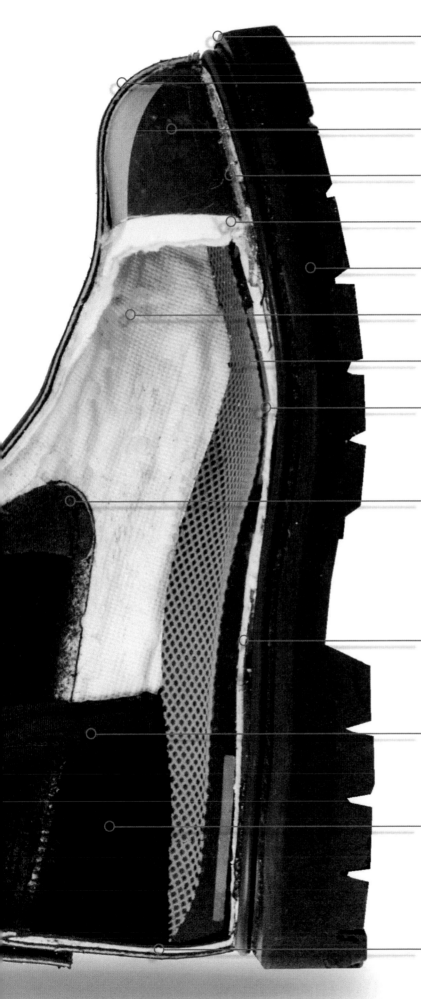

Goodyear welted outsole:
extruded PVC plastic rand

2.2mm full-grain leather:
chrome tanned, waterproof

Safety toe: 2.3mm carbon steel,
ANSI rated

Lasting board: 3mm high density,
steel toe support layer

1.5mm EVA padding protects
the foot from the steel toe edge

Double density Polyurethane midsole:
Durometer Asker "C" 50° and 35°

Vamp lining: double layer 200gsm

Sockliner cover:
100% polyester open knit

Double density PU footbed:
Durometer Asker "C" 25° and 35°

2.2mm full-grain leather:
chrome tanned, split surface lining

Lasting board: 3mm, full length,
heavy duty paper fiber

20mm nylon binding tape:
seam reinforcement covers rough stitching

Heel counter inner lining:
1mm PU synthetic suede

Heel counter: 1mm chemi-sheet
fiber board

180

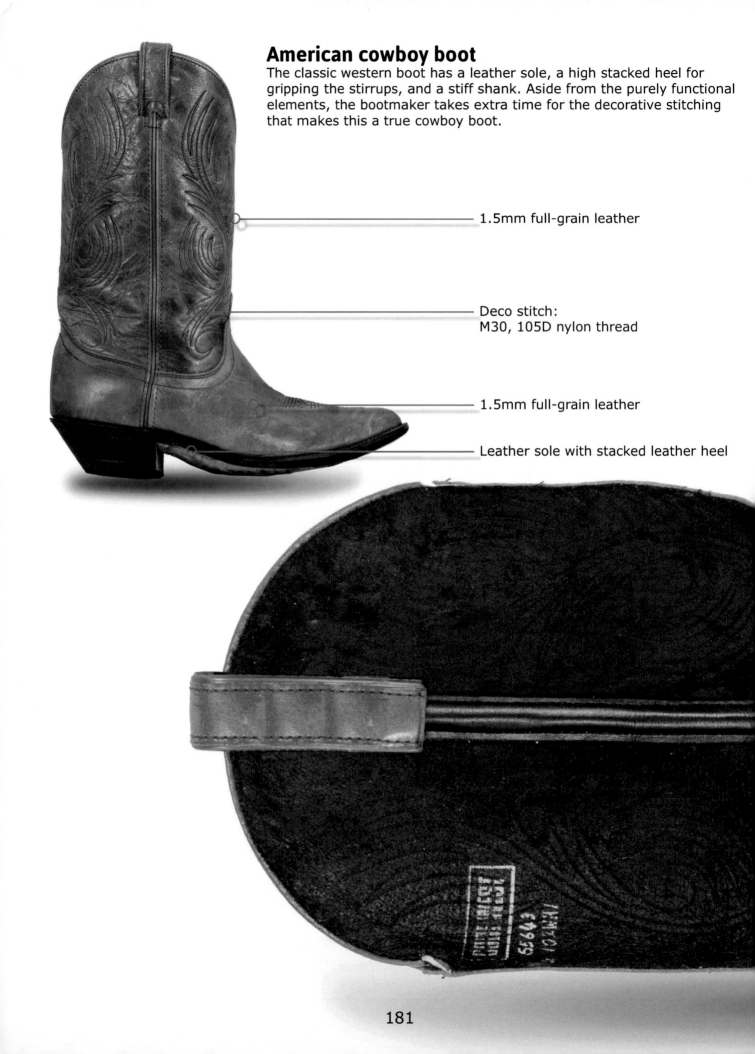

American cowboy boot

The classic western boot has a leather sole, a high stacked heel for gripping the stirrups, and a stiff shank. Aside from the purely functional elements, the bootmaker takes extra time for the decorative stitching that makes this a true cowboy boot.

1.5mm full-grain leather

Deco stitch:
M30, 105D nylon thread

1.5mm full-grain leather

Leather sole with stacked leather heel

Cowhide leather:
6mm, vegetable tanned

Hardwood filler

1mm toe reinforcement:
skived Surlyn plastic sheet

5mm latex and cork
cushioning filler

Vamp leather reinforcement:
100% polyester, 230gsm, bonded to leather

Full length lasting board:
2mm fiber board

Sockliner skin:
polyester fabric

Footbed padding and
2mm EVA foam

Injection molded nylon shank

1.5mm full-grain leather

1.0mm PU leather reinforcement

PVC seam cover: 20mm wide

9mm high density rubber heel:
Durometer Shore "A" 85°

Wooden heel:
6mm, stacked leather slabs

Heel reinforcements:
2mm paper lasting board

Heel pocket: 1.5mm
non-woven polyester fabric

1.5mm leather filler layer

Heel counter: 1.0mm Surlyn plastic

The jungle boot

First adopted in 1942 for use in the jungles of the Pacific, this lightweight canvas and leather design has served army troops well into the 1970's. Conditions on the ground during the Vietnam conflict required the addition of a thin steel plate. With many updates and improvements, the jungle boot continues to serve armies around the world today.

Action leather: 1.8mm, chrome tanned, 1.00 PVC leather backing

Webbing: 45mm x 1.25mm polyester, M10, 270D nylon thread

Cotton canvas:12oz., unbacked

Action leather: 1.8mm chrome tanned

Direct attach high density PU outsole: Durometer Shore "A" 50

Webbing: 20mm x 1.25mm polyester, M10, 270D nylon thread

Action leather: 1.8mm chrome tanned, 1.00mm PVC leather backing

Tongue and gusset: 12oz. cotton canvas, unbacked

Thread: nylon, M10, 270D

Cotton canvas: 12oz., unbacked

Webbing: 24mm x 1.25mm polyester, M10, 270D nylon thread

Webbing: 24mm x 1.25mm polyester, M10, 270D nylon thread

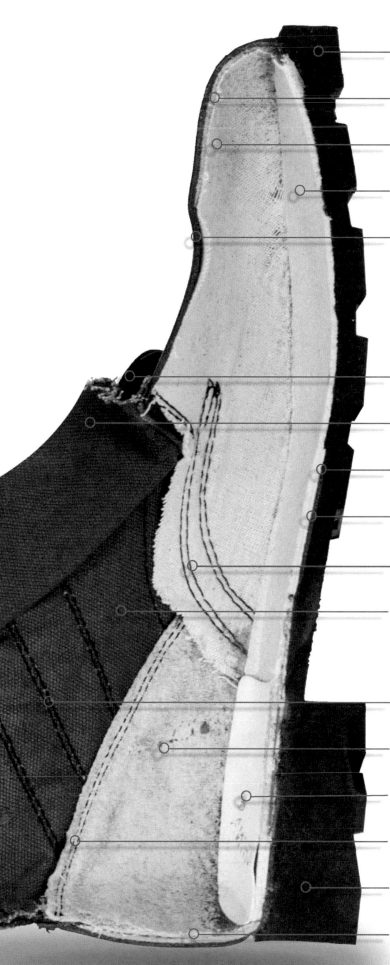

Direct attach high density PU outsole: Durometer Shore "A" 50°

Toe reinforcement: 1.5mm plastic coated fiber board

12oz. cotton canvas: unbacked and undyed

Lasting board: 2.0mm paper fiber, full length

Toe cap and vamp: 1.8mm, chrome tanned action leather

1.8mm chrome tanned action leather with 1.00mm PVC leather backing

Tongue and gusset: 12oz. cotton canvas unbacked

Lasting board: 1.0mm paper fiber, 3/4 length

Steel shank: 1mm thick spring, 15mm x 110mm

M10, 270D nylon thread

Upper canvas: 12oz. cotton canvas, unbacked

M10, 270D nylon thread

Heel counter: 1.0mm chrome tanned, split suede leather

Screen printed logo: 1mm PU leather with woven backing

M10 270D nylon thread

Direct attach high density PU outsole: Durometer Shore "A" 50°

Heel counter reinforcement: 1.5mm plastic coated fiber board

The "CVO" circular vamp oxford

First made in Liverpool in the 1830's as a beach shoe, this classic is also known as a plimsole or pumps. The standard for English school children's indoor physical education for over 100 years, the design spread to every corner of the British empire. Still worn as a casual summer shoe, this style remains popular worldwide. Its vulcanized construction makes it durable, washable; if not a bit heavy.

Vamp:
1oz. patterned cotton veil,
10oz. cotton canvas

Foxing tape:
2.5mm vulcanized rubber

Outsole rubber bottom: 3.5mm
outsole Density Shore "A" 60°

Steel eyelet:
8.5mm OD, 4.0mm ID

Shoelace:
100% polyester, braid 8mm

Tongue face:
1oz. patterned cotton veil,
10oz. cotton canvas

Cotton edge binding:
double roll

Cotton edge binding:
double roll

Tongue face: 1oz. patterned cotton veil,
10oz. cotton canvas

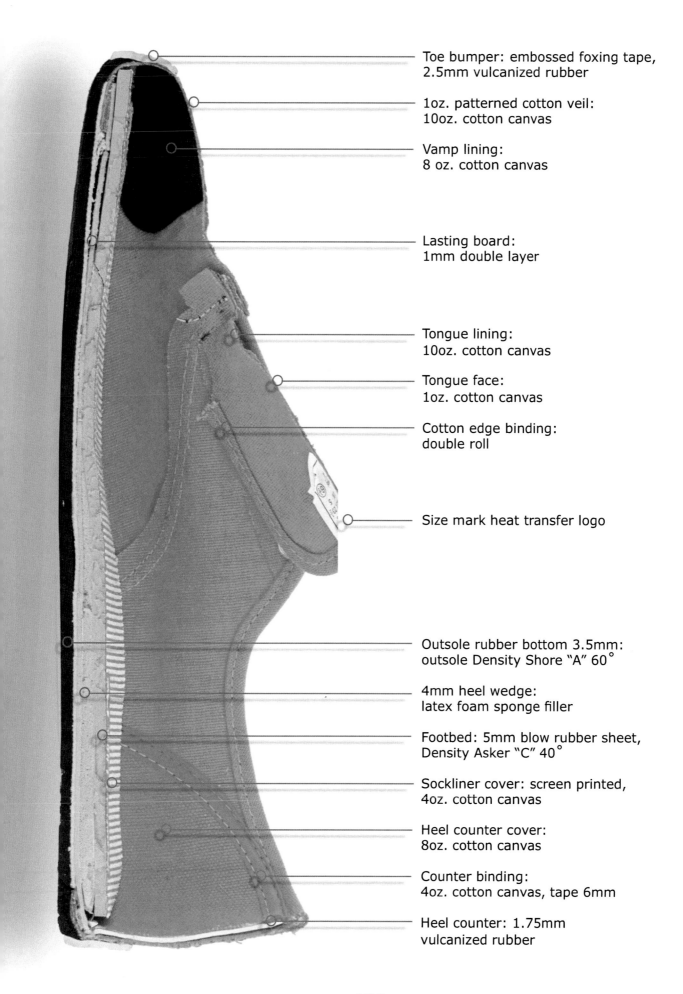

Toe bumper: embossed foxing tape, 2.5mm vulcanized rubber

1oz. patterned cotton veil: 10oz. cotton canvas

Vamp lining: 8 oz. cotton canvas

Lasting board: 1mm double layer

Tongue lining: 10oz. cotton canvas

Tongue face: 1oz. cotton canvas

Cotton edge binding: double roll

Size mark heat transfer logo

Outsole rubber bottom 3.5mm: outsole Density Shore "A" 60°

4mm heel wedge: latex foam sponge filler

Footbed: 5mm blow rubber sheet, Density Asker "C" 40°

Sockliner cover: screen printed, 4oz. cotton canvas

Heel counter cover: 8oz. cotton canvas

Counter binding: 4oz. cotton canvas, tape 6mm

Heel counter: 1.75mm vulcanized rubber

The high heel shoe

While the high heel shoe looks simple on the outside, the internal construction required to support a 4" heel can be complicated. Under the footbed, you can see the heavy layers of lasting boards that sandwich a contoured steel shank. A steel shaft supports the narrow heel.

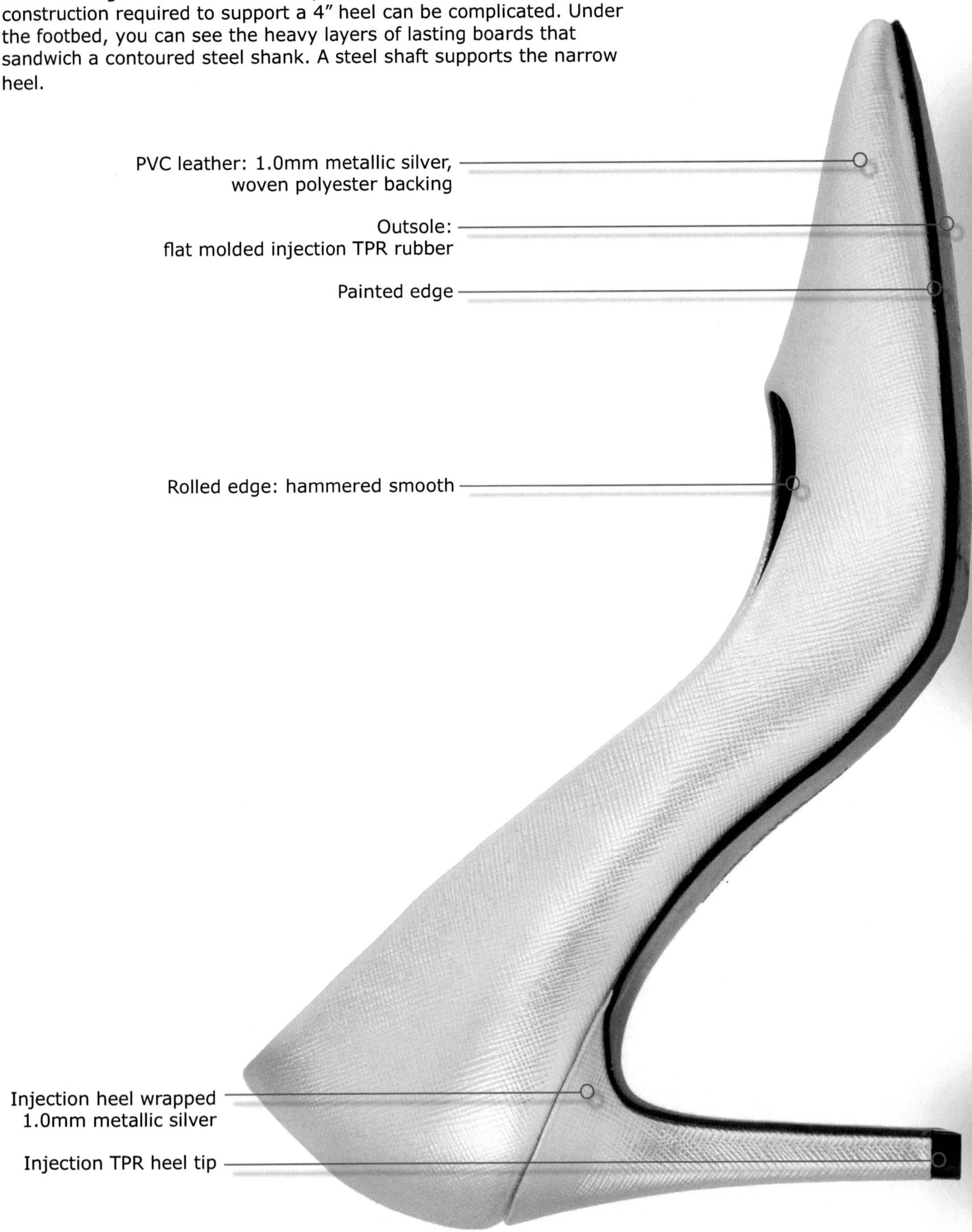

PVC leather: 1.0mm metallic silver, woven polyester backing

Outsole: flat molded injection TPR rubber

Painted edge

Rolled edge: hammered smooth

Injection heel wrapped 1.0mm metallic silver

Injection TPR heel tip

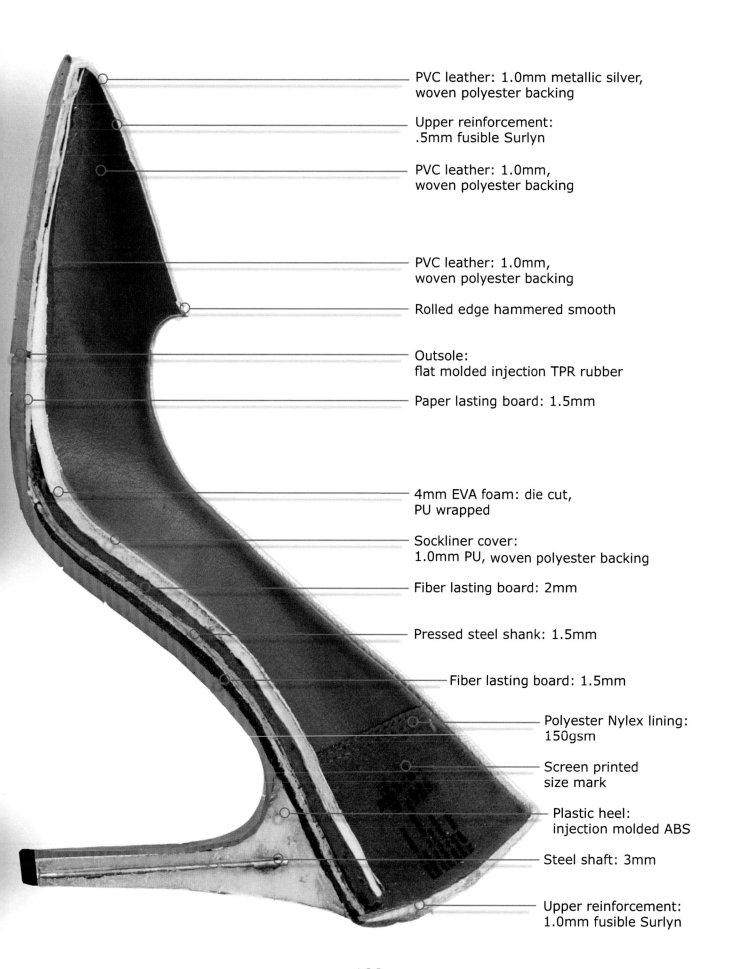

PVC leather: 1.0mm metallic silver, woven polyester backing

Upper reinforcement: .5mm fusible Surlyn

PVC leather: 1.0mm, woven polyester backing

PVC leather: 1.0mm, woven polyester backing

Rolled edge hammered smooth

Outsole: flat molded injection TPR rubber

Paper lasting board: 1.5mm

4mm EVA foam: die cut, PU wrapped

Sockliner cover: 1.0mm PU, woven polyester backing

Fiber lasting board: 2mm

Pressed steel shank: 1.5mm

Fiber lasting board: 1.5mm

Polyester Nylex lining: 150gsm

Screen printed size mark

Plastic heel: injection molded ABS

Steel shaft: 3mm

Upper reinforcement: 1.0mm fusible Surlyn

Women's casual shoe

Designed for low impact comfort, this casual shoe is soft and feather lite. The EVA sole is molded in one piece without rubber. The footbed is PU memory foam with an extra spongy latex foam wedge. This shoe will be very comfortable in the store but the comfy feeling will not last more than a few months due to its lack of support, EVA outsole, and soft foam footbed.

1.0mm PU nu-buck: non-woven polyester backing

Vamp: 100% polyester, 120gsm "hex" mesh, 3.5mm KFF PU foam

Midsole: hot pressed EVA Durometer Asker "C" 43°

Elastic tape: 20mm, polyester knit with elastic rubber inside

Edge binding: 10mm, lycra with zig-zag stitching

100% polyester, 120gsm jersey knit, 3.5mm KFF PU foam

Vamp: 100% polyester, 120gsm "hex" mesh, 3.5mm KFF PU foam

1.0mm PU nu-buck: non-woven polyester backing

Webbing: 10mm nylon, .5mm thick

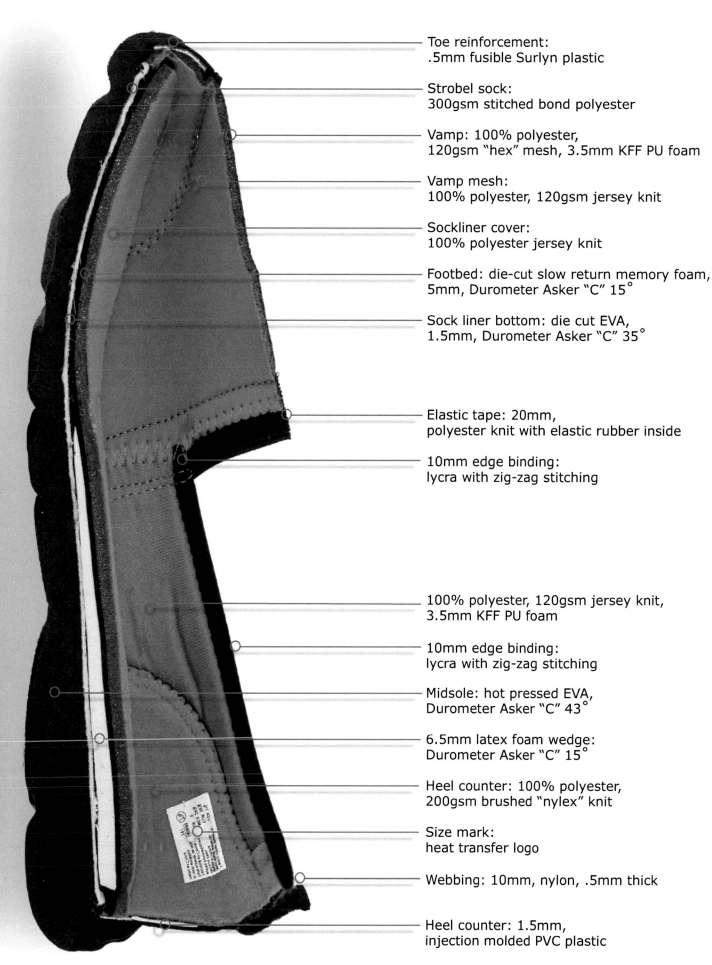

Toe reinforcement:
.5mm fusible Surlyn plastic

Strobel sock:
300gsm stitched bond polyester

Vamp: 100% polyester,
120gsm "hex" mesh, 3.5mm KFF PU foam

Vamp mesh:
100% polyester, 120gsm jersey knit

Sockliner cover:
100% polyester jersey knit

Footbed: die-cut slow return memory foam,
5mm, Durometer Asker "C" 15°

Sock liner bottom: die cut EVA,
1.5mm, Durometer Asker "C" 35°

Elastic tape: 20mm,
polyester knit with elastic rubber inside

10mm edge binding:
lycra with zig-zag stitching

100% polyester, 120gsm jersey knit,
3.5mm KFF PU foam

10mm edge binding:
lycra with zig-zag stitching

Midsole: hot pressed EVA,
Durometer Asker "C" 43°

6.5mm latex foam wedge:
Durometer Asker "C" 15°

Heel counter: 100% polyester,
200gsm brushed "nylex" knit

Size mark:
heat transfer logo

Webbing: 10mm, nylon, .5mm thick

Heel counter: 1.5mm,
injection molded PVC plastic

CHAPTER 28

SHOE MATERIAL VENDOR LIST

Real leather

Asiatan
www.asiatan.com

Wei Tai Leather Co., Ltd.
www.weitai.cn

Auburn Leather
www.auburnleather.com

Sadesa
www.sadesa.com/

Korea Institute of Footwear & Leather Technology
www.kiflt.re.kr/

The Leather Group
www.theleathergroup.com/

PrimeAsia Leather Corporation
www.primeasialeather.com/

Corlam Co Ltd Hong Kong
www.internationalleatherdirectory.com/
fullcompanydetails.php?comp_id=corlamco

Wolverine Leathers
www.wolverineleathers.com/

S.B. Foot Tanning Co.
www.sbfoot.com/

HELCOR-LEDER-TEC GmbH (Split & Action leather)
www.helcor-leder-tec.com/

Pony Leather Corporation
www.pony.com.tw/english/index.aspx

Synthetic leather
Baiksan Co., Ltd
www.baiksan.co.kr

Clarino
www.clarino-am.com/

Nan Ya Plastics Corporation
www.npc.com.tw

San Fang Chemical Industry Co., Ltd.
www.sanfang.com

Yuan Feng Synthetic Leather
www.szyongfeng.com.cn

Textile

Bu Kwang Textile Co., Ltd..
www.bukwang.com/

Dae Young Textile Co., Ltd.
www.daeryong.co.kr/

Dongguan Boyi Textile Co., Ltd.
www.en.boyi-tex.com

Faytex Corporation
www.faytex.com/fabricbooks.html

Faure Corporation
www.faure-textile.com/en

Ducksan Co., Ltd.
www.ducksan.biz

Yuan Ling Knitting Ind. Co., Ltd.
www.yuanling.com.tw

Cosmo
www.cosmofabric.net

Tiong Liong Industrial Co., Ltd. (fabric, textile manufacturing, dyeing, hi-tech coating, and lamination etc.)
www.tiongliong.com/

Schoeller Textile USA, Inc.
www.schoeller-textiles.com/en/

Kolon International Corp.
www.kolonindustries.com/

Nantex Industry Co., Ltd.
www.nantex.com.tw/en/

Nam Liong Group
www.namliong-group.com

Armortex Fabric
www.namliong.com.tw/tech-textile/category/armortex/

SeaMate Neo-Prene
www.namliong.com.tw/sponge/

Bu Kwang Textile Co., Ltd.
www.bukwang.com/

More Shoeparts
www.aplf.com/en-US/23518/more-shoeparts-co-Ltd.

Winiw
www.shoe-materials.com

Dongguan Fushan Textile
www.fushantex.com

Thread

American & Efird, Inc
www.amefird.com/

Coats Thread
www.coatsindustrial.com

Outsoles

Jones & Vining, Incorporated
www.jonesandvining.com/footwear.html

Framas
www.framas.com/en/products/#c48

Vibram
www.vibram.com/

Meramec Group
www.meramec.com

Jiarong Shoes Material Co. Ltd.
www.globalsources.com/si/AS/Jiarong-Shoes/6008827324404/Homepage.htm

Eclipse Polymers (EVA and Foamed Rubber Products)
www.eclipsepolymers.com/

Dongguan Zhengyong Industry Co., Ltd.
www.dgyongzheng.cn/

Vibram
www.us.vibram.com/

Skydex (impact and cushioning technologies)
www.skydex.com/

Chemicals

Bayer
www.bayer.com/

Sung Woo Chemical Co., Ltd.
www.sungwoochem.co.kr/

Footwear molds
Well Progress Plastics
Simon@wellprogress.com

Ting Yi Mould
www.tingyimould.com/

Jiang Men Mold Co., Ltd.
www.jiangmen.com.tw/

Dae Sung Precision Co. /
www.daesungpm.co.kr/

Metal accessories
Dae Sung Co., Ltd.
www.daesung.net/

Qing Can Hardware Accessories., Ltd.
www.qingcanwj.com/

Oudi Hardware co.
www.oudihardware.com

Trimmers
www.trimmers-pro.com

Lining fabric
Trendware
www.trendwaremarketing.com

Cosmo
www.cosmofabric.net

Yuan Ling Knitting Ind. Co., Ltd
www.yuanling.com.tw

Winiw
www.shoe-materials.com

Shoelaces and trim
Paiho Group
www.paiho.com

Jun may Label Mfg. Corp.
www.jmlabel.com

Lasts
Jones & Vining, Incorporated
www.jonesandvining.com

Framas
www.framas.com/

The Shoe Last Shop
www.shoe-last-shop.com

Footbed foam
Rogers Corporation
www.rogerscorp.com/

Ortholite
www.ortholite.com

Ultralon Foam
www.ultralon.co.nz

Lasting boards
Bontex, Inc.
www.bontex.com

Texon International
www.texon.com

TecnoGi Spa
www.tecnogi.com/index.php/en/products

Cosmo
www.cosmofabric.net/

Jones & Vining, Incorporated
www.jonesandvining.com

Winiw
www.shoe-materials.com

Molded logo
Guanglida Apparel Co
www.dgguanglida.com

Shoe manufacturing equipment
G-Shine Qixin Shoe Making Machine
www.dg-qixin.com

Plastic parts
Duraflex
www.duraflexgroup.com

Nifco Buckle
www.nifcobuckle.com/en/

IWT Nexus
www.global.itwnexus.com

DSM Engineering Plastics
www.dsmep.com

Foam
Flextech foam
www.flextechfoam.com

Rogers Corporation
www.rogerscorp.com/

Ortholite
www.ortholite.com

Ultralon Foam
www.ultralon.co.nz

Shoe test equipment
GoTech
www.gotech.biz

Haida Test Equipment
www.haidatestequipment.com

Asian Test Equipments
www.asiantestequipment.com/footwear-testing-equipment.html

Teclock Durometer testing equipment
www.teclock.co.jp/product-2/

Upper reinforcements
Winiw
www.shoe-materials.com

Texon International
www.texon.com

TecnoGi Spa
www.tecnogi.com/index.php/en/products

Libo shoe material
www.libo-shoematerial.com

Online Shoemaking Courses
Shoemaking for Designers and Brand Builders
How to Select Shoe Materials
Sneaker Authentication Basics
Creating Footwear Specifications
Footwear Cost Calculation
Footwear Cost Engineering
Footwear Inspection and Quality Control
Building a Modern Shoe Factory
Footwear Sustainability Strategies
Footwear Fitting & Comfort
Footwear Import Duty
Starting Your Shoe Business
Shoe Types and Constructions
How to Design Shoes
DIY Shoemaking for Beginners
The Footwear Process Development to Production
Footwear Development Factory Communications
Footwear Marketing & Merchandising
and more!

Text Books Available Now:
How Shoes are Made
Footwear Pattern Making and Last Design
Shoe Material Design Guide
How to Start Your Own Shoe Company
How to Spot Fake Sneakers
Cómo se hacen los zapatos
Cómo empezar tu propia empresa de calzado
Guía para el diseño de materiales de calzado
Patronaje de calzado y diseño de hormas
鞋子是怎样制成的

Made in the USA
Monee, IL
03 June 2024

59365390R00119